RAILWAY.

DRAWING No

General Elevation

General Plan

BRUNEL'S ROYAL ALBERT BRIDGE

Isambard Kingdom Brunel (1806 - 1859)
S K Jones (Brunel Society) Collection

'This stupendous structure, remarkable for the boldness of its conception, and for the ingenuity of its construction ... unprecedented in magnitude, will stand forth to future generations, a lasting and worthy monument to the skill of the justly celebrated engineer by whom it was planned'

Humber 1861

'As a triumph of engineering skill and enterprise, it stands second to none in magnitude, even in this age of scientific progress, and will constitute a monument to the ability of the gentleman who has designed and superintended its construction, that will hand down his name to all future ages as one of the most remarkable men of his time'

Plymouth & Devonport Journal 3 September 1857

For Val

BRUNEL'S ROYAL ALBERT BRIDGE

A Study of the Design and Construction of his 'Gateway to Cornwall' at Saltash

BY

JOHN BINDING

TWELVEHEADS PRESS

TRURO 1997

CONTENTS

The endpapers are a copy of one of Brunel's original drawings of the Royal Albert Bridge reproduced by coutesy of Railtrack Great Western.

TWELVEHEADS PRESS

First published in 1997 by Twelveheads Press, Chy Mengleth, Twelveheads, Truro, Cornwall TR4 8SN.

ISBN 0 906294 39 8

British Library Cataloguing-in-Publication Data.

A catalogue record for this book is available from the British Library.

Designed by Alan Kittridge. Printed by The Amadeus Press Ltd., Huddersfield.

SOURCES & ACKNOWLEDGEMENTS

The Bibliography lists works which were consulted to provide background and general information relating to the building of the Royal Albert Bridge. However, as far as possible, my narrative has been developed from primary sources of information, duly referenced as appropriate; where continuity has demanded conjecture, the text has been qualified accordingly.

The most valuable original material has been derived from copies of many of Brunel's drawings of his design and adaptations introduced during the building of the Bridge, which are held in the archive of Railtrack Great Western, at Swindon. I am indeed most grateful to the Records Manager for permission to consult and use this information; and to the Engineers at Swindon for all their help and assistance during my research, the relevant illustrations being acknowledged 'RtGW'.

Further information was derived from the Minutes of the Cornwall Railway and other related reports housed in the Public Record Office at Kew, which my Record Research Agent, Mrs Betty Thomson, diligently investigated on my behalf. Mr Nick Lee was most helpful in furnishing information regarding the Saltash and Chepstow Bridges from the Brunel Archive at the University Library, Bristol.

I am also most grateful to the Archivist of the Institution of Civil Engineers, Mrs M. K. Murphy and her staff, in providing copies of relevant papers from their Proceedings and in investigating my several enquiries. Robert Sharp of the Science Museum Library, and Philip Atkins of the NRM, York, kindly furnished information from their respective records (acknowledged 'SM/SS') as did Tim Bryan of the Great Western Museum, Swindon, and John Powell of the Ironbridge Gorge Museum.

Additional details of the contemporary scene were culled from local newspaper reports, for which I am indebted to the staffs of the Local Studies Libraries at Redruth and Plymouth, and the Railway Studies Collection at Newton Abbot. Mrs Elizabeth Sharpe and her colleagues of Saltash Heritage kindly contributed details from the history of Saltash as it affected the building of the Bridge, while Roger Penhallurick and the staff of the Royal Cornwall Museum, Truro, provided a number of illustrations, duly acknowledged 'RIC'.

I wish to acknowledge the considerable interest and assistance which I have received from many individuals and institutions, including loan of photographs from their collections. Among those whom I would especially like to mention are: Derrick Beckett, John Beckett, Dr L. G. Booth, Tony Bowden, Pat English, Mr & Mrs Larry Crozier (and other retired members of railway staff who kindly recalled events of the past), Steve Jones, Sir William and Lady Miles for their kind hospitality, Steve Rowson and Brian Ward; while, in particular, I wish to thank Michael Messenger and his colleagues at Twelveheads Press for their editorial expertise in preparing this work for publication.

Finally, my special thanks are due to all my family and many friends, without whose help and encouragement the work would not have been completed; and above all, to my wife, Val, for her ever present support.

Rock, Cornwall
December 1996

INTRODUCTION

The magnificent Royal Albert Bridge which Isambard Kingdom Brunel (1806–1859) designed and built to carry the Cornwall Railway at a height of 100 feet across the waters of the River Tamar at Saltash, must surely be recognised as one of his most outstanding works. Its unique design and handsome proportions, set in an idyllic location between the hills of Devon and Cornwall, give it an aura of grace and majesty all of its own. As the 'Gateway to Cornwall' it forms a fitting and lasting memorial to this great Victorian engineer.

This, then, is the story of that Bridge, known to the thousands of holiday-makers who cross the Tamar each year, either by rail or road, on the way to their destination in Cornwall. The saga of its construction over nearly fourteen years, from Act of Parliament in 1846 to Royal Opening in 1859, presents a story of achievement in the face of adversity.

Granted, Brunel's attainments in other fields may be considered equally worthy of recognition, for it is said that of all his projects, the Great Western Railway was perhaps his favourite, despite the stormy history of its construction. 'I am engineer to the finest work in England' he wrote. However, the gentle gradients and sweeping curves of the route to Bristol, famed for the high speeds of the steam era, are rarely noticed by the passenger in today's Intercity 125 express.

With the passage of time, memories grow dim, and we can easily forget all his other works, particularly within the City of Bristol. His first great project, the Clifton Suspension Bridge (where, following the deferment of the contract due to financial problems, the original chains were to be incorporated in the Saltash Bridge); the City Docks; the original Temple Meads Station; and, of course, his contribution to the design and building of the three great steamships. Of these, the *Great Britain*, now resting in the centre of that city, where she was built, is another lasting memorial to this brilliant engineer. It was quite remarkable that one man could successfully embrace so many different engineering disciplines, but his Saltash Bridge stands supreme today to remind us of the vision and talents of this exceptional man, whose reputation has ever remained on an illustrious pedestal.

Thus, it was to this Tamar crossing that he brought his own particular skills, in investigating the most economical way of bridging that stretch of water. His great love of timber initially projected an arch design, but this fell foul of Admiralty requirements; he even considered a massive single span. But in the end, he evolved a development of the design then under construction in wrought iron for his bridge across the Wye at Chepstow. It was to prove unique and as enduring as any other contemporary structure. Significantly, it was much lighter and cheaper than the Britannia bridge across the Menai Straits, recently completed by his great friend and rival Stephenson.

Amongst those immediately acquainted with Brunel or who served under him in creating these great undertakings, he seemed to possess an extraordinary amount of influence. They almost worshipped him, despite his sometimes unpredictable behaviour. He punished himself harder than any of his assistants, working during the day on his plans and then, at night, travelling by any means available to some distant site or other meeting. Inevitably, such a strenuous routine was to affect his health in later years.

He was at his best in argument, reflecting his brilliant, volatile personality and eager spirit, particularly when answering criticism of his proposals before Parliamentary and other committees. How else could he have convinced the directors of the South Devon Company to retain his services, following the outcome of the 'Atmospheric Caper'?

This background to his personality is no better in evidence than in the long struggle to build the Cornwall Railway and the Saltash Bridge; the frustration of the early Parliamentary hearings, the endless disruption arising from the Company's perpetual lack of capital, the immense engineering difficulties in building that centre pier, the repercussions of the bankruptcy of the main contractor, the floating out and raising of the main spans – all leading, eventually, to the completion of an outstanding structure.

Significantly, much of the work was undertaken by his engineering assistants, working under his direction; men like W. Bell, W. Glennie and C. E. Gainsford (who had recently returned to this country following a difficult time as resident engineer under C. B. Vignoles during the construction of his Kiev Suspension Bridge, completed in 1853). They reported to R. P. Brereton (1818–1894) who, through Brunel's enforced absence due to his other commitments and then his failing health, assumed overall responsibility for the final construction. Brereton was a modest but well qualified man who seemed content to live in the shadow of his illustrious chief. We appear to know little of his personal life yet he made a most valuable contribution to the building of the Bridge.

This was recognised by the Cornwall Railway Chairman at the celebration *dejeuner* held in Truro to mark the opening of the line, in his statement that in Brunel's unavoidable absence, Brereton 'was always ready, always able, always full of energy' to see the contract through to a satisfactory conclusion.

However, it must not be forgotten that this great work could not have been completed without the hard work and dedication of the ordinary working man. Firstly, there were those, some probably hailing from the mining community who, using only bare hands and the basic working tools of their trade (mallet, chisel, crow bar, shovel etc) and working in the most appalling conditions of darkness, flooding and often, of necessity, in a pressurised environment, had the necessary stamina to construct the foundation for the central pier.

Then, there were the stone cutters and trowel masons who, working in exposed conditions and at great height, without scaffolding, built the massive masonry land piers and the twin piers supporting the approach spans.

Nevertheless, the greatest skills must surely be attributed to the platers and metal workers who developed the patterns, sheared, rolled and punched the 2 feet wide wrought iron plates which, when riveted together, formed the elliptical sectioned main tubes, with their well known parabolic elevation. Each completed truss, with its massive main chains, bridge decking and associated supporting linkage, weighed over 1,000 tons. The subsequent lifting of these two massive spans over 100 feet to their final position was no mean engineering feat.

Brunel was, indeed, fortunate to have working for him such a devoted team of engineering assistants and workmen who, defying all the difficulties, finally helped to bring this project to fruition.

The following story sets out the background to this immense undertaking, from the political intrigue which surrounded the Parliamentary bills of the alternative railway routes to Falmouth, the decision to build a bridge at Saltash Passage (in place of the original steam ferry at Torpoint) and then through the years of construction to the final opening, with all the pomp and splendour of a Royal occasion, Sadly, Brunel's failing health kept him away from that great day; he died later in the year, after having only once viewed his completed masterpiece.

Today, however, we are reminded of the man every time we cross the Tamar, whether by train or by road, as we see those striking letters 'I K BRUNEL ENGINEER 1859' set high on the portals of his Bridge; even as we use the magnificent Tamar suspension bridge that spans the river but a short distance from its venerable neighbour, opened just over 100 years after Brunel's masterpiece was completed.

CHAPTER ONE

THE GREAT DIVIDE

A stranger standing on Plymouth Hoe and viewing the Sound, could be forgiven if he assumed that the rolling wood covered hills to the south west were part of Devon. On closer study, he would notice that they are cut off from his location by an arm of the sea (called The Narrows) extending between Devil's Point on the eastern shore and Wilderness Point to the west, which reaches in from the Sound to form the estuary of the Hamoaze. This extensive landlocked area of water drains the River Lynher and the River Tamar, and from Plate 1.1 will be seen to divide Cornwall from its neighbouring county, Devon. However, it is interesting to note that, according to Carey's map of Cornwall, dated 1820, an area of the righthand bank opposite Saltash extending to the parish of St Budeaux, was at one time deemed to be part of Cornwall.

The source of the Tamar is in the distant north, not far from the Bristol Channel coast, from where it flows almost due south to reach the Hamoaze. Until the mid nineteenth century, not only did it form a natural barrier that divided Cornwall, a Duchy, in almost every respect unique and independent, from the unmistakeably English County of Devon, but it had also acted as a cultural divide between the two.

In earlier times, the Romans reached the river at the narrows opposite the present town of Saltash, beyond which it is generally thought that they made little significant progress. The early history of this borough is closely identified with that of Trematon Castle, to which it was for many years appended (Polsue). From that time the Mayor was believed to take precedence over the Mayor of Plymouth, and by virtue of his office as Mayor of Saltash, was also coroner to the Borough of Plymouth. Once famed for its local cockles and for the 'toughness of the thaws and sinews of its boatwomen' in the local regatta the borough was deemed worthy of being appointed the ruler of the liberties of the Tamar.

During the times of the Civil Wars, from 1642 to 1646, Saltash had assumed importance as one of the entrances into the County. It was taken and retaken several times by the Royalists, the men of Cornwall, who remained loyal to the King, and the Parliamentarians, the Puritans of Plymouth, thus perpetuating divisions between the two communities which lasted generations.

There can, therefore, be little doubt that with their natural isolation from the rest of the country, the Cornish had developed as a people different from the English. In the far west of the county their economy was one of the first in the world to become industrialised. The early and successful application of steam power to pumping water from the deeper mines, facilitated the development of mining tin and copper ores. Thanks to the work of men like Richard Trevithick this achieved for Cornwall an enviable place in the forefront of technological innovation, to complement its indigenous activities of agriculture and fishing.

Over the years, the allocation of the ferry rights to ply across the Hamoaze was jealously protected and in that respect at Saltash, until about 1829, the usual clumsy ferry boats had been used. However, about that time a Steam Floating Bridge, or ferry, was proposed by J. M. Rendel (1799-1856), a civil engineer who had been a surveyor under Telford. In about 1822 he had established a practice in Plymouth, and in 1824 had been entrusted with work on the construction of the Lary (or Laira) Bridge near Plymouth[1].

The layout and details of construction of the ferry are shown in Plates 1.2 and 1.3, but for some unknown reason, according to history, this innovative proposal failed to

1.1 (Opposite page) *A copy of part of Colonel Coleby's original 1813 survey of the Tamar, updated in 1839 and subsequently revised to show the routes of the South Devon and Cornwall Railways in the Plymouth and surrounding areas. The extensive land locked waterways which comprise the Hamoaze, creating an effective barrier between Devon and Cornwall, will be clearly appreciated; and the local narrowing at Saltash which provided Brunel with the site of his famous bridge.* CORNWALL LOCAL STUDIES LIBRARY

Burcomb
Whitsome
Down Fm
Dunstone
Woolaton
St. Mellion
Halton
Halls Hole
Hall F.
Collytown
Lephill
Clifton
Saunton
Briston
Tinnel
Liphill
Egypt
Beer Ferrers
Nattom
Dunwood
Pounds
Ford
Villaton
Elbridge
Wheatland Green
Hay
Leigh
Heaton
St. Anns
Carmeen
Horsham
Blackstone
Ashley
Ramscombe
Hall
Kingsmill
Cross
Park
Landulph
RIVER TAVY
Topham
Villaton
Doghole
North Coombe
Whitestone
Wooten
Botes Fleming
Warleigh
Tamerton Foliot
Notter Hill
Notter
Landrake
Warren Point
Stoketon
Broad moor
Carkeel
Skinham Fm
Budshead
Holes Fm
Mid Pill
South Pill
Witley
Trematon
St. Erney
Ernsettle
Woodland Fm
RIVER TAMER
Burraton
St. Budeaux
Wadgeworthy
Royal Albert Bridge
SALTASH
Kings Tamerton
Dock Lea
Burell Place
St. Stephens
Passage
Manadon
Trevollard
Trerun
Trematon Castle
Burrington
Weston Mill
Beckhall
Weston Peverell
Chapel
Grove
Kinterbury F.
Tredown F.
Orchard
Prospect
Wilcove
East Antony
Mile Ho.
Stoke Damerel
Merrifield
Barrow
Keyham Dock Yd
Torpoint
Cemetery
Sheviock
Cleave
Trevol
Hay
DEVONPORT
HAMOAZE
Antony
Dock Yard
STONEHOUSE
St. John's Lake
W. Trelay
Sunwell
St. Johns
Lr. Tregantle
Empacombe
Barn Pool
Mt. Edgcumbe
St. Nicholas Island
Kings Brewhouse
Inceworth
Hr. Tregantle
Bridgmoor
Frathy

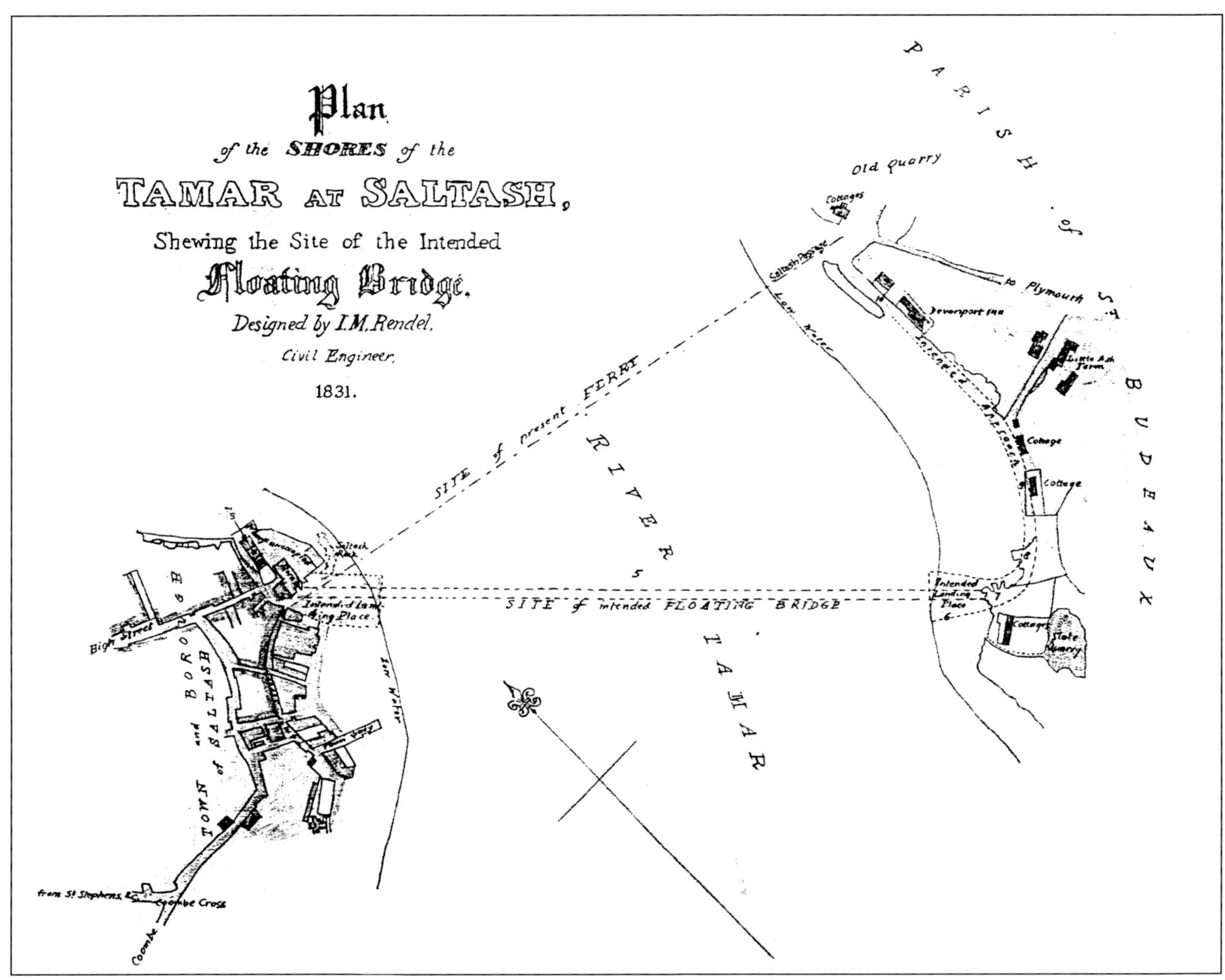

1.2 *This plan shows Mr Rendel's proposal for a Floating Bridge at Saltash Passage c1831. It portrays the line of the chains across the passage and the arrangements for the terminals on either shore.* SALTASH HERITAGE

answer the expectations of the proprietors and it was scrapped, to be replaced once more by the original ferry boats.

Earlier, in the lower reaches of the Hamoaze, local enterprise had operated a similar ferry service dating from 1791, using ordinary foot passenger boats, followed in 1831 by an attempt to introduce a steam powered paddle ferry boat *Jemima*[2]. Sadly, this craft had insufficient power to overcome the strong currents and was withdrawn from service, to be replaced once again by the original passenger boats.

Then, on 11 April 1834, Rendel established his 'Steam Floating Bridge', probably based on the same design as the above Saltash project, to operate between Torpoint, on the Cornish shore, and the Devon shore adjoining the village of Stoke Damerel. The layout and details of construction of the Saltash ferryboat should be noted for it is reasonable to assume that a similar arrangement would have applied in the case of this Torpoint ferry, which is of concern later in our story.

The coming of the railway was to bring many changes to a scene which had changed little over the years, the South Devon Railway Bill having received the Royal Assent on 4 July 1844. Despite the trauma and frustration of the 'Atmospheric Caper', the line between Exeter and Plymouth was finally completed, under Brunel's direction, on 2 April 1849, with the opening of the terminus in Plymouth. This was built between Union Street and Millbay Road – an unpretentious wooden erection, with the usual all over roof which so characterised Brunel's stations – and it was, of course, eventually to form the terminus for the Cornwall Railway.

Having reached this far corner of Devon, further progress to the west depended on the crossing of that great divide – the estuary of the Hamoaze or River Tamar. Meanwhile, in the far west of Cornwall, some of the populace had viewed the developments beyond that natural barrier more with concern and suspicion as to how they would affect their mode of life, rather than as the opportunity to form closer ties with the rest of the country. In particular, the Government threat, followed by its action of 1843, to deprive Falmouth of its Packet Boat status, had caused alarm within the shipping fraternity.

Nevertheless, with the projected arrival of the railway in Plymouth, the more progressive of the mine owners and merchants of Cornwall had already been casting envious eyes to the east, to see if their isolated county could be linked to the burgeoning network of railways which were beginning to spread across the English countryside. Accordingly, in co-operation with the shipping interests they were spurred to action.

But, first they had to find a means of bridging that great divide.

1.3 *Contour of the channel and details of the ferry itself and how it was self propelled between the two shores. It is thought that the 'steam bridge' across the Hamoaze at Torpoint was of similar construction but probably larger. Certainly, involving a longer crossing in a strong tidal environment, the contour of the chains would have been anything but straight between the two shores, hence the concern regarding how rail vehicles were to be loaded from the rail tracks at each terminus.* SALTASH HERITAGE

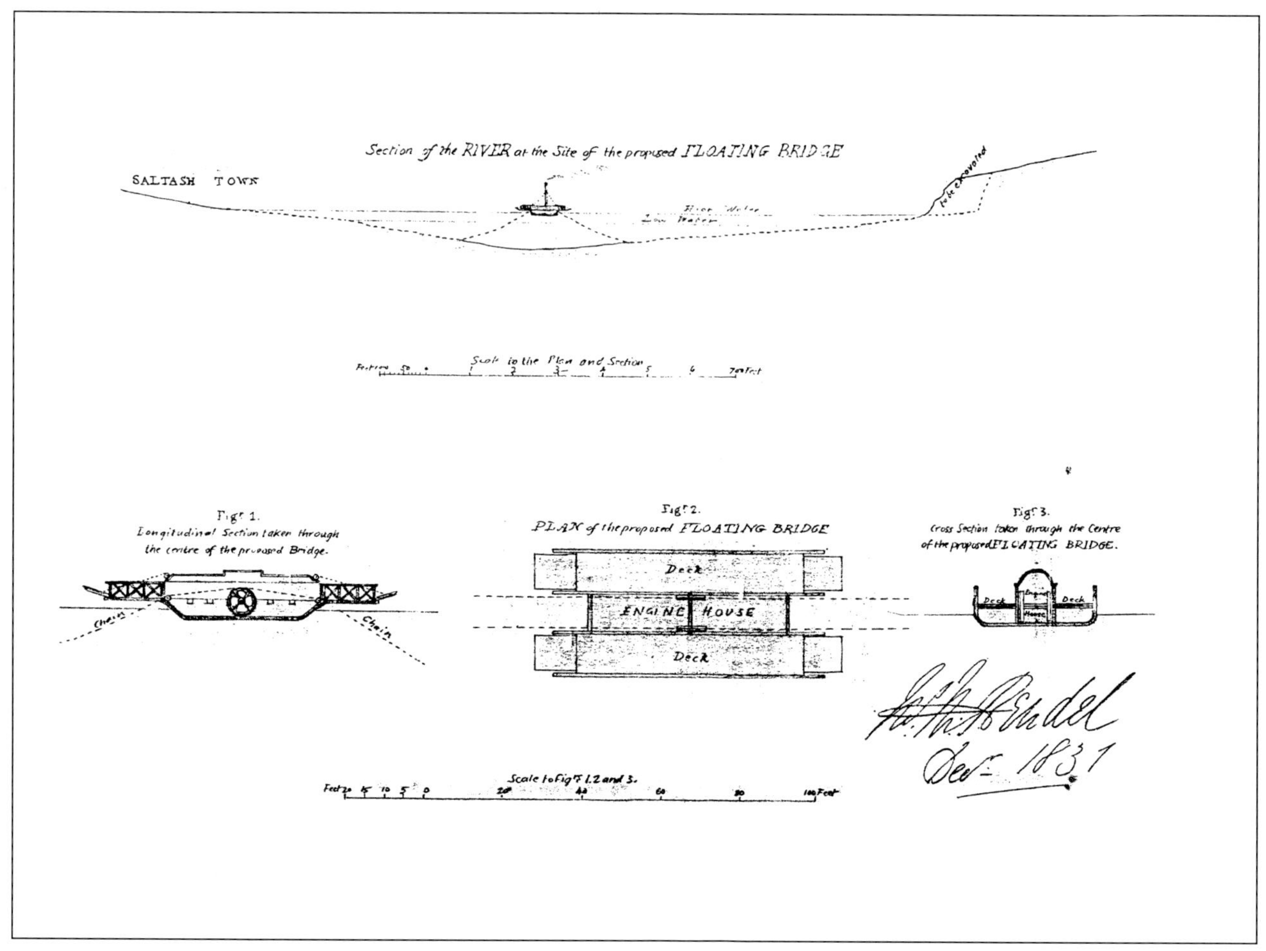

CHAPTER TWO

THE COMING OF THE RAILWAY

1835 to 1859

In 1835 a scheme had been mooted by Colonel George Landmann (Biddle 1990) to build a railway from London to Salisbury, Exeter and then to Falmouth by way of Okehampton and Launceston – thus crossing the Tamar at its upper, narrower reaches – and so down the spine of the county to Bodmin and Truro. According to the prospectus, the engineer was to be Charles Dean but it appears that the proposals lacked detailed consideration of how the line was to overcome the considerable natural difficulties of the route. It seems doubtful whether the scheme proceeded beyond a prospectus, and it was rejected by Parliament the following year.

However, under the threat of the loss of the packet services for Falmouth, the project was revived at a most influential County Meeting[1] held at Bodmin on 29 October 1839, led by the Earl of Falmouth, which resolved

> ...it is essential that the meeting should promote the progress and completion of a Railway communication between London and the West of Cornwall as far and as early as any means now available...will allow.

This resolution represented the real beginning of the Cornwall Railway and a Committee was appointed to further the whole project. Sadly, very few of the gentlemen who formed that committee lived to see the eventual opening of the line. The reader may find the map Plate 2.1 of help in studying this chapter.

The route was surveyed by Captain W. S. Moorsom (1804–1863), that indefatigable ex-army officer who seems to have been involved, one way or another, with many of the railway projects of that time. It was to follow a line from a junction with the Bristol & Exeter Railway at Cowley Bridge, just north of Exeter, and then down through Launceston, Bodmin, St Austell, Truro to Falmouth, again crossing the upper reaches of the Tamar. A line from Plymouth was to join the trunk a little west of Lidford. In April 1841 Captain Moorsom gave a preliminary report[2] to the Committee in which he outlined his proposals. Somewhat optimistically he commented that

> ...there is no work in the whole line which is not within the compass of ordinary design and of ordinary execution.

A sub committee was appointed to prepare a report for the next county meeting, to be convened as early as possible after the current Parliamentary session.

However, early in 1842, before this committee could complete its work, and make recommendations, the Earl of Falmouth died and the project lost the impetus of its indispensable leader. It would appear that matters then languished for a while until the Government announcement on 29 May 1842 that the packet station was to be moved from Falmouth to Southampton. This led to renewed exertions and, following meetings during July of that year in Truro and Redruth, Mr Tweedy and Mr Bond were appointed to confer with the directors of the Great Western Railway, to seek their support. This was duly promised on completion of the South Devon Railway; not, however, for the route as provisionally surveyed but for a line from Plymouth to Falmouth.

Through the latter part of that year the Committee was actively engaged in enquiries and negotiations to further the project and they had the offer of £413,000 from parties in London. However, the conditions governing the finance were not acceptable and the offer was therefore declined.

Formation of the Cornwall Railway

Then, at a meeting in Truro in January 1844 the Company was formally constituted and its officers provisionally appointed – Mr Treffry, Chairman; Captain Moorsom, engineer; and Mr Bond as Secretary. Later in

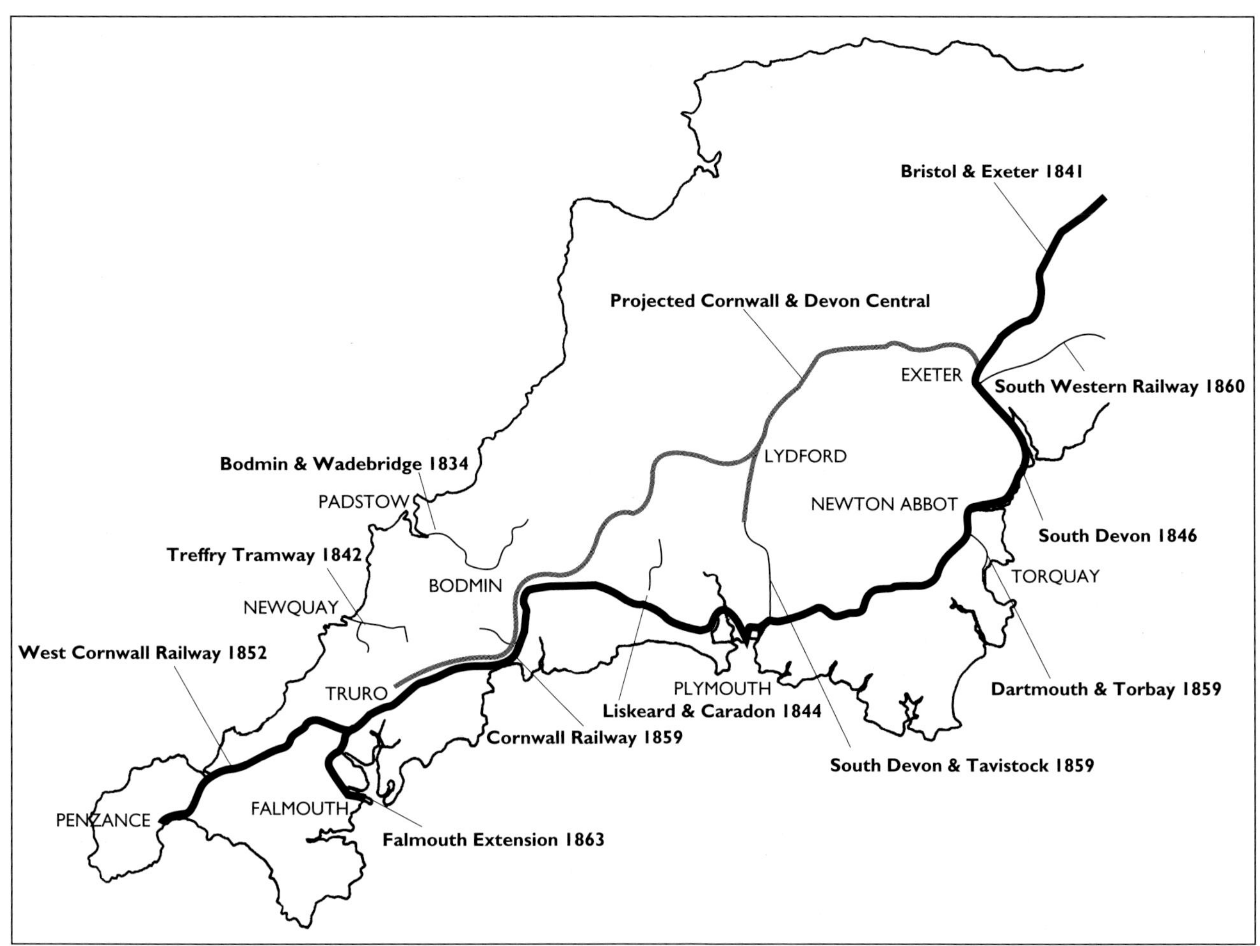

2.1 *Map showing the development of the railway system west of Exeter, up to the date of the opening of the Cornwall Railway in 1859. It includes what is believed to have been the projected route of the abortive Cornwall & Devon Central Railway.*

that year, the Great Western, the Bristol and Exeter and the South Devon companies, officially announced their intention to support this new enterprise, a decision which with the pending arrival at Plymouth of the South Devon Railway spurred Captain Moorsom to proceed with his survey of this southerly route to link Falmouth with the South Devon Railway.

The prospectus for this project was published[3] in September 1844, indicating an issued capital of £900,000 divided into 18,000 shares of £50 each. The initial deposit was £3 per share with interest thereon of 4% p.a., on all paid up calls from date of payment until the railway was completed. Of this total, the Associated Companies, namely, the Great Western, Bristol & Exeter, South Devon and Bristol & Gloucester were to contribute a total of £250,000. The document gave details of the likely operational benefits of the line, together with an outline of the proposed route. From Falmouth this was to run to Truro and then, following the southern slopes of the county, to approach the Hamoaze along the southern bank of the St Germans or Lynher river, past Antony, and then clinging to the northern shore of St John's Lake, to sweep round into the site of the existing Torpoint Ferry. The crossing of the Hamoaze would, therefore, be by steam ferry at one of its deepest and widest locations at Torpoint, as shown in Plate 2.2, a copy taken from the 1844 section of the Cornwall Railway, prepared by Captain Moorsom. Significantly, the prospectus was singularly lacking in any detail of how this was to be achieved.

However, the subsequent Notice[4] of the intended application to Parliament did include more information in that the Act would

...incorporate a company, and to enable the proprietors of...a certain Ferry, known as the Torpoint Steam Ferry, at Torpoint, to sell or let the said ferry, and the machines, vessels, wharfs, quays, landing-places, staiths, works, and other conveniences thereto belonging or used therewith...and the tolls and duties payable in respect thereof and all or any of the powers of such proprietors or persons in connection therewith respectively, to the Company so to be incorporated...and to enable such last mentioned Company to purchase or rent, and hold and use the said ferry, and to exercise all such powers as aforesaid.

It was further proposed to amend the powers and provisions of the original Act which had established the ferry (in the thirtieth year of the reign of King George III) to alter the tolls and rates payable. At the same time the Company would be empowered to establish a ferry across the Tamar from Torpoint to the opposite bank in the parish of Stoke Damerel, to include the construction of the associated quays, wharfs and landing places necessary in connection with the intended railway.

CORNWALL & DEVON CENTRAL RAILWAY

In the face of these developments, the South Western Railway began their policy of supporting a line to link Exeter and Falmouth, by following the route over the moors to the north, generally along that of Captain Moorsom's first survey, the so called Central Line. The supporters of this original line, the Cornwall and Devon Central Railway, led by Thomas Harvey, published their prospectus in 1844, having meanwhile appointed a committee[5] to

> ...open communications with the Directors of the South Western Railway Company, and such parties as may be disposed to join in carrying out a direct railway communication from Falmouth to the Metropolis by Exeter and Salisbury.

In due course the London & South Western promised pecuniary support, once their Bills for an extension from Salisbury to Exeter were passed.

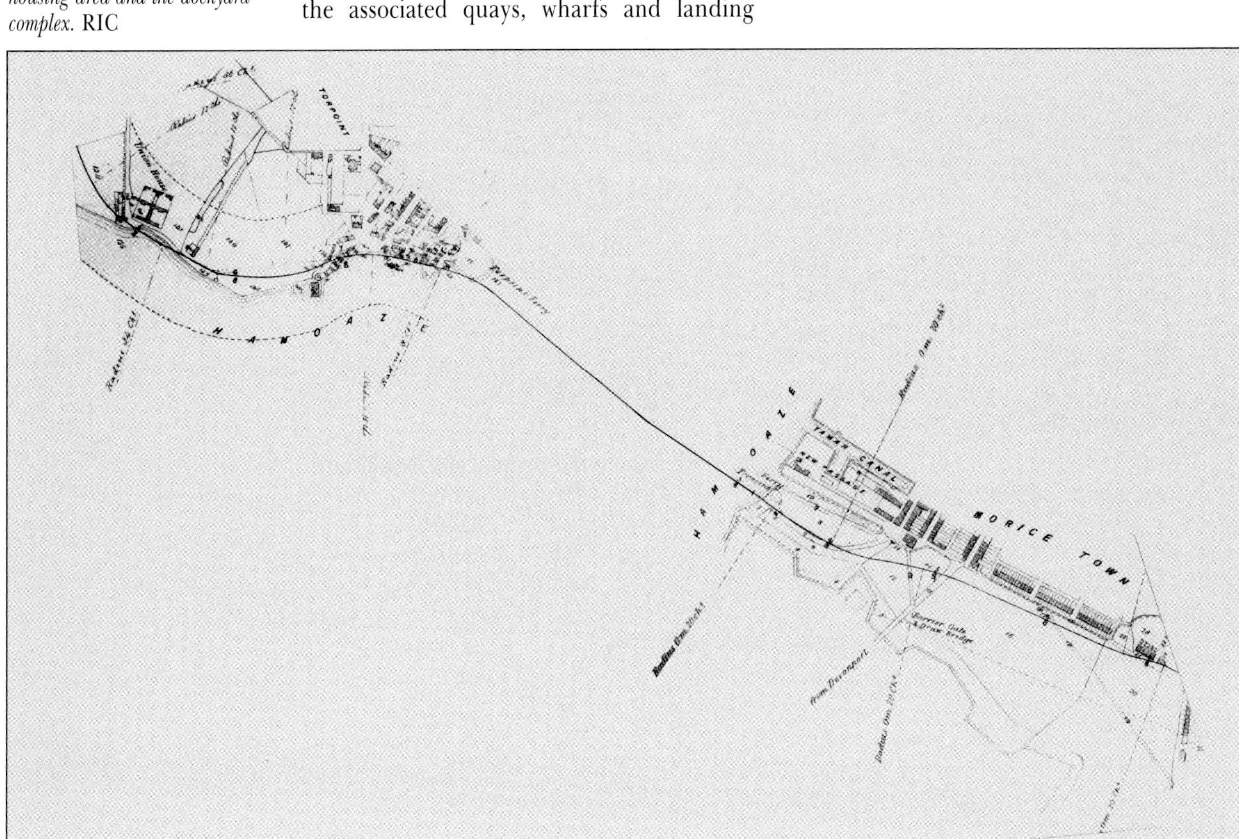

2.2 *A copy of the route at the proposed Torpoint Ferry crossing of the Hamoaze as surveyed by Captain Moorsom in 1844, showing the line sweeping in along the shore of St John's Lake to reach the western terminus of the ferry. On the opposite shore the route climbs away through the local housing area and the dockyard complex.* RIC

The Rival Routes

Sadly, the prospect of two alternative routes to link Falmouth with the rest of the rail network divided the efforts of the promoters. In fact, *The Royal Cornwall Gazette* maintained that many were deceived by the South Western's promise of help for the so called Central Line, even though this route appeared to enjoy more popular support. Hence, during 1844 the two rival groups actively promoted their respective proposals, seeking support and finance from the populace of Cornwall. Indeed, from a reading of the local press it would appear that through the autumn of that year the County was gripped with railway mania, the pages of the *West Briton & Cornwall Advertiser* were filled with reports of 'highly respectable and influential meetings' organised by the rival supporters at the principal towns in the Duchy.

An editorial[6] commended the prospectus of the Cornwall Railway and 'strongly urged on those who wish to take shares, the importance of an early application'. What a striking contrast to the difficulties which were to plague the Company in later years, through lack of subscription for its capital.

At the same time, in support of the benefits of the Cornwall Central Railway its promoters emphasised[7] that

> ...the projected coast line of railway from Falmouth to Torpoint, with a very doubtful passage across Hamoaze on the lower part of the Tamar...would be of little comparative advantage, if effected, and is highly objectionable, as tending to prevent the formation of a central line of railway, which alone would be beneficial to the county of Cornwall.

To add further strength to their case, the Central Railway then published[8] a detailed analysis comparing the respective merits of the two routes, identifying among many others, the following aspects:

1. Distance to Exeter – the Central route was some 22 miles shorter.

2. Engineering difficulties – few on the Central route but 'many and formidable' on the coastal line, including a very doubtful passage across Hamoaze.

3. The time taken to cover the increased distance and the crossing of the Hamoaze would add an hour to the journey time to Exeter.

4. The ruling gradient of the Central route would be significantly easier than the southern route, having regard to the gradient profile of the South Devon Railway.

The report concluded that the Central Railway could satisfy all the criteria laid down by the Board of Trade in connection with a new railway, and no real opposition could be offered to this line upon any grounds. On the other hand, the Coast Railway (or southerly route) could not meet these requirements to any extent, while the 'Great Western Company will not assist in making the best line'. Consequently, the smallest amount of opposition must destroy the Coast Line.

Matters did not rest there, for a few weeks later the promoters of the Cornwall Railway responded with a detailed 'Exposure'[9] to the points made in the Central Company's analysis, refuting the negative criticisms. It pointed out, in particular, that the Central route included no less than 24 [*sic*] tunnels in its 98½ miles whereas the Coastal line had but one in 66 miles, while the crossing of the Hamoaze was calculated not to exceed 15 minutes. So the arguments flowed across the County between the rival factions until eventually, the two schemes were to come before the appropriate Parliamentary committee.

Meanwhile, to add further complication, a Committee appointed by the Board of Trade to examine schemes for extending Railway Communications in Cornwall and Devonshire, had reported[10] in March 1845 that insofar as the Central line was concerned they

> ... had no hesitation in arriving at the opinion that it must be considered ... as altogether impracticable as a commercial undertaking [and that the] proposed Cornwall Railway from Plymouth to Falmouth affords the only practicable means of extending Railway communications to Cornwall.

The Parliamentary Hearings

The Cornwall Railway Bill was introduced into the House of Commons on 24 February 1845, and in due course was subject to examination by committee. On 29 May 1845 Captain Moorsom faced close questioning[11] regarding the route, particularly in Plymouth where, from the ferry terminus it was to cut through 'Navy row and Stoke' to reach the South Devon station. To this plan the inhabitants of Torpoint presented considerable opposition, supported by the dockyard authorities[12], while the proposals for the crossing of the Hamoaze attracted sharp criticism. Apparently trains were to use 'the ferry boats at present in use, but various alterations and improvements would be rendered necessary'.

He reported that the boat was a double boat, with a division in the middle housing the engine (see Plate 1.3). It was

> ... proposed to divide the train and break it up, and run down three of the carriages, one on one rail and three on the other[*sic*].

Captain Moorsom was again cross examined by the Committee during their meeting of 30 May[13], in particular with regard to the Hamoaze crossing, in which learned counsel of the Committee inferred

> ...that the boat or floating bridge, and the electric telegraph, in crossing that passage, would be exposed to considerable danger by ships dragging their anchors.

In reply he pointed out that the 'present boat-bridge was found to be sufficient for all the purpose of trade'. From experience, vessels did not frequently drag their anchors and foul the chains of the bridge, while the wires of the electric telegraph 'would be conveyed across, preserved dry from external damp in a tube, which would be under water in the mud on the bottom'. He stated that the passage of the Hamoaze could be completed in six or seven minutes, and while the present boat would accommodate six of the largest Great Western carriages in practice they might not convey so many.

At a subsequent session of the Committee on 2 June[14], Mr Brunel was called to give evidence. In view of their projected investment he had been retained by the Associated Companies to approve the plans on their behalf. When asked by the Committee 'will you state generally, whether you consider the plan for crossing the Hamoaze will succeed', he replied 'I think so, or I should not have agreed in recommending it'.

The Committee also queried the difficulty arising from the affects of wind and tide on the approach of the ferry to the shore; in particular, the need 'to draw the boat up at right angles'. When asked if he was prepared to suggest to the Committee how he would achieve this objective, his sanguine reply was

> No; I am prepared to say that I consider there is no difficulty whatever in doing it.

When questioned on how the trains were to be loaded on the ferry, his response was to the point; that is was 'a very easy and simple thing to do'. The carriages would be run on the boats in the same way as private carriages, and removed in a similar manner; the procedure was simple and 'no longer time would be consumed here than two minutes' [*sic*]. This was not more than was occupied in other lines in breaking up trains and starting them afresh. Finally, the boat might easily be made to carry six carriages. On reflection, we must marvel at Brunel's optimism regarding this aspect of the crossing, which was surely anything but a simple operation, and question whether or not he had some ulterior motive in adopting this point of view.

It is significant that other witnesses called to give evidence were strongly opposed to this coastal route and, in particular, the crossing of the Hamoaze. They favoured the direct Central connection to Exeter, a route which it was maintained should carry more of the ore produced in the County.

On 17 July the bill came before a Committee of the House of Lords, with Lord Ellenborough in the chair, and the crossing of the Hamoaze was subject to further consideration[15]. Mr J. M. Rendel, who had earlier been involved in the construction of a floating bridge or steam ferry at Saltash (see Plate 1.2), gave evidence of having constructed the present steam ferry boats or bridge at the Hamoaze. These were worked by chains which extended to either shore, and when the wind and tide were strong, the chains formed an arc such that the platform of the boat was not at right angles to the landing place. He was of the opinion that considerable difficulty would arise in bringing the rails of the bridge immediately in contact with the rails of the landing place, so that the carriages might easily be run on and off the bridge. In addition, the considerable rise and fall of the tide, which amounted to eighteen feet at springs, would impose further difficulty. On reflection, despite Brunel's optimism, there was much merit in his submissions, and it should be remembered that he was speaking from some considerable experience in the operation of these 'steam bridges'.

He indicated that a train being stopped, divided, placed upon the steam bridge, landed on the opposite shore, recoupled and finally put in motion, would incur a delay of from eight to twelve minutes on each side, in addition to the seven or eight minutes for the crossing. It should be noted that the totals of these times do not compare with the 15 minutes quoted in the above 'exposure'. This witness further considered that a dock should be constructed on each shore of the Hamoaze to allow the floating bridge to get under a platform and the trains to be 'dropped on or raised from the bridge'.

Evidence of a general nature was given by Mr Locke and Mr Stephenson, against the Cornwall line but in support of the Central route, which was confirmed by further supportive contributions at subsequent meetings on 18 and 19 July. In this respect, Mr Rowe addressed the Committee on behalf of the opponents to the Cornwall Railway and stated that the scheme 'was a great delusion'; its success to date was, in a great measure, due to the support of the Great Western Railway, aided by a report from the Board of Trade in its favour. However, there could be no doubt that the Cornwall line was 'highly disagreeable to a great mass of the inhabitants of Cornwall and Devon, for 150 petitions had been laid on the table of their Lordships House against it'. In truth, the Cornwall line was a most impracticable line which would never answer the purposes for which a railway should be established; he was most critical of the Board of Trade and its decisions.

In the face of such condemnation the Committee retired to consider their decision, and later reconvened in the evening of 19 July 1845, to give their answer. 'The noble Chairman, intimated that the committee were of opinion that the construction of a railway from Plymouth to Falmouth...would be of great public advantage'. However, without a further and more accurate survey, to obtain more favourable gradients and curves and, if possible, to avoid the crossing of the Hamoaze, 'the bill should not now be further proceeded with'.

This announcement was received with cheers from the bill's opponents, 'which were instantly checked'.

Appointment of Brunel as Engineer

Notwithstanding the popular support throughout the County for the Central route, the Cornwall Company promoters were encouraged by the obvious preference of the Government officials for their project. At a meeting of the Directors and officers of all the Companies involved, held at Paddington on 25 July 1845, a resolution was entered into to carry out the recommendations of the Lords.

This was implemented by the Directors of the Cornwall Company, who now turned to Brunel; a Resolution[16] was passed on 26 August 1845, appointing him Engineer of the Cornwall Railway Company. He was 'requested carefully to survey the country for the purpose of recommending such improvements or alterations in the line of the railway as may seem to him expedient', with a view to introducing a new bill to the following session of Parliament. In particular, while retaining the option of crossing the Hamoaze by means of a steam-bridge, he was to investigate an alternative arrangement for bridging this Great Divide.

In all the circumstances, his relations with Moorsom became obviously strained, and in an endeavour to assuage the latter's wounded pride, Brunel suggested to the Directors that Moorsom should furnish assistance as and when required – a situation which, in practice, proved quite unworkable. His contribution proved more a hindrance than a help and eventually culminated in the arrangement being cancelled by Brunel at the end of the year (Vaughan 1991). Meanwhile, on 2 December 1845, the Company Finance Committee was instructed to advance Brunel the sum of £2,500.

THE DEVON & CORNWALL CENTRAL BILL

In the interim, Parliament had been considering the Devon & Cornwall Central bill, and on 31 March 1846 this projected line came before the Standing Orders Committee of the House of Lords, chaired by the Earl of Shaftesbury. It attracted great opposition on behalf of both the Cornwall and the West Cornwall Railway Companies. On examination, it appeared that the promoters' submissions were technically flawed due to the improper deposit of the relevant plans. They included so many blunders, that the Committee considered it was impossible to suppose that they were serious in promoting the Central line (one report[17] mentions the detection of 'some three thousand errors'), 'and thereupon declared the standing orders not to have been complied with'. The bill was therefore 'thrown out', but the preparations for its submission had cost some £96,000, in order, as another report[18] commented, to 'gratify the professional rapacity of men whose only object appeared to be the reckless expenditure of the shareholders money.' When it is realised that the South Western Railway did not reach Exeter until 1860, the efforts of the Devon and Cornwall Central Railway were indeed proved abortive.

This decision was a great disappointment to the population of Cornwall, arising as it did not from the merits of the bill but from an administrative failure - as evidenced in an editorial in the *West Briton & Cornwall Advertiser* of 10 April 1846:

> What is to be done with the Cornish Railways?
>
> This is a question that is on everyone's mouth. Great, indeed is the disappointment that is felt throughout the county at the failure of the central line before the Committee on standing orders in the House of Lords. There seems to have been some grievous mismanagement somewhere... [and] we cannot, however, withhold an expression of strong reprehension at the neglect that has occasioned this mischance, and of equally strong regret that so important an undertaking is thus delayed, if not entirely overthrown.

The editorial went on to extol the advantages of the Central line, a project which the paper claimed it had always supported, and sought to question the most appropriate steps to be taken in the future, including an amalgamation between the two Companies. In this respect it was understood that such an offer had been made by the promoters of the Central line; a solution which 'would have been satisfactory to the county gentlemen on both sides of the question'. This offer had, however, been refused by the committee of the Cornwall line.

The future of the Central line was, therefore, in doubt but the promoters endeavoured to hold the Company together. They continued to make vigorous protest against the development of the Cornwall line until eventually their Company expired during 1847.

BRUNEL'S PROPOSALS

In the meanwhile, Brunel had completed his initial survey and came forward with a fresh concept, which reflected the approach to the problem of a man of genius, compared with the very ordinary proposals previously submitted by Moorsom. (The latter could not be called a successful engineer since only one of the many schemes for which he became engineer actually got through Parliament).

With boldness and imagination Brunel's route while, in general, following Moorsom's original line, adopted adjustments to the alignment which eased the curvature and kept gradients within a maximum of 1 in 60. Significantly, it included the building of a high level bridge to carry the double-track line across the Tamar at a location some two miles upstream from Moorsom's alternative ferry crossing at Torpoint. There, the river narrowed to a width of 1,100 feet , with the banks rising steeply on either side. On the

Cornish bank the small town of Saltash, in picturesque muddle and disarray, (Plate 2.3) struggled up the hillside. At first sight it appeared to be a poor insignificant place, with its sixteenth century houses (one dated 1584) down in Tamar Street and the late seventeenth and eighteenth century properties up Fore Street Hill, all crowding together in a variety of small shapes to form this fishing town. However, the surrounding hills, with the great expanse of inland water, lent a picturesque setting for what was to become the site of one of Brunel's greatest achievements, to form a lasting memorial to his genius. In selecting this site his impish nature may also have played a part, since an early map of the area by John Cary, c1818, shows the opposite (Devon) bank, extending as far as the village of St Budeaux, as actually being part of Cornwall. From this crossing, it was proposed that the line would follow the banks of the Hamoaze, inland from the dockyard at Devonport, then swing south and east to reach the South Devon terminus at Millbay. However, in submitting his plans for the overall route, Brunel maintained[19] that

> ...the character of the county of Cornwall is such that no railway can be constructed at any moderate expense without either sacrificing all consideration for the interests of localities and the position of population to the mere choice of levels, or without steep gradients and sharp curves.

At a special meeting of shareholders held in Truro on 15 May 1846, with about one hundred members in attendance, the Chairman, Mr J. T. Treffry, confirmed that following the meeting's approval of that day's proceedings, their bill was set to receive a third reading in the House of Commons. Although last year it had been finally rejected by the House of Lords, it had received approval in principle. However, Parliament had said 'we approve of your measure, but we think you have not adopted the best means to carry it out; you may get a better line if you will try'. That trial had now been made, under the able supervision of that eminent engineer, Mr Brunel, who had laid out a line between Plymouth and Falmouth, and in addition, between Doublebois and Launceston, with a line to connect Bodmin and Padstow.

This network, together with the connection to the West Cornwall line, provided a system to cover the needs of the County as a whole 'and could not fail to meet the requirements of Parliament and give an ample return to the shareholders who might embark in the undertaking'. There was an overwhelming majority in favour of the proposal.

2.3 *A view of Saltash from the Devon shore, c1824, showing the site which was eventually to form the location of Brunel's Royal Albert Bridge. It will be seen that the ferry, conveying a coach or cart across the passage, is hand propelled while the horses have apparently already been brought over; a tedious and time consuming operation.* SALTASH HERITAGE

Further Parliamentary Considerations

The bill came before the House of Lords Committee, chaired by Viscount Morpeth, on Friday, 12 June 1846, and was once more subject to detail scrutiny, with strong opposition from representatives of the original Central route. Again, Mr Rendel submitted evidence, this time to the effect that the navigation of the Tamar required that the bridge should be at least 100 feet high. 'In the plans the crown of the arch appeared to be seventy feet and the rails eighty two feet above high water', possibly indicating that Brunel originally had in mind a massive single arch bridge across the Tamar. The witness had estimated that a suspension bridge at Saltash would cost £83,000. 'A bridge with piers to bear a railway, such as that proposed, would cost considerably more; it certainly could not be constructed for £40,000'. The piers, working through 40 feet of water at low water, involved work of a difficult and expensive nature. 'No bridge should be allowed to be constructed across the Tamar under 100 feet in height'.

A number of witnesses, including Locke, submitted evidence of a general nature in criticism of the overall route, including the South Devon line, and in support of the alternative Central Company's proposals. When called before the Committee Brunel fiercely defended his overall plans, including the then operation of the South Devon atmospheric system. His Tamar bridge would be built about 95 feet above mean high-watermark, although it is thought[20] that at that time 'Brunel had not determined on the mode of crossing the Tamar', but the means should not be ruinous to the Company. We can only conjecture that, such was his reputation and the validity of his argument, the Committee were prepared to accept the broad scope of his proposals.

At a meeting on 15 June, the Committee, under Viscount Morpeth, had decided that the preamble of the Cornwall Railway, 'with the exception of the Doubleboys branch' [sic] was proved and further, recommended that the bridge at Saltash should be made (by consent) of the greatest practicable height. Subsequent meetings of the committee were held through June and July 1846; at that of Saturday, 18 July, with Lord Denbigh in the chair, Brunel gave detailed evidence with respect to the renewed survey of the line made by himself after the original bill had been thrown out in the session of 1845. He was of the opinion[21] that

> ...notwithstanding the steepness of some of the gradients, the line could very well be worked, and would most certainly pay. The line was in most respects the same as that of last year, and he thought any line that might be made through this district must occupy very nearly the same ground as this would. The curves and gradients were much more favourable on this line than on that originally proposed...the gradients on the old line were in some cases as steep as 1 in 40, but on this there were none steeper than 1 in 60...The total length of the main line was 63 miles [and] the total estimate £1,600,000 [excluding the cost of] the Launceston or Doublebois branch. The crossing of the Hamoaze, which was objected to by Lord Ellenborough's committee of last year, has been avoided...The height at which the line crossed the river Tamar, at Saltash, was, according to the sections, eighty or eighty five feet above high water mean mark, but he thought it more likely that it would be made at about ninety five feet...there was nothing to prevent the Company from making the arch at ninety or ninety five feet above high water mark. There were no piers.

The supporters of the Central line hung tenaciously in the argument; in the meeting of 23 July they maintained that at a height of 85 feet the bridge across the Tamar would effectively obstruct the navigation of the river where vessels of 300 tons burden came up to export the ores of the county. Even to that extent the bridge could not be raised within the limits specified in the bill except by consent or a supplementary act next year. However, the chairman, Viscount Torrington, ruled that the construction of the bridge across the Tamar at Saltash was a question which remained with the Admiralty; they had it within their power to order the bridge to be of what height they pleased, and that work could not be commenced till all the plans and specifications had been submitted for their approval, so that they were cognisant of all the facts of the case. It was, therefore, better that the responsibility of the matter should remain in their hands.

Eventually, the supporters of the Central route had to concede that their battle was lost. In its issue of 31 July 1846, the *West Briton & Cornwall Advertiser* included an editorial regretting that the Cornwall Railway bill would shortly become law. Undoubtedly, there was still very strong support for the Central line and the editorial concluded

> ...We are unwilling to pass any comments on the Committee of the House of Lords, and the very restricted light in which they were pleased to treat the Cornish Railways. It was anything but in accordance with the report that lately emanated from their lordships' house; and certainly not the way to remove the complaints that are so commonly made of the imperfect state of our legislation as regards railway matters.

Cornwall Railway Act, 3 August 1846 (9 & 10 Victoria c.335)

Thus, Brunel's proposals were eventually accepted, the Bill being passed by the Lords on the 30 July; and the Cornwall Railway Act, incorporating the Company, received the Royal Assent on 3 August 1846. The expenses of this successful application were just half those incurred for the abortive Central scheme[22].

Among its many Sections, the Act specified that

> ...the said Railway shall cross the River Tamar at Saltash by a Bridge to consist of Four Spans only, with straight soffits, all of which Spans shall be of such Dimensions, Height and Construction as shall be previously approved of by the Lord High Admiral.

Furthermore, the Act required that the Company should pay an annual rent of twenty five pounds in perpetuity to the Duchy of Cornwall

> ...for such use of the said water of Tamar...for the liberty of doing all things needful or convenient for the Construction of the said Railway over and across the same.

It was thus left to Brunel to interpret these broad stipulations as best he could, which we shall consider in the next chapter. Meanwhile, there followed a few weeks when there seemed every prospect of work starting on the project, leading to its speedy completion. However, in the autumn of that year there was a general panic in railway shares, leading to the value of even the most prestigious and well established companies being more than halved. Hence, the facilities for raising capital for new projects were no longer available and all new undertakings, however well founded, were suspended. Inevitably, the shares of the Cornwall Railway fell into this category; they became unmarketable and the Company was forced to await the emergence of better times. As MacDermot says, 'the Company went to sleep for three years'.

Then, sadly, in 1850 the zealous and hardworking chairman, Mr J. T. Treffry, died; his loss was a severe blow to the Company's prospects and Mr M. Williams was appointed his successor. In the prevailing economic climate the Company's fortunes waned for a further two years. Meanwhile, Brunel had in 1851 revived its plans when he came forward with the proposal for a single line of rails, which would enable completion of the line from Plymouth to Falmouth for £800,000, including the building of the Saltash Bridge. This proposal decided the Directors to take steps to rearrange the Company's capital but it was another year before these plans were formalised at a shareholders' meeting in April 1852. With some improvement in market conditions, the new Chairman was able to bring fresh confidence and a sense of purpose to the enterprise, leading to the Associated Companies once again giving their support.

Through the ensuing years the difficulty of raising money still remained, but eventually the route from Plymouth to Truro was completed in 1859, with the opening of the Saltash Bridge; thirteen years after the granting of the Act. It was a further four years before trains finally reached Falmouth, in 1863. Sadly, the railway had been a long time in coming.

CHAPTER THREE

THE INITIAL DESIGN INVESTIGATION

1847 to 1849

First Thoughts

While the building of the Cornwall Railway involved a series of major engineering works throughout its eventual length of 65 miles from Plymouth to Falmouth, including no less than 42 timber viaducts, by far the most significant work was the bridge to cross the Tamar at Saltash. Understandably, Brunel directed his effort to evolving the most economical and suitable design for this major undertaking. As we have already noted, in preparing his initial recommendations for the revised line, it [1] is thought

> ...very probable that at this time Mr Brunel had not determined on the mode of crossing the Tamar – for it was needful not only to have the means of crossing, but that such means should not be ruinous to the Company.

According to both his son's biography and MacDermot, apart from the approach spans, he had initially envisaged bridging the water by a single span of 255 feet and six spans each of 105 feet, with a clearance above high water of 70 feet. Following his great love of timber, their superstructures were to have been formed as trussed arches and, as such, would have represented magnificent specimens of timber design, probably supported on timber piles driven down into the mud to reach rock foundation. However, it would appear from the evidence submitted to the Parliamentary Committees that these initial proposals were open to different interpretations. For instance, reference is made at the meeting of 12 June to 'a single arch with piers' and a height of 70 feet; at the meeting of 18 July 1846 'there were no piers', and height of 95 feet; while the meeting of 23 July 1846 quoted heights of 85 feet and over.

Significantly, it was established at the meeting of 23 July 1846 that the Admiralty would have the final say in this matter, and in due course they decreed that, in the interest of navigation, the spans should be altered to two of 300 feet and two of 200 feet with straight soffits and a clear headway of 100 feet. Such an arrangement would have required no less than three piers in deep water.

At one time, Brunel had also considered a design comprising a single span of 850 feet. He had previously carried out calculations for a span of 1,000 feet and taking account of 'a proper thickness of ballast, and a possible load of a train of engines without tenders, and a limitation under such a load of 5 tons strain per square inch' he concluded that a span of 1,000 feet could 'be made in England of the very best workmanship' (Brunel 1870).

He was now faced with the Admiralty requirement involving the daunting task of constructing three massive piers in deep water, a situation which finally determined his decision to have a single central pier in mid stream with two spans each of 465 feet, which were subsequently reduced to 455 feet. Notwithstanding his extensive experience, even Brunel could not contemplate these structures in timber, and he would have to turn to the only alternative material available, wrought iron. In making this decision he was, doubtless, influenced by the work of his friend and professional rival, Robert Stephenson, who had recently had to face problems of a similar magnitude for the bridges across the Conway and Menai Straits on his Chester & Holyhead Railway.

The Introduction of Wrought Iron

Here, in the early 1840s Stephenson had considered the use of beams formed from rivetted wrought iron plates and angles, and in April 1845 had formed a productive collaboration with two other engineers, William Fairbairn who was experienced in the application of wrought iron, and Eaton Hodgkinson, well versed in the theory of structures. In this respect, they would have taken due note of the theoretical work carried out by the Rev Henry Moseley as published in his book *The Mechanical Principles of Engineering and Architecture*, in 1843. While this was probably the first comprehensive treatise on what might be called modern engineering mechanics to appear in English, it paid due acknowledgement to the works of the French scientists Coulomb, Poncelet and Navier.

Thus, this team had carried out a series of tests on different forms of wrought iron tubular structures with the results carefully analysed in a report published in 1846. This established

> ...wrought iron on a more rational basis than any other material and at the same time they made it almost impossible for engineers to proportion beams, as they had done previously, on the basis of some hunches and a little "ad hoc" experimental work.[2]

It is reasonable to assume that, through his close relationship with Stephenson, this information would be available to Brunel, for application in due course to the design of the Saltash Bridge. Meanwhile, as we shall see, he was able to complete the design of his bridge across the Wye at Chepstow, using wrought iron, founded on the sound technical premise of Stephenson's work. In passing, we should note that although Brunel became one of the boldest designers in wrought iron in the late 1840s and early 1850s, he never claimed any credit for its introduction.

To complete the story of Stephenson's investigation, unfortunately, following the initial success of their earlier collaboration, Stephenson and Fairbairn were subsequently in dispute, although by December 1848 the two tubes of the Conway Bridge, spanning 400 feet, had been completed and opened for traffic; followed by the completion in 1850 of the Britannia Bridge across the Menai Strait. Thus, the success of these two fine structures gave further credence to the application of wrought iron tubular construction and on the basis of these results Brunel sought to build his own unique designs.

It will be appreciated that Brunel was carrying out these preliminary engineering studies at a time when the Company had been unable to attract the necessary investment. Consequently, he was under constant pressure to reduce the cost of his work but it was noted[3] in the Board Minutes of 19 January 1848 that Brunel stated

> ...he had endeavoured to reduce the Engineering staff...and operated such reductions as would bring the Expenses at present within £2,000 per annum and that he did not consider it would be advisable to reduce it below that sum.

The Site Investigation

In selecting the location for the bridge at Saltash, advantage was taken of a greenstone dyke, described by Brereton[4] in the contemporary but now obsolete term as a 'trap', that outcrops to the surface above high water on the western bank of the river. During 1847, a preliminary exploration was carried out by divers to see if this reef extended to the centre of the stream which would thus form a suitable base for a central pier. In spite of the difficulties posed by the depth of water and the strength of the current, not to mention the deposit of silt and mud which extended to depths of between three and sixteen feet, exploratory borings had been carried out. Unfortunately, this initial investigation failed to yield sufficiently reliable information on which to base the design of the central pier.

Brunel then determined that a thorough examination should be made of the river bed where he intended to locate the central support. For this purpose he constructed a wrought iron cylinder, of six feet diameter and some 85 feet in length, to act as a coffer dam, from which trial borings could be made. On the outside of the cylinder heavy lugs and lifting eyes were fixed, in spiral formation, to which slinging cables were attached. This unit was then slung between two gun-brig hulks and supported from a suitable framework mounted on their decks. This combination was then towed out and anchored in the river over the proposed site of the centre pier. The spiral location of the cylinder's cable attachments allowed the cables to be brought up to windlasses placed at different points on the decks of the hulks; thus the cylinder could be controlled in its descent to the bed of the river and allowance made for the rise and fall of the tide.

Brunel's report[5] of 22 February 1848 advised that

> ...the preliminary works for the purpose of more accurately determining the nature of the bottom of the river and the thickness of the deposit above the rock upon which the pier will be founded and thus determining the exact position of the pier are still proceeding. I expect in a few weeks to have sunk a cylinder of sufficient size to enable me to examine the bed of the river.

The day to day operation of this investigation was under the control of one of Brunel's assistants, W. Glennie who had earlier been the resident engineer during the construction of Box Tunnel on the Great Western Railway. On 27 April 1848, he reported[6] to the Cornwall Company Secretary, W. H. Bond, that the cylinder had been launched the previous day at 10.30 a.m. and positioned in mid stream at low water, 4.30 p.m. His letter records that... 'everything went beautifully – there was not a single mishap.' He was sorry Mr Brunel could not be present.

In a progress report[7] of 1 May 1848 he advised that they

> ....had met with some rock or hard ground near the surface of the mud which prevents it [the cylinder] from going down. I am now probing to see what it is. If it is not rock I hope to force the cylinder down by weight but if it is rock we might shift it to a softer place.

However, by 17 May Glennie was reporting[8] that 'our cylinder is performing admirably', although, unfortunately, they had broken the clutch box in lifting the cylinder. Furthermore, we infer that the necessary pumping equipment was not yet operative, since he goes on to describe how by means of the cranes he had lowered the water level to 40 feet below the top of the cylinder. This was 30 feet below high water mark, and in the following 16 hours it had only risen 5¼ inches. Some of that may have been due to leakage in the cylinder itself but he confirmed that they

> ...have got a perfect coffer dam so far. The cylinder is 10 feet in the mud and within 18 inches of the rock at the bottom.

By 25 May Glennie had the satisfaction of reporting[9] that the previous evening he had stood 'in the mud at the bottom of the Tamar' and examined it minutely:

> ...It is most favourable for our operations being very adhesive and stiff and perfectly water tight. We had to dig it with a spade. It contains a small portion of sand and broken shells but no gravel as far as we have examined it.

With obvious reference to Brunel, he reported that he had smoked a cigar at the bottom of the river.

With the cylinder firmly positioned, trial borings were made into the rock surface, a total of five such borings being made from within it, before the whole assembly was moved to a new location and the process repeated.

Coincidentally with this investigation, it had been arranged that the proposed route of the line across the Tamar at this location should be fully surveyed. This was carried out over the period 4 March to 31 May 1848 by a Mr Johnston, of Plymouth, who produced a detailed plan of the proposed alignment. The centreline of the bridge was determined by triangulation, set up from a baseline between 'a location D' on the pier at Saltash and a 'location C' on a 'Lower Stone at Ferry Beach' on the Devon shore. It appears that the location of Glennie's cylinder on 16 May 1848 was included as part of this survey, for its position is recorded as location 'E' on that plan.

An extract from Johnston's plan incorporating these details is shown in Plate 3.1. Sadly, during the period of this initial investigation the prospects for the Company declined in the face of the 'monetary affairs of the Kingdom'. In spite of these difficulties Brunel[10] was, nevertheless, anxious that

> ...with the view to our future proceedings when the time may come for carrying on the works – it will be a very great relief and add much to public confidence if we have determined every thing connected with the Bridge at Saltash – ascertained the exact state of the rock at the points which

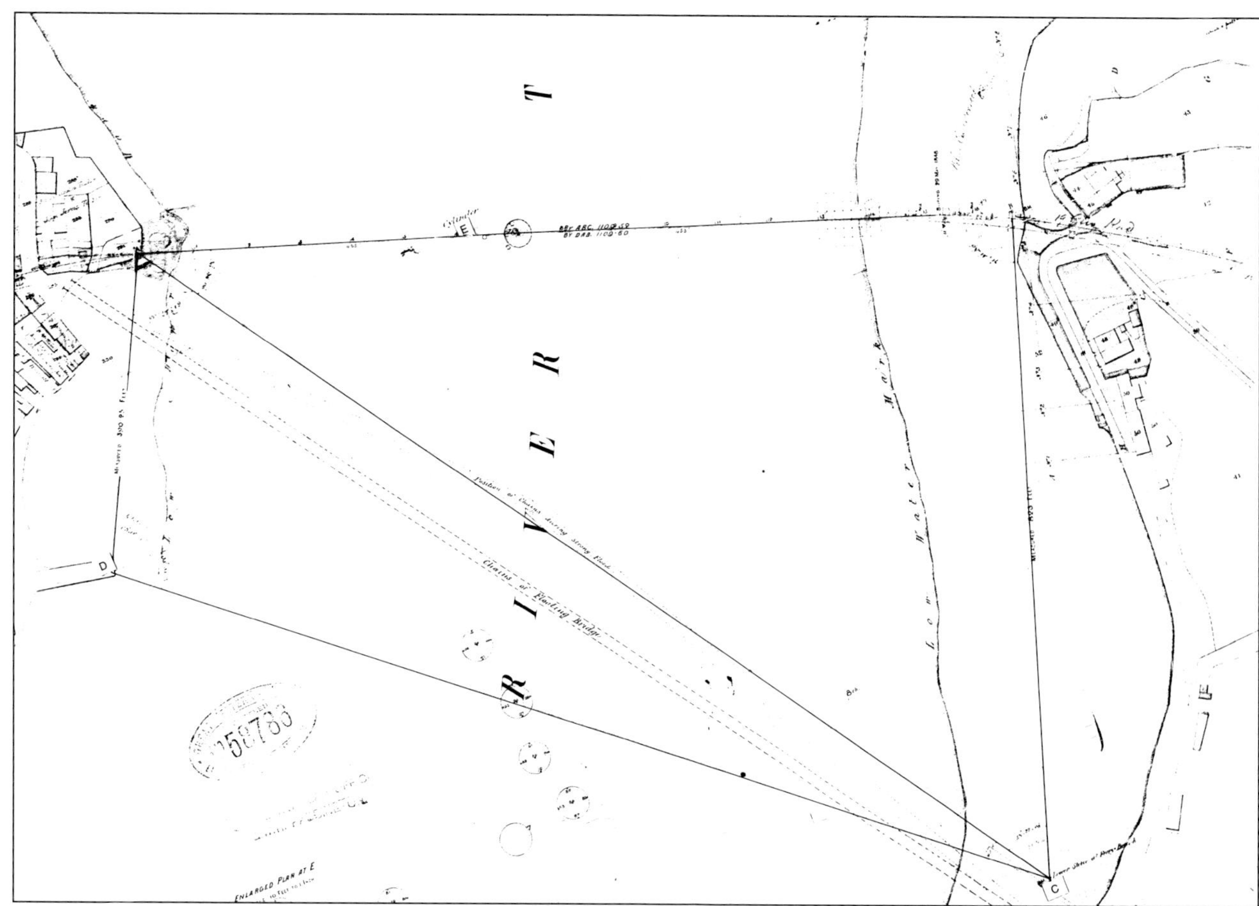

3.1 *A reproduction of part of Johnston's survey of the Tamar crossing of May 1848, showing the centreline of the proposed route, the baseline of the triangulation, locations 'D' and 'C'; the cylinder position 'E' and the proposed positions of the centre pier and the two landward piers. Note also the line of the chains of the original floating bridge.* RTGW

appear likely to be suitable for the pier and proved the practicability of getting down to the rock through a cylinder such as the one we are using for the soundings and borings and of keeping the water out if need should arise by closing that cylinder and using it as a diving bell.

Partial Suspension of the Works

Nevertheless, in spite of this encouraging engineering investigation and following the most careful consideration of all the factors involved, the Directors, at the shareholders' meeting in Truro of 20 August 1848, reported that they had deemed it prudent to suspend the bulk of the operations in connection with the construction of the railway. With unpaid calls of over £20,000 on issued shares and the Associated Companies declining to furnish further capital in this situation, they had no alternative.

However, one of the areas where they had decided work should not be suspended concerned the investigation into the soundings at the Saltash passage, since it was reported[11] that

> ...we have all the machinery there, and it will cost £350 to complete those soundings, so that we shall then be able to proceed whenever it is thought advisable to go on with the works, whereas if we suspend working at that place we shall have to remove the vessels there, and there would be great difficulty in resuming that part of the work.

Accordingly, throughout the following autumn and into the cold winter, Glennie was able to continue his investigation, assisted by Captain Dance and 'some excellent men whose services' Brunel had secured. By their 'zealous and laborious exertions' they were successful in making 'a detailed examination and minute survey of the rock which would form the foundation of the centre pier of the bridge'; and had satisfied themselves regarding its excellent quality. This investigation included ascertaining the exact state and form of the surface so as to determine the proper site for the pier.

At the same time, these experiments had also tested the efficiency of Brunel's proposals for the construction of the centre pier. By sinking the cylinder through the tenacious clay which covered the rock, it had been possible to make a light coffer dam from which the water had been withdrawn, thus enabling the engineers to descend and examine the rock at their leisure.

Altogether the cylinder was pitched at 35 different positions, to make a total of 175 borings over an area 50 feet square. Their detail position and result were carefully recorded, so as to furnish an accurate survey of the surface of the rock. From all these data, a model of the rocky base could be made which would enable the proposed position of the central pier to be precisely determined. Before removing the cylinder from the final location of the investigation the clay was cleared away and the rock excavated to a depth of two or three feet. It was found to be exceedingly tough and sound and a trial wall of masonry was built, in order to complete the experiment.

The fifth Half Yearly ordinary meeting of the shareholders, held in Truro on 23 February 1849, gave a depressing report of the Company's affairs; works suspended, suspension of payments of interest on deposits made by shareholders and a shortage of funds due to unpaid calls. In contrast, Brunel's report[12] regarding the outcome of the examination of the bed of the river Tamar was one of success and hope for the future. The works carried out by his assistants, at a depth of some eighty feet below high water mark and in a strong current

> ...determined most satisfactorily the nature of the foundation [and] have also tested the efficiency of the plan by which it has been proposed hereafter to construct the pier and I am happy to say that nothing could have proved more satisfactory or more completely have realised my most sanguine expectations.

He considered that the success which had attended these trials and their outcome, had removed all doubt regarding the proposed facility of constructing the central pier, by sinking a wrought iron cylinder of the requisite diameter to form a 'perfect coffer dam'. This would enable a substantial stone pier to be built in the centre of the river, in eighty feet of water 'at the ordinary cost of masonry'. He concluded

> ...with this centre pier (and the pier on either side can be built without any difficulty) and with the present known and proved plans of construction of large spans in wrought iron the work becomes one of ordinary difficulty and moderate expense and can as I have ascertained be contracted for as a whole and without any large charges for risk.

Despite this encouraging prospect, the overall shortage of finance imposed a continuing curtailment on the works connected with the project and for a period of some three years no further progress was made in the building of the Bridge, other than work on the drawings, based on the results of these encouraging experiments.

CHAPTER FOUR

THE PROTOTYPE

1849 to 1853

During the period Brunel was working on plans for the Cornwall Railway, and in particular the design of the Saltash Bridge, among the many other projects in which he was involved was the building of the South Wales Railway. This entailed the construction of a bridge across the River Wye at Chepstow. Again, through his love of timber, his first thoughts had been to use timber-trussed arches but because the Admiralty had insisted upon a bridge having a level soffit, giving 50 feet of uninterrupted headroom over a width of 300 feet, he had to turn to alternative materials.

As we have seen, he had taken due note of the work of Stephenson and his colleagues in connection with the application of wrought iron in bridge construction, and in the light of these results he decided to adopt it for Chepstow; work starting on the crossing in May 1849. In that connection, with his characteristic attention to detail, he made arrangements for the mathematician and astronomer Airy to take measurements at the site (Pugsley 1976); writing to the site engineer, W. G. Owen, 'Mr Airy is a man who of course can thoroughly understand and appreciate such works - being a first rate mechanic as well as mathematician'.

Accordingly, before examining the details as finally established for the Saltash Bridge, it would be appropriate to consider the experience which Brunel was thus to obtain in the employment of wrought iron in his designs and the Chepstow Bridge can, therefore, be considered the precursor or prototype for Saltash.

He had, of course, closely observed the work of Stephenson during this period and it would be reasonable to assume that those overall results influenced his decision to use wrought iron. However, in no way would he slavishly follow his rival's practice and, while taking due heed of Stephenson's basic concept,

4.1 *An engraving taken from an 1856 pamphlet published to commemorate the opening of Brunel's Tubular Suspension Bridge over the River Wye at Chepstow in 1852; a structure which 'merits an extended notice, from the novelty of its construction, the difficulties with which the engineer has had to contend during the progress of the works, the cost at which it will be completed, and the almost perfect rigidity of the structure, as evidenced...under a very heavy weight'. Edward Finch's Bridge Works can be seen on the right hand bank.* MOSS ROSE PRESS

Brunel's approach involved a more fundamental analysis of how best to apply a tubular construction, with meticulous attention to the detail design and erection procedures. These were worked out in his Duke Street office, to avoid the number of set backs and hold-ups which he had observed when attending the erection of his rival's projects. The outcome was an original and imaginative bridge design which, by comparison, was to prove most cost effective. A contemporary engraving of the final structure is shown in Plate 4.1.

On the eastern bank of the Wye crossing Brunel was faced with a limestone precipice some 120 feet high, being the edge of a wide sweep of tableland; the western bank was only a little above high water level, rising gradually over a considerable distance. It was composed partly of clay and partly of loose shingle interspersed with large boulder stones.

In order to provide a clear headway of fifty feet under the bridge at high water, for navigation purposes, a long embankment was necessary on this side while a cutting, some 21 feet deep, had to be cut in the opposite cliff. This left a total distance of 600 feet to be bridged, divided into a river span of 300 feet and three land spans each of 100 feet. This overall layout of the crossing will be apparent from the drawing in Plate 4.2.

The bridge design involved spans of riveted wrought iron construction, incorporating two lines of broad gauge track, each carried on independent plate girderwork. The cliff provided an excellent foundation for the abutment at one end of the main span, but on the opposite bank the land throughout was soft and treacherous. There was, however, rock at a depth of 30 feet below the bed of the river.

To build a masonry foundation, using a coffer dam, was almost impracticable, since the rock was 84 feet below the level of high water, while the building of a stone pier on a foundation of piles was abandoned on account of expense. However, Brunel experimented with the application of a screwed pile[1] near the site, formed of a cast iron cylinder, 3 feet external diameter and 12 inches thick, cast in lengths of 10 feet. These were joined together by 'internal socket and joggle joints, secured with pins and run with lead'. The bottom cylinder incorporated a 12 inch circular projection in the form of a helix, with a pitch of 7 inches, secured by a wrought iron hoop.

This cylinder was screwed into the ground, using capstan bars worked manually, to a depth of 58 feet, through stiff clay and sand down to the rock. Progress was intermittent, owing to the time needed to clear out the core, etc, but this depth was reached after 142

4.2 *The layout of the Chepstow Bridge as illustrated in Brunel's biography by his son, showing the novel and simple construction he adopted for this crossing. This he was able to develop with confidence for the longer crossing of the Tamar at Saltash.*

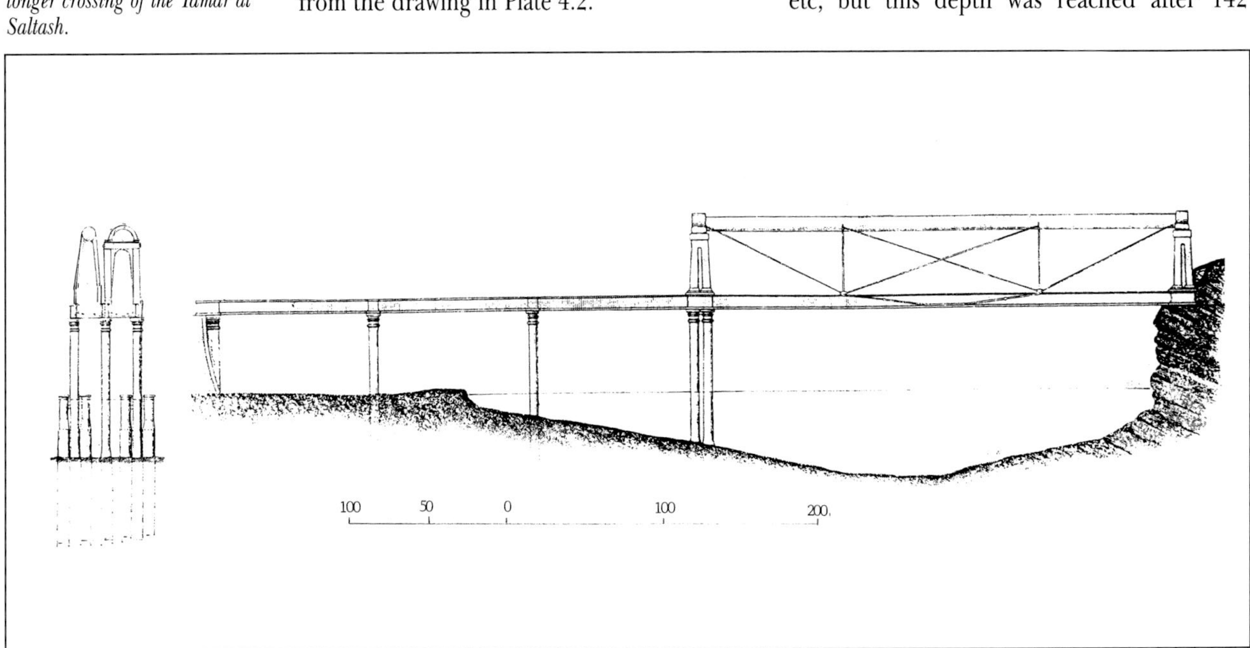

revolutions in an overall time of 48 hours, 14 minutes. In the light of this experiment he had intended to try a cylinder of 6 feet diameter; then, in spite of this early success and for no apparent reason, he abandoned the screwed pile as a basis for forming the western abutment. Instead, he turned to the well established use of cast iron cylinders, forced down by weights, and then filled with concrete.

Consequently, for the western support of the main river span Brunel settled on a construction which comprised a double row of cylinders, six in all, the lower parts of which were 8 feet in diameter, joined together in lengths of 6 feet; the leading edge of each bottom cylinder being made with a cutting edge, so as to penetrate the ground. The land piers for the 100 feet spans were of similar formation; each consisted of three cylinders, 6 feet in diameter, joined together in lengths of 6 feet.

The majority of the cylinders were sunk by excavating the ground within them and weighting the tops, the water level being kept down by pumping. However, there was a difficulty that as the ground was of wet sand and shingle, water tended to run in from the outside while excavation was in progress, and thus would have disturbed the lateral stability of the cylinders. Accordingly, care was taken not to excavate too close to the bottom of each cylinder, the ground round the cutting edge merely being loosened and the cylinder forced down by weights. On reaching the rock, the latter was dressed to form a level foundation, and the cylinders then filled with concrete.

In the case of the main pier, the nature of the strata included large boulders and pieces of timber, which frustrated the smooth execution of this work. When still some distance from the rock base, a length of one of these large cylinders cracked on meeting an obstruction. Timber struts were then fitted within it, until the obstacle was passed; it was then strengthened by means of a wrought iron hoop, and the cylinder forced down to the rock.

Sekon (1895) gives a detailed and colourful description of the operation:

> ...In sinking the cylinders...the workmen had first to pass through 29 feet of blue clay and sand, below which they met with a thin bed of peat containing timber, some solid oak, hazel nuts, and other similar substances. They next came to several feet of fine blue gravel, and then they reached a bed of boulders, upon which the cylinders were originally intended to rest. After this was a bed of red marl, beneath which was solid rock like millstone grit, and into this the cylinders were sunk. The mode in which this part of the work was performed was curious. The cylinders were placed on planks to prevent their cutting into the soft mud. One by one cylinders were added until they had reached the top of the stage (about 100 feet in height) which had been erected for the purpose of sinking them. The weight of the column now cut through the planks, and the cylinder sank about six feet into the mud. Two or three men then descended into it and, as they removed the contents, the cylinder continued to sink, and as it descended fresh cylinders were added at the top. This process continued without interruption till a depth of about 17 feet was attained, and then a spring was tapped, and without a moment's notice the water broke in from below in such force as to require the constant action of two 13 inch pumps worked by an engine. A remarkable fact attending this occurrence was, that the spring water invariably rose in the cylinder exactly at the height to which the tube [*sic* - Sekon probably meant the tide] was standing in the river at that moment. That it was not an interruption from the Wye was considered to be beyond dispute, inasmuch as the river at this point, from the action of the tide, was always heavily tainted with mud, while the water which rushed into the cylinder from below was of exceeding purity, and did not contain a particle of salt.

Sadly, Sekon does not relate how the incursion of the spring was overcome nor

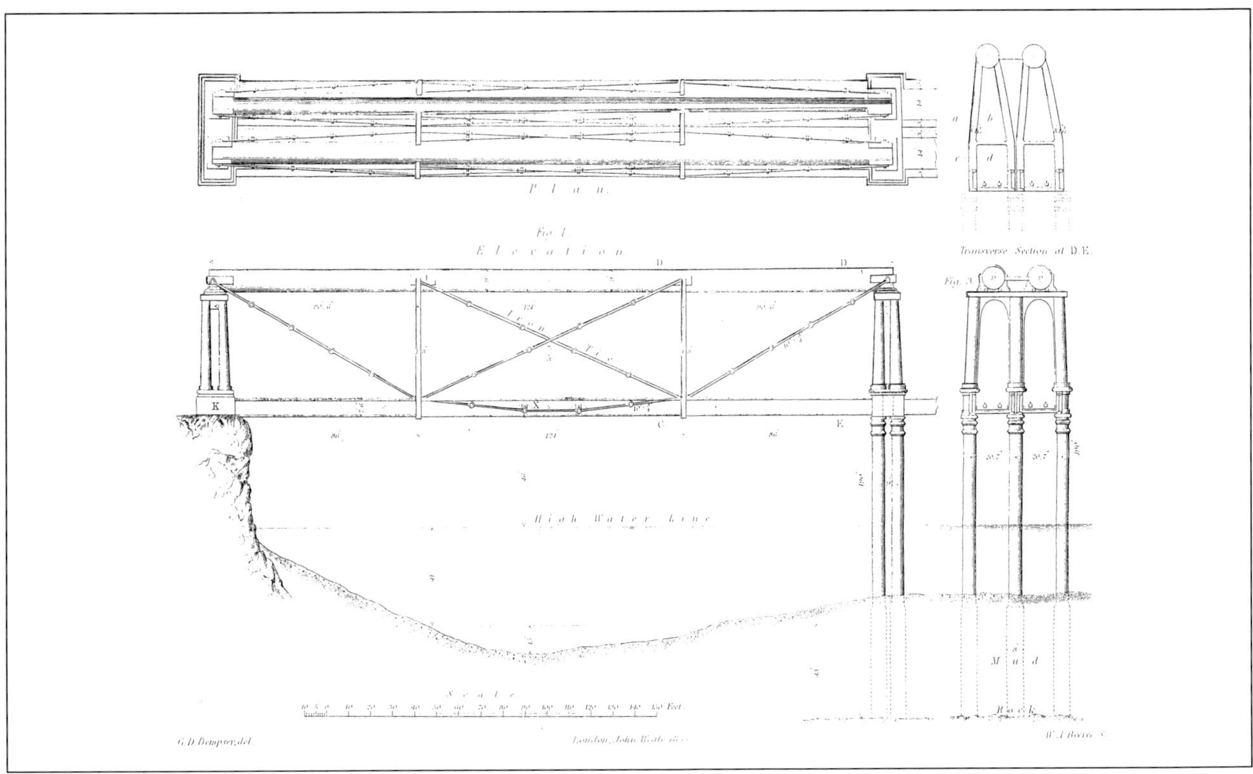

4.3 *A general arrangement drawing of the 305 feet main span over the navigable channel of the River Wye, showing the twin tube construction for the two lines of rails, the layout of the chains and the diagonal ties of wrought iron links which stiffened the central panel of the span.* DEMPSEY

does he add any further relevant information to our story.

Although by April 1851 the majority of the cylinders had been sunk into position, it was apparent from the delays due to the influx of water, this aspect of the contract would not be completed in time to be ready to receive the superstructure. Brunel therefore resorted to pressurising the cylinders to force out the water, with workmen inside excavating material to speed its sinking. For this method, it was necessary to close off the top of each cylinder and incorporate an intermediate chamber as an air lock, through which men and materials were passed.

Meanwhile, alongside the main pier, four supplementary columns, formed from 7 foot diameter cylinders, were placed in position, connected to the 8 foot cylinders by heavy brackets, thereby providing additional bearing surface for this main support. Any slight inaccuracy of the position of the cylinders was corrected at ground level by means of adjusting cones, and on this foundation three pairs of 6 foot diameter cylinders were built up to the level of the railway.

Turning now to the overall design of the main span, this was in the form of a Trapezoidal Truss, (Rankine 1885) as shown in Plate 4.3. The details of its construction are shown in Plate 4.4, being copies of drawings prepared in 1855 for G. D. Dempsey. Each line of railway was carried on two longitudinal wrought iron girders, $7\frac{1}{2}$ feet deep; having a triangular top flange, a plate iron vertical web and a slightly curved plate for the bottom flange. With the land span girders, which were of similar construction, these members were continuous throughout the bridge length, this overall design reflecting the investigation carried out by Brunel's assistant, Bell, in 1849 into the behaviour of continuous beams. In the overall construction, the diagonal layout of the cross girders and timber decking as shown in Figs. 9 and 11 of Plate 4.4 should be noted.

Over the main navigable span, the horizontal girders were carried by 'suspension' chains, one set on each side of the roadway, hung from either side of the ends of an arched horizontal circular tube, Fig 2 Plate 4.4. Each tube was 9 feet in diameter, of uniform section, fabricated from 16 equal-sized plates, $\frac{5}{8}$ inch

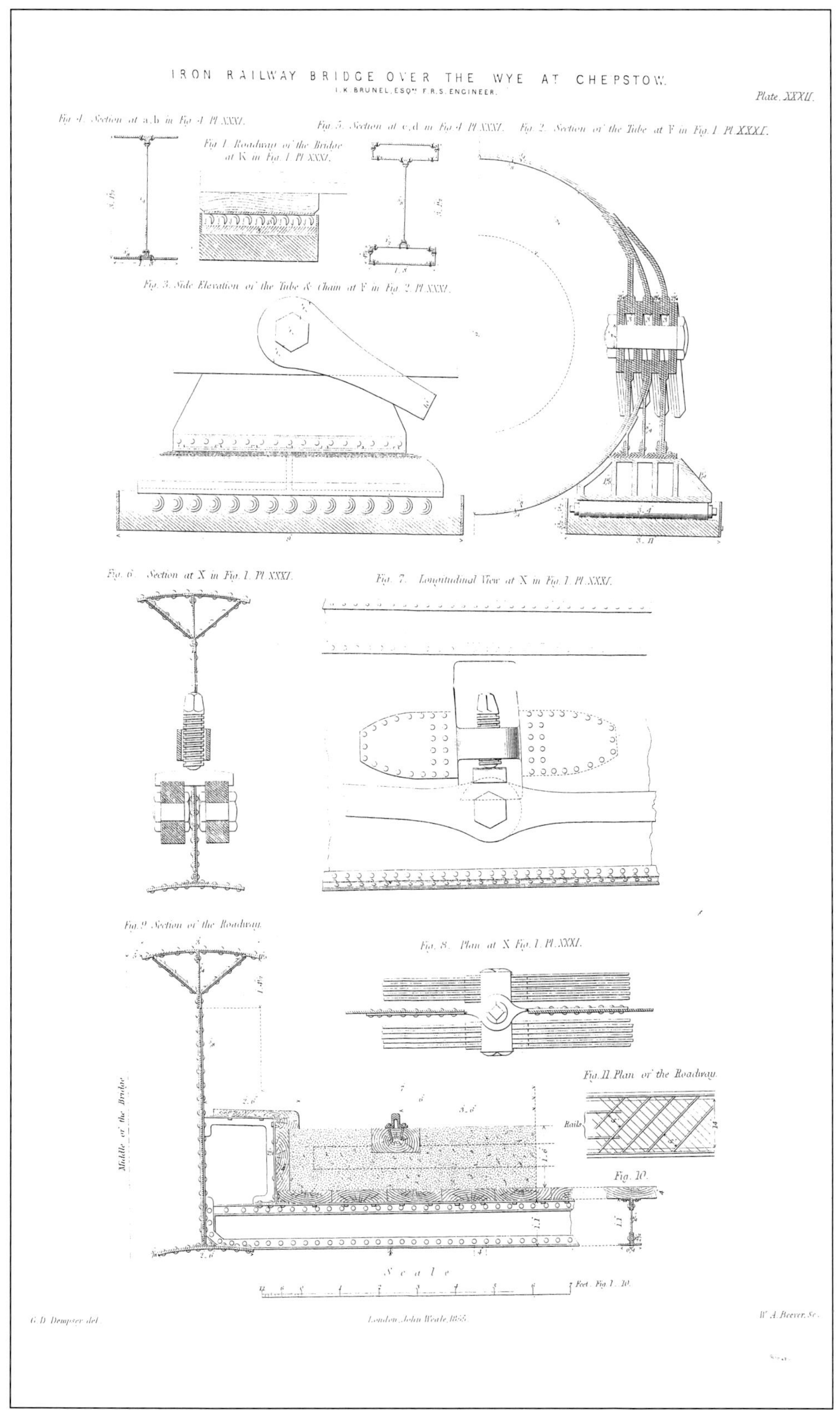

4.4 *Details of the main span, as shown in Plate 4.3.*
DEMPSEY

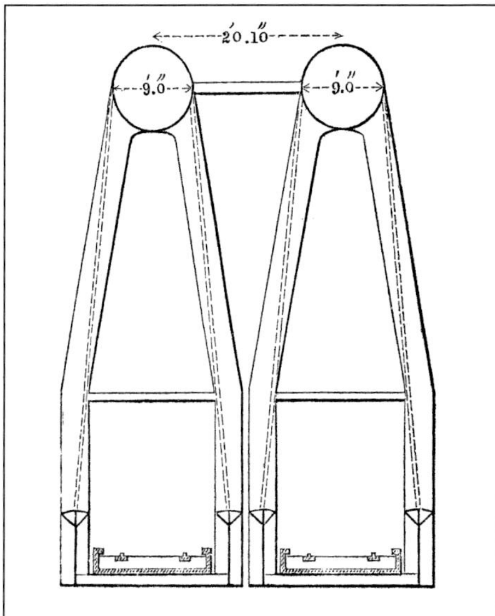

4.5 *A section through the bridge, showing the intermediate struts for each track linked to the corresponding overhead tube, the fall or 'cascade' of the chains from each tube to their respective roadway girders; the latter following Brunel's favourite construction.*
EDWIN CLARK

thick, and two side-plates 5/8 inch thick. The plates were all 10 feet in length, lapped together at the sides, and butt-jointed at the ends with double butt-plates, and double rivetted[2]. The tubes were stiffened at 26 feet intervals by a series of diaphragms, while their ends rested on the tops of the main towers, located about 50 feet above the level of the rails. The tower at the eastern or 'land' end was built of masonry while the western or 'river' one was constructed from cast iron sections, seated on top of the set of tubular piers as described above. Two archways within each tower formed the portals through which the trains passed.

Within this structural formation, the tubes were in compression with their respective roadway girders supported by the two suspension chains, each of which comprised a series of links, 20 feet long. These were composed alternately of 12 and 14 links, 10 inches deep, and varying from 3/4 inch to 11/16 inch in thickness, rolled as single pieces without welding of the eyes, see Plate 4.3 and Fig 3 of Plate 4.4. The 'cascading' of the chains within the bridge structure can be seen from

4.6A (opposite page bottom) *and* **4.6B** *Probably among some of the earliest of railway photographs, these two illustrations show the Chepstow Bridge under construction in the 1850s. 4.6A taken from the land span is of the down line (opened 14 July 1852) with the up line under construction. 4.6B is a similar view from the western shore.*
BRISTOL UNIVERSITY

Plate 4.5, which also shows the two intermediate struts. These resting on the chains on either side prevented the overhead tube from sagging. Hence, while the weight of the structure was supported somewhat in a manner similar to a suspension bridge, the inward drag of the chains was resisted by the massive overhead tube. Furthermore, to reduce the characteristic distortion of a suspended structure, introduced by a rolling load, diagonal ties of wrought iron links stiffened the centre panel of the truss.

Each tube was located on rolling-bearings set on the masonry abutment tower on the eastern bank (Fig 2 of Plate 4.4) and 'fixed' bearings on the cast iron tower at the 'river' or western end. Likewise, the roadway girders were mounted on rolling-bearings on the masonry abutment at the eastern end (Fig 1 Plate 4.4). At the points where the roadway girders were intersected by the inclined chains, they were not fixed to the chains, but rested upon them, through a system of rollers and saddles. The ends of the short horizontal links, in the middle of the span, included screws for adjusting the level of the girders (Figs 6, 7 and 8 of Plate 4.4), this arrangement being intended to minimise the strain on the roadway girders arising from the slight alteration in the form of the truss which took place when a load came on the bridge.

On completion of the ironwork for the first truss, it was assembled on the river bank with the ends supported on temporary piers and the structure uniformly weighted with a load of 770 tons, or $2^{3}/_{4}$ tons per foot run. This test proved satisfactory and arrangements were then made to dismantle the truss in preparation for its erection. Since river traffic could not be interrupted for more than a single tide, it was made so that it could be divided into parts, each of which could be lifted separately and quickly. The tube was temporarily stiffened by parts of the main chains, arranged to form a truss so that it could be suspended from its ends for lifting and thus carry its own weight without deflection.

This tube assembly was first slewed on to a platform at right angles to the river, in preparation for it being rolled out so that as the tide rose its outer end could be supported by six pontoons. Hawsers attached to the pontoons guided them across the river, in the face of the fast current, to position the assembly between the two towers. Through the course of the day, by means of lifting tackle attached to both ends of this assembly, it was hoisted to the level of the rails, and eventually to the top of the towers. This part of the project was carried out on 8 April 1852, under Brunel's meticulous planning and control. It was followed by the attachment of the suspension chains and the lifting and fixing of the roadway girders, all this work being completed by 14 July 1852, when this single down line of railway was opened for traffic. The erection of the second tube followed in due course, and the up line was finally completed and opened in April 1853.

Illustrations of the bridge under construction are shown by the early photographs of Plates 4.6A and 4.6B. It is interesting to note that the drawings and calculations for the bridge were prepared by R. P. Brereton, working in Brunel's London office[3], while the resident engineer of the line was one of Brunel's assistants, W. G. Owen. The contractors for the iron-work were Messrs Finch & Willey, of Liverpool.

According to details[4] issued by Brunel in 1850, an analysis of the approximate weights involved in the Chepstow Bridge are shown in the accompanying Table. These figures differ from the information later given by Berridge[5], who quotes the total weight of the load carrying structure for each of the main navigable spans as 558 tons, for an actual span length of 308 feet. A further weight analysis is given in the Moss Rose Press publication, amounting to a total of 1,400 tons for both tracks; accordingly, there does seem to be some confusion regarding the actual weight of materials included in the structure.

	TONS
298 feet run of tube and butt plates	127 1/2
Hoop of tube over piers	7 3/4
Side-plates, bottom-plates etc for attachment of main chains	15
Side-plates for attachment of diagonal chains	2 1/4
Stiffening diaphragms, 26 feet apart	4 1/4
Rivet heads etc	4 3/4
Total weight of one tube	**161 1/2**
Main chains, eyes, pins etc	105
Diagonal chains, eyes, pins etc	23
Vertical trusses	18 1/2
Saddles, rollers etc at points of suspension	22
Main roadway, girders, transverse floor girders etc	130
Total weight of wrought iron in one roadway	**460**

Nevertheless, the resulting overall design was a relatively light and cheap construction for a double track, nominal span of 600 feet, having been completed for a total cost of £77,000, (compared with £145,190 for Stephenson's 400 feet long Conway Bridge). This unique structure remained in service until 1962 when the main spans were replaced by a pair of steel trusses, to show in turn, a saving in overall weight of the load carrying structure of over 45%.

From this brief résumé of the design and building of the Chepstow Bridge, it will be appreciated that Brunel had gained considerable experience, not only in the design of the wrought iron structural elements of the bridge, but also in the excavation and preparation of the foundations in a difficult terrain, with the men eventually having to work within a pressurised environment. This experience was to stand him in good stead when, in due course, he came to build the centre pier at Saltash.

CHAPTER FIVE

THE FINAL DESIGN

1852

While from 1847, due to the difficulties in attracting the necessary finance, there had followed a lull in the immediate work associated with the Cornwall Railway, it would appear that Brunel continued to give consideration to the most economical approach to further the whole project. As previously noted, in this respect he came forward in 1851 with the proposal that only a single line of rails should be laid between Plymouth and Falmouth, with suitable passing places; the Saltash Bridge, of course, also to be single track. This aspect he discussed with the Board of Trade in 1852, to secure their agreement.

Thus, supported by his experience of the Chepstow crossing, Brunel had by 1849 settled the broad principles of his design. The Bridge was to comprise two main spans supported on a single deep water pier set in mid stream, with a substantial masonry pier built on each foreshore; together with a series of approach spans from each bank. While Stephenson had in 1850 completed spans of 460 feet in his Britannia tubular bridge across the Menai Straits, in no way would Brunel simply copy the work of his friend and professional rival. Instead he chose to adapt the results of the fundamental test work which Fairbairn and Hodgkinson had carried out for Stephenson, to develop his own design. Hence, for each main truss, following on from his experience

5.1 *The south west aspect of the Royal Albert Bridge, an illustration from the book The Forth Bridge by Phillip Phillips published in Edinburgh in 1889. This view, taken in the late 1880s, from the foreshore at Saltash, shows the simple yet elegant framework of the two main spans as initially devised by Brunel, free from the auxiliary bracing introduced in later years to counter the affect of increased train loads on the suspension system.* SM/SS

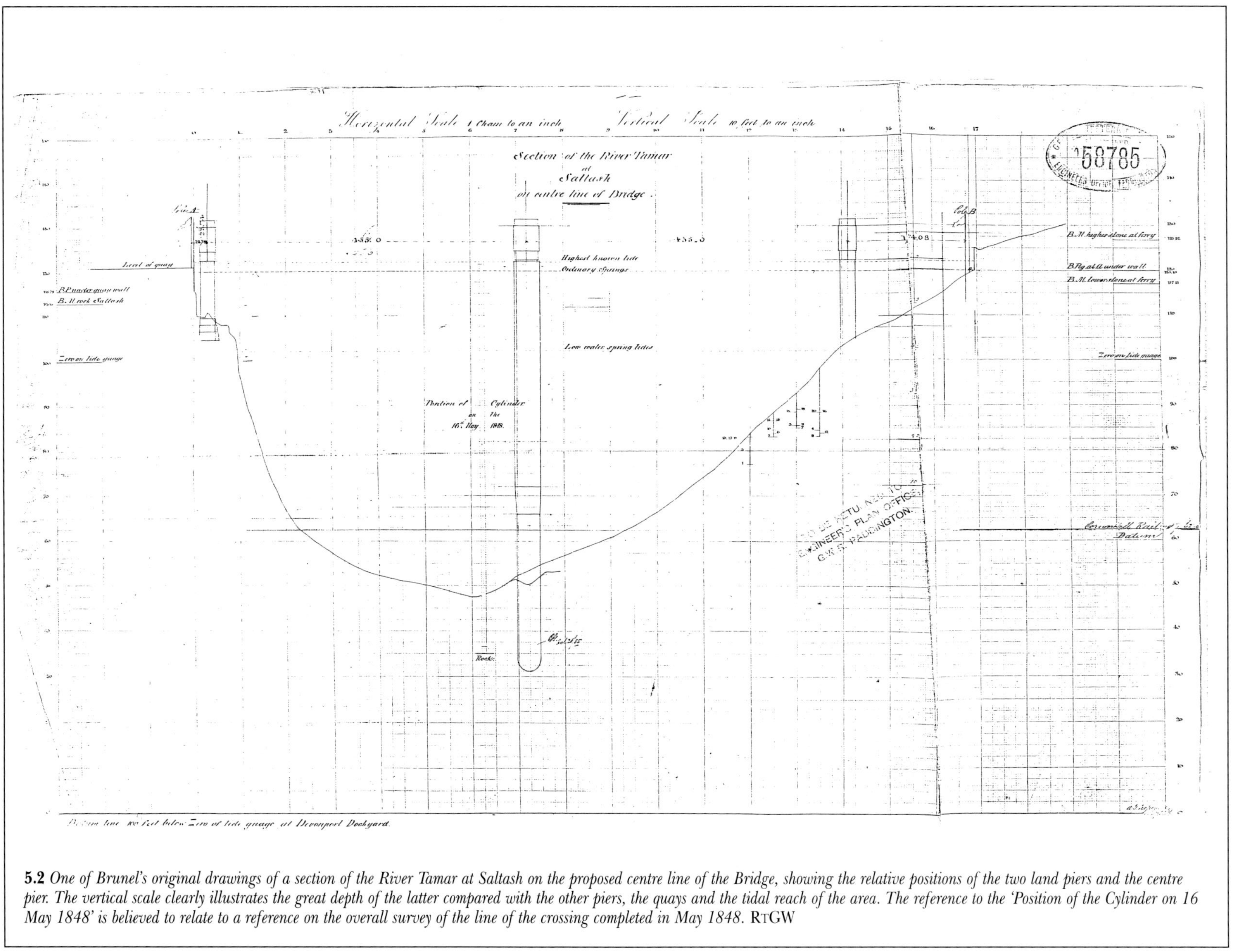

5.2 *One of Brunel's original drawings of a section of the River Tamar at Saltash on the proposed centre line of the Bridge, showing the relative positions of the two land piers and the centre pier. The vertical scale clearly illustrates the great depth of the latter compared with the other piers, the quays and the tidal reach of the area. The reference to the 'Position of the Cylinder on 16 May 1848' is believed to relate to a reference on the overall survey of the line of the crossing completed in May 1848.* RtGW at Chepstow, he proposed a structure in the form of a Bowstring Suspension Bridge (Rankine 1885) comprising a wrought iron tubular arch or bow, having a profile generally in the form of a parabola, in combination with sets of suspension chains hanging on each side of the tube in a catenary curve. The tube included as great a rise as the chains had dip at the centre of each span, where the overall depth of the truss was 72 feet (Plate 7.13). From the centre of the tube to the top of the chains was 56 feet 3 inches (Plate 8.2).

The plate girder roadway, which was to carry the railway track, was slung below each tube from eleven pairs of vertical members. These passed through and were connected to the chains, while intermediate hangers located midway between these verticals, were attached solely to the chains. It will be appreciated, therefore, that the two main spans were in fact based on the principle of the suspension bridge, thus making Saltash unique today as the only one of that type carrying main line trains. To overcome the shortcomings of the suspension system - the tendency for the chains to change shape under the influence of a train moving across the structure - the verticals were restrained through a continuous system of diagonal bracing.

This comprised a series of long wrought iron members, each pinned at both ends to connect the main tube and the chain links, while each pair of verticals was braced together by transverse struts and sets of diagonal stays. The overall result was a construction of simple yet graceful design, which will be apparent from the view of the Bridge taken from the Saltash foreshore in the late 1880s, and reproduced in Plate 5.1.

While it would appear that this design was able to accommodate the traffic needs of the late nineteenth century, the coming of heavier locomotives and trains accentuated the inherent weakness of the suspension system. Consequently, over the years additional bracing has been introduced to combat this situation which, sadly, has tended to detract from the simple elegance of Brunel's original conception.

Reverting to the original design, with its broad features now settled, and once he was satisfied regarding the constructional details of his Chepstow bridge, it is believed that work then started on the detail drawings for the Tamar bridge at Brunel's offices in 18 Duke Street (Berridge 1969). His notebooks and general calculation books over the period of the early 1850s include several outline calculations, showing how his design was developed. Then, on 27 October 1852 he reported[1] to the Board that, apart from some details relating to the masonry, the drawings and specifications of the Saltash Bridge were ready.

DESIGN CALCULATIONS

With regard to the final design calculations, which presumably would also have been carried out at his offices, it must be appreciated that at that time the theory of engineering structures had not yet been developed sufficiently to enable engineers to design a large iron structure safely and economically by calculation alone. While the dead and live loads on the bridge could be reasonably accurately estimated, the assessment of the other loading affecting the strength of the structure, was then quite beyond such analysis. The interpretation of the mathematical investigation of structures, evolved in the seats of learning by Moseley and his disciple Pole, based on the earlier works of Navier, had not yet been developed to achieve, certainly in Britain, an enduring unity of theory and practice. This was to follow from the works of Rankine, published after the death of Brunel.

With regard to the operating load which the Bridge was to accommodate, there does not appear to be any evidence in the literature of the precise figures adopted by Brunel. However, from the details of the design of the Landore viaduct, prepared at around the same time (1847/1850) we know from Fletcher[2] that viaduct was calculated to carry:

Ballast: 1 foot thick, 7 feet wide,	
per foot run, each rail	7 cwt
Permanent way, per foot run	0¾ cwt
Load of locomotive engine,	
per foot run	12 cwt
Total load, per foot run,	
to each rail	19¾ cwt
Say, 1 ton per foot run, to each rail.	

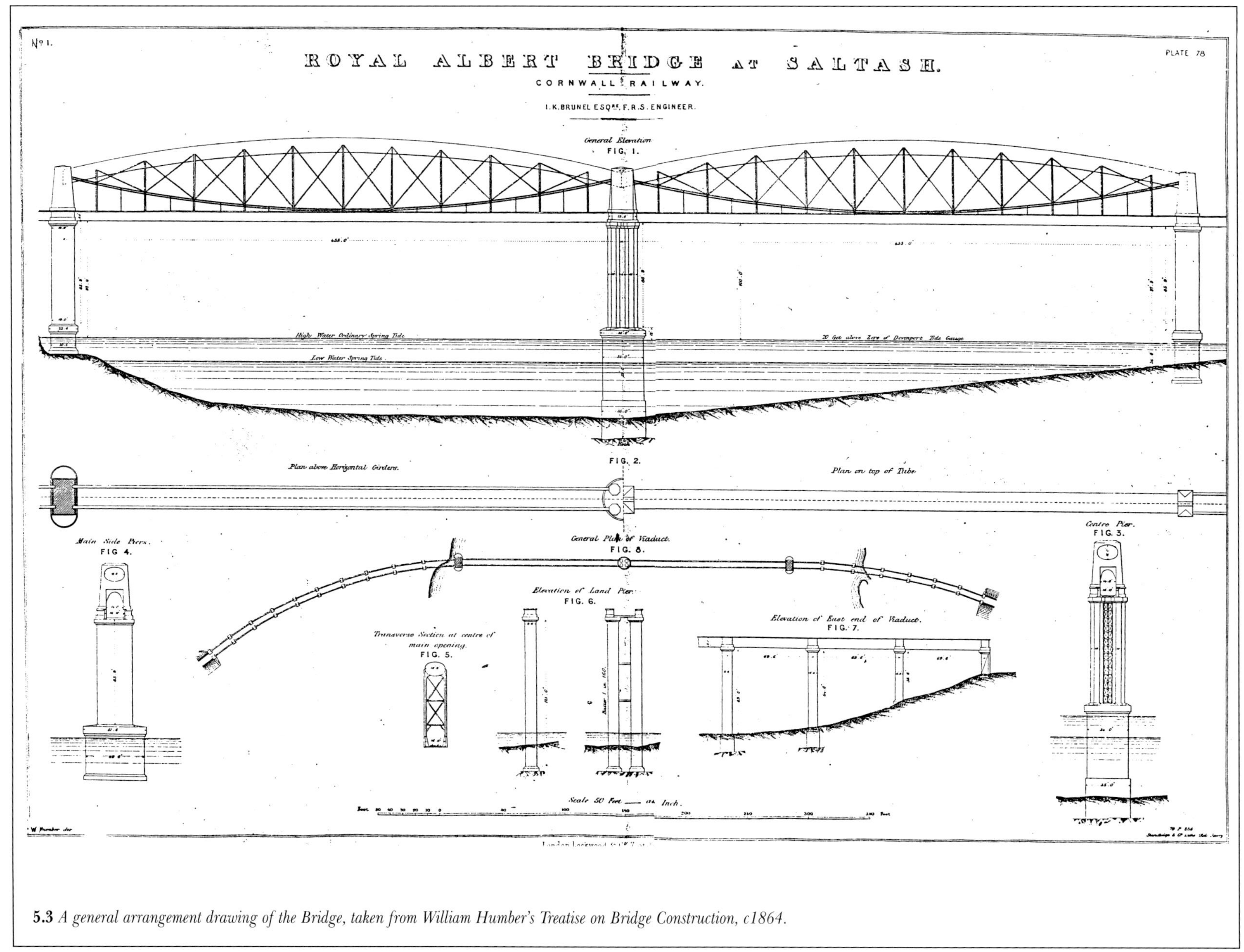

5.3 *A general arrangement drawing of the Bridge, taken from William Humber's Treatise on Bridge Construction, c1864.*

It would, therefore, not be unreasonable to assume, initially, a similar level of loading for Saltash although, as we shall see, this was significantly exceeded in later years.

Surprisingly, it would appear that the effect of wind loading received only superficial consideration as it was not until the tragic failure of the Tay Bridge in 1879 that the full significance of this force was appreciated. However, in spite of its exposed position, the Tamar Bridge has withstood the onslaught of the south westerly gales without significant distress - ample testimony to its original design. In this respect the later comments by Brereton (see below) are relevant.

Having regard to his close association with his friend and professional rival, Robert Stephenson, it would be reasonable to assume that Brunel consulted either with him directly or with Fairbairn and Hodgkinson, in connection with the scope of these formal calculations and, in this respect, that they would have taken due account of Moseley's work on continuous beams. As we have already noted, the results of the extensive testwork and its analysis which had been carried out in this connection had been published in 1846, including the establishment of formulae for circular and elliptical tubes; sadly, by around this time relations between Stephenson and Fairbairn were strained.

However, insofar as Saltash is concerned, whatever limited calculations were made by Brunel, or his assistant Bell working to his instructions, they do not appear to have survived. Against this overall background, and notwithstanding such final calculations as were undoubtedly made, acceptance of the design was subject to the results of suitable testing on completion.

5.4 *A magnificent view of the Bridge from the slopes on the Devon bank, taken soon after completion, with the track laid but with some work in hand on the eastern portal as evidenced by the scaffolding and crane at that position. There also appears to be scaffolding around the top of the centre pier, while the difference in overall colouring would indicate painting still to be completed.* SM/SS

5.5 *A distant aspect of the main centre spans taken from down stream at sea level in 1861, which again emphasises the graceful lines and simple formation of Brunel's original design. A miscellaneous collection of 'wooden walls' appears anchored off Devonport, while the main Devon pier can be seen on the right, with the main Cornwall pier on the foreshore at Saltash on the left.*
REPRODUCED WITH PERMISSION FROM THE GEORGE WASHINGTON WILSON COLLECTION, ABERDEEN UNIVERSITY LIBRARY: REF F2570.

The Drawings

It is fortunate that many of Brunel's original drawings for the Saltash Bridge, together with sketches of his interim solutions to problems as they arose during building, have been carefully preserved within the Records Office of Railtrack Great Western (RtGW) at Swindon. From an examination of these drawings, we can make a meaningful study of the details of construction of his original design, as reflected in the elegant formation illustrated in Plate 5.1. As already noted, over the years a number of modifications have been incorporated and the scope of these changes form the subject of a later chapter.

The Location

Following on from the investigation for the site of the centre pier and the corresponding site survey, Brunel was able finally to settle the exact location for the crossing. Plate 5.2 shows a section of the River Tamar at Saltash on the proposed centre line of the Bridge, believed to have been developed from Johnston's survey, since it includes the reference of the date of 16 May 1848, quoted as the 'Position of Cylinder'. It would seem that this must refer to the cylinder involved in Glennie's investigation of the river bed, as previously described in Chapter 3.

The illustration of Plate 5.2 is, however, of particular relevance in connection with the various levels, and demonstrates better than any description, the immense depth of the centre pier foundation relative to the levels of the other piers, and the magnitude of the work involved in its construction.

The following paragraphs offer a broad description of the design of the complete Bridge as originally built; Plate 5.3 being a general arrangement drawing of the overall structure. Plate 5.4 is a photograph of the finished Bridge, viewed from the Devon shore, and dates from around the completion of the structure, in view of the crane still in position on the eastern portal. Plate 5.5, a view from a distance of the high centre spans taken in 1861 which, in conjunction with Plate 5.1, exemplifies their graceful contour and the overall symmetry of Brunel's design.

Plates 5.6 and 5.7 illustrate some of the details of construction as recorded by Humber (1864) which should be studied in conjunction with the descriptions that follow, together with the copies from Brunel's original drawings, Plates 5.9, 5.10, 5.13 and 5.14. Although these are indistinct in certain areas, they are included to furnish contemporary information of the details of his work.

The Main Tubes

Brunel's experiments and tests on various models had demonstrated that the most efficient form of strut was that with an oval or circular cross-section; for instance, he had used 9 feet diameter struts as the upper tubes on the 300 feet spans at Chepstow. However, for the 455 feet spans at Saltash he decided to use a tubular strut of elliptical cross-section; 16 feet 9 inches in width and 12 feet 3 inches in depth. The greater width increased the lateral stiffness of the tube and also permitted the suspension chains and bracing to lie in a vertical plane on either side of it. Having regard to the exposed position and height of the Bridge, this shape also offered less wind resistance, a factor on which Brereton was to comment in some detail at a later date[3], during a meeting of the ICE in 1882. He then considered that for each tube the area subject to direct wind pressure amounted to approximately 9,000 feet^2. Taking wind pressure to be calculated on the then latest Board of Trade requirements of 56lb/ft^2, assumed to represent a velocity of about 110

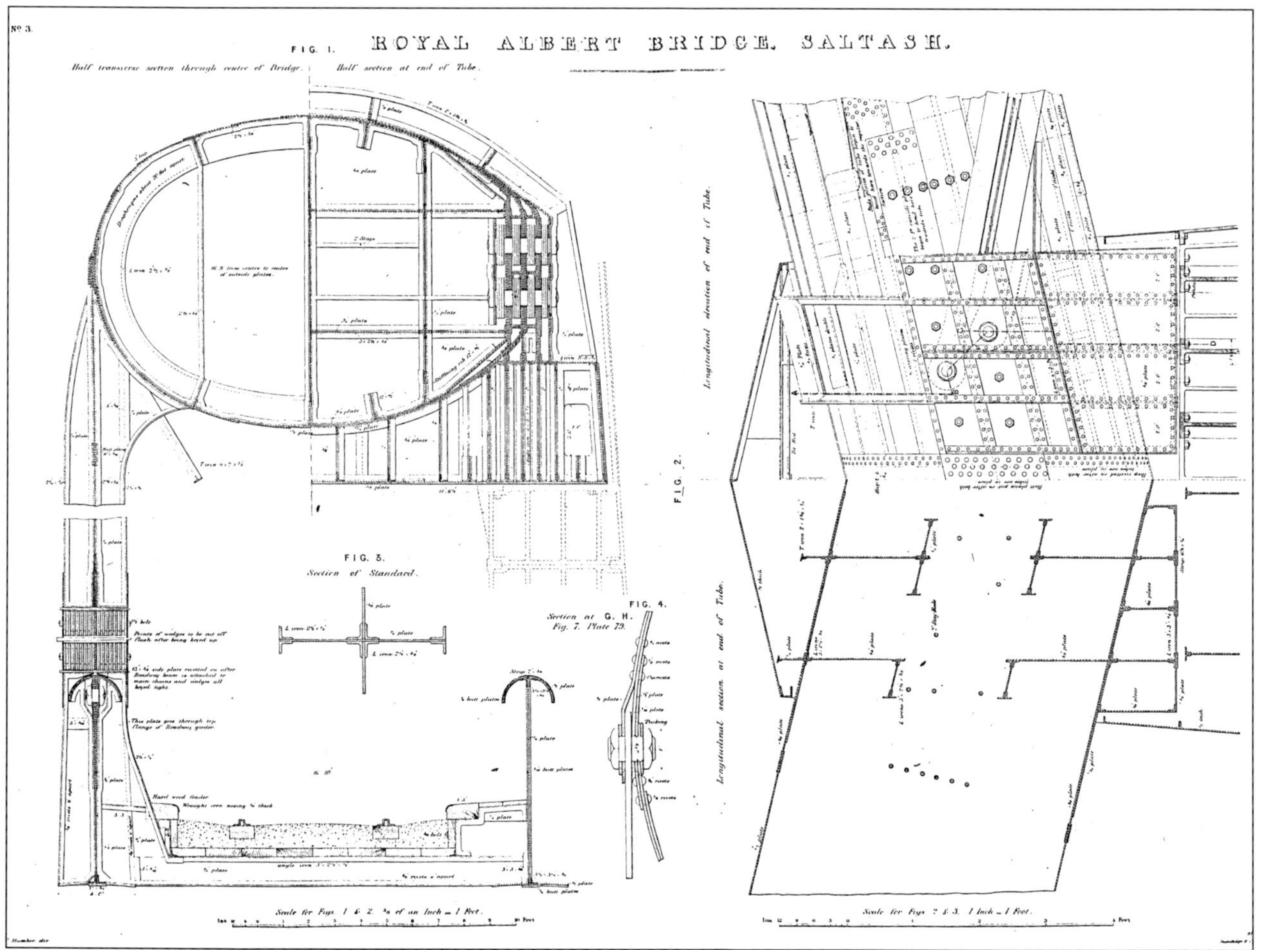

5.6 *Details of construction from drawings by William Humber c1864.*

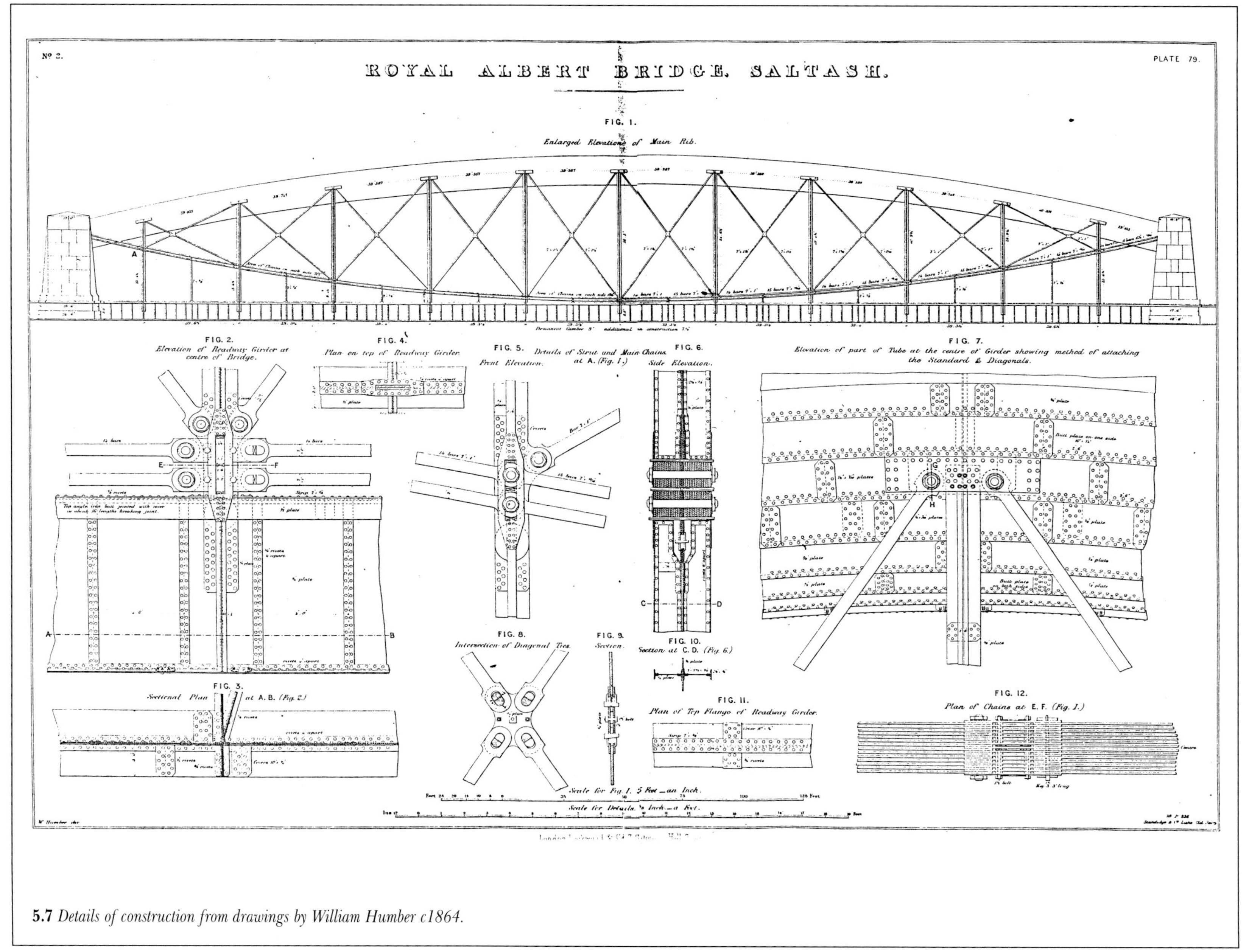

5.7 *Details of construction from drawings by William Humber c1864.*

m.p.h., the lateral pressure would have amounted to about 224 tons, or 112 tons at each end of a tube. He considered even half the above velocity to be well in excess of that experienced by railway structures of large magnitude and accordingly, that the design of the Royal Albert Bridge was well able to cope with the wind loading likely to be experienced at Saltash.

In an earlier discussion[4] regarding the strength of the tube, he also pointed out that the radius at the sides was about five feet; and there, in the line of the greatest strain, the plating of the skin was doubled. At the upper and lower parts the radius of curvature was 12 feet and at these flatter portions, several longitudinal ribs or webs were incorporated, after the manner of the Britannia tube. Brereton quotes a total length of each tube of 461 feet. They were fabricated from $^{1}/_{2}$, $^{5}/_{8}$ and $^{3}/_{4}$ inch thick wrought iron plates, generally 10 feet long x 2 feet wide, rolled and joggled as necessary and rivetted together. At the longitudinal joints the plates were lapped but the transverse joints incorporated double-covered butt joints; $^{3}/_{4}$, 1 and $1^{1}/_{4}$ inch diameter rivets being used, according to position. An examination of Plate 5.8A, besides showing the general quality of the fabrication, in particular the edge preparation of the plates and standard of riveting, reveals that the tubes were straight between each vertical hanger or chain connection.

As already mentioned, extending throughout the length of both tubes were sets of internal stiffeners, formed from 12 x $^{1}/_{2}$ inch plates set on edge, three at the top and three at the bottom. Spaced at about 20 feet centres within the length of each tube were annular stiffeners, 15 inches deep with $2^{1}/_{2}$ x $^{5}/_{8}$ inch edge angles, additionally reinforced by two single vertical angles 2 $^{1}/_{2}$ x $^{3}/_{8}$ inch and a double vertical angle on the centre line. These details will be evident from Fig 1 of Plate 5.6 and the photograph of the tube interior shown in Plate 5.8B.

The ends of the tubes incorporated closed diaphragms, while 2 inch diameter solid iron cross ties provided additional lateral stiffening, their number increasing towards the ends. To ventilate the interiors, a number of 2 inch diameter holes were drilled in the undersides, thus mitigating the damaging affect arising from the onset of any condensation.

According to Brereton, the longitudinal distance between the eye attachments of the suspension chains was nominally 450 feet and, as already noted, the distance apart of the two sets of suspension chains on each side of the bridge was 16 feet 9 inches, the same as the overall width of the tube. Each set comprised two chains and to connect them to the ends of the tube, the adjacent plates of the tube shell were locally formed inwards and reinforced by

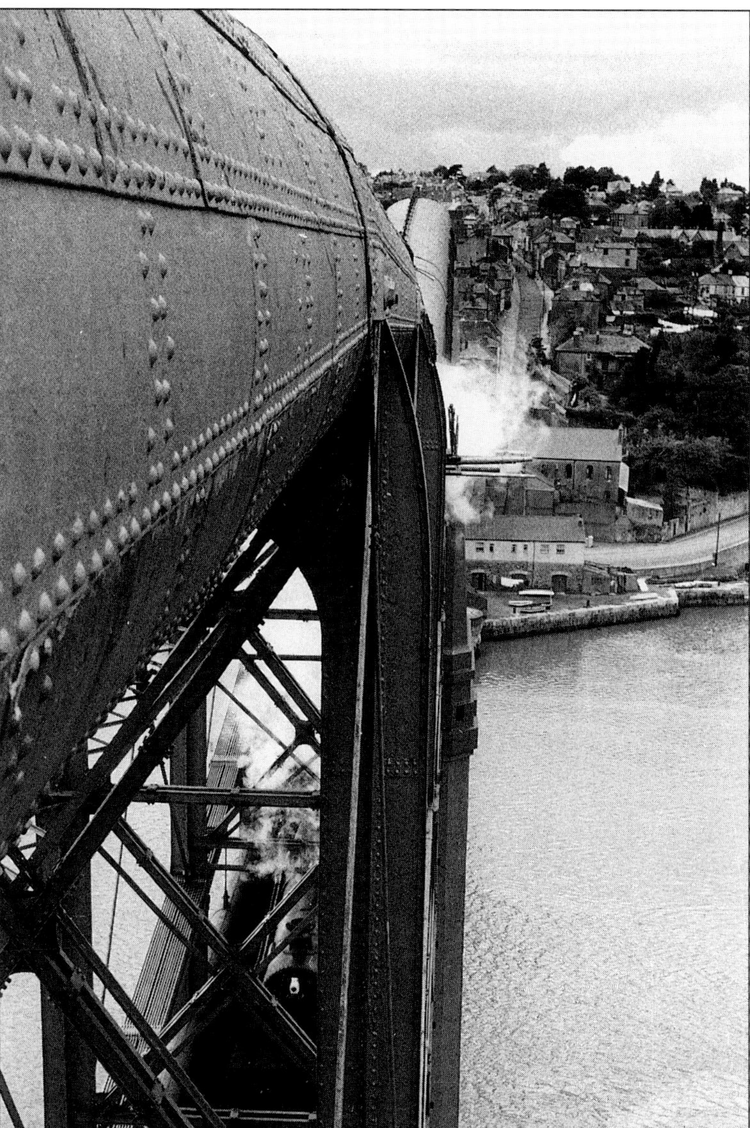

5.8A *As a steam hauled train slowly crossed the Bridge a brave photographer took this view from the side of one of the tubes, since he must have been leaning well out from the structure, probably in a bos'ns chair or similar support. The illustration shows the excellent quality of the rivetting, the cropped edge preparation of the plates and, most significantly, that the tubes were straight between standards.* RTGW

5.8B *A view inside one of the tubes, again showing the excellent quality of the rivetting, the stiffening flanges and the dual colour scheme.* RTGW

three intermediate walls, each made up from 5/8 inch thick wrought iron plates shaped and rivetted together so as to provide four spaces. The chain links were gathered together in suitable groups to fit these spaces for attachment to the tube by wrought iron bolts, 7 inches diameter, with an overall support length of 2 feet. These bolts, located approximately 2 feet from the ends of the tube, were staggered to accommodate each pair of chains, consequently, the upper chain of the pair was approximately one foot longer than the lower, this difference being accommodated by the pairs of end connecting links - see below.

While the above arrangement solved the problem of securing the chains to the tube, the detail design has posed an ongoing maintenance problem, since the spaces between the plates and the chains are inaccessible for cleaning and painting - essential in the exposed environment of the structure. However, the application of non oxidising paint in the spaces has assisted in this situation since it tends to remain plastic and thus provide protection to the ironwork (Pugsley 1976).

Immediately adjacent to these connections two additional 3/8 inch thick plates formed internal diaphragms, stiffened with angle irons, and also incorporating pairs of transverse diaphragm plates, all to provide a substantial reinforcement of the ends of each tube. These details will be apparent from a study of Fig.1 of Plate 5.6, while the orientation between the two tubes over the centre pier, the relative position of the chain centres and the reinforcement of the tube supports will be appreciated from the details shown in Plate 5.9.

The Suspension Chains

These extended on each side of the tube, and each chain was formed from two groups of wrought iron links, spaced one above the other at approximately 14 inch centres. Each tier was built up of a combination of 14 links, 1 inch thick or 15 links 15/16 inch thick, side by side, in alternate panels. The links were 7 inches deep throughout their length, with each end enlarged to form an eye to accommodate a 4 1/8 inch diameter hole, at nominal 20 feet centres, with a tolerance of ±0.020 inch.

In practice, two types of link were involved; the first, dating from 1843 were originally intended for the Clifton Suspension Bridge, and incorporated a welded head and eye with a clamping cheek forged into one end of each link. This provided a grip for handling, to assist in aligning the links, bearing in mind that a set of links weighed around 3 tons; see the relevant detail in Plate 5.10. The second type dated from 1857 and were rolled as a one piece unit, and while still incorporating a 4 1/8 inch diameter hole, the head was profiled and shaped to provide a more efficient connection, as shown in Plate 5.11. For both types, the links were interlaced and connected through the eyes by wrought iron pins, 4 inches diameter, thus providing a nominal clearance of 1/8 inch.

While this would not be considered good practice today, it was no doubt done to avoid the great difficulty which would have occurred in erection had a close fit been adopted. This is particularly significant bearing in mind that the vertical supports (suspension standards, below) were regularly spaced across the span while the chain links, in the form of a catenary, were of fixed centres. Consequently, some compromise of the pin locations must have been necessary in effecting the overall

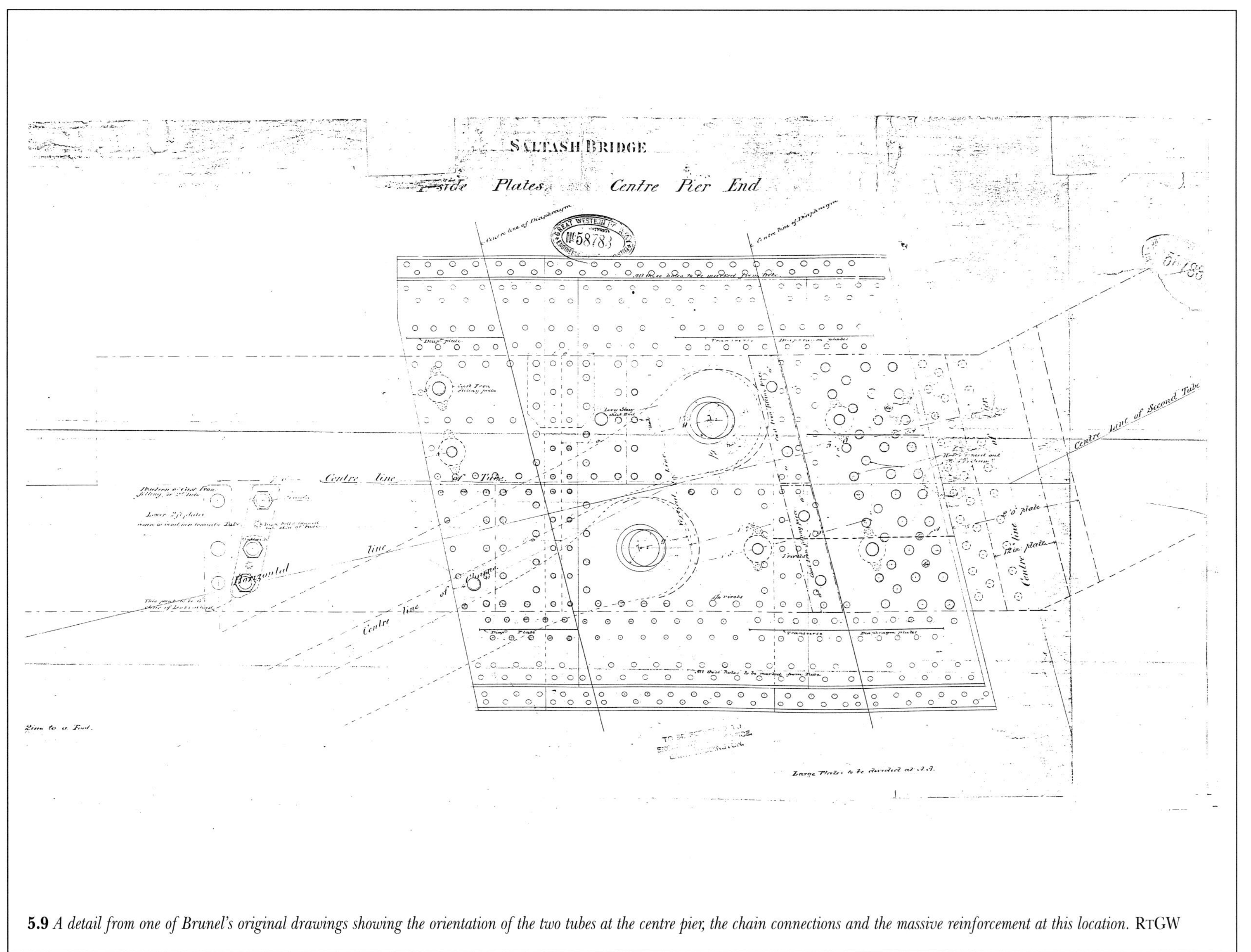

5.9 *A detail from one of Brunel's original drawings showing the orientation of the two tubes at the centre pier, the chain connections and the massive reinforcement at this location.* RtGW

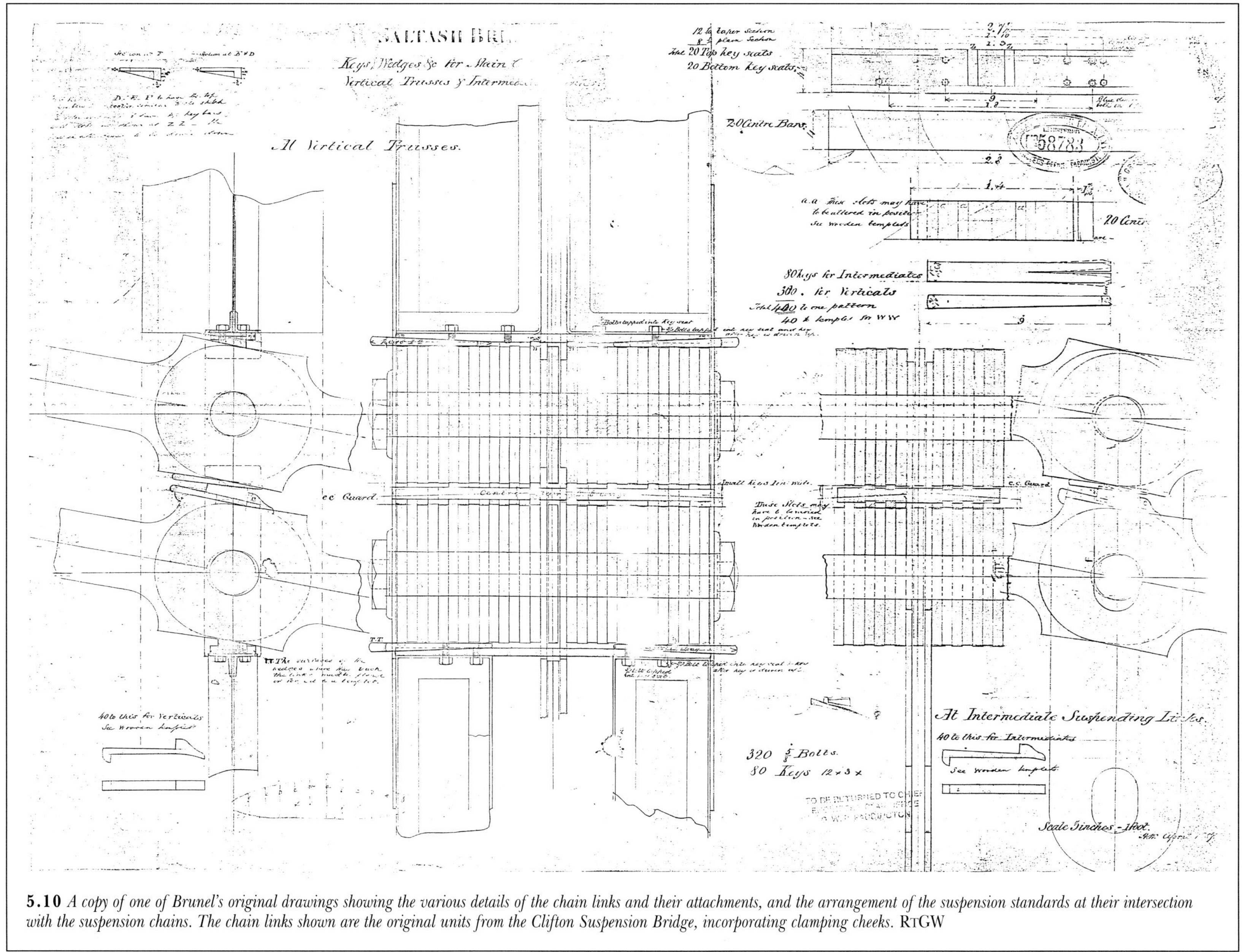

5.10 *A copy of one of Brunel's original drawings showing the various details of the chain links and their attachments, and the arrangement of the suspension standards at their intersection with the suspension chains. The chain links shown are the original units from the Clifton Suspension Bridge, incorporating clamping cheeks.* RtGW assembly. It would appear that this was achieved by an elongation of one of the chain link holes and the insertion of two half pins, tightened in position by a tapered key, as shown in Figs. 2 and 12 of Plate 5.7. In the case of the normal connections, the ends of the pins were screwed and secured by nuts; see details of Figs. 2, 5 and 6 of Plate 5.7.

Each tier comprised 24 sets of links, each link of nominal 20 feet centres, including a pair of special links at each end to connect the chains to the massive 7 inch diameter anchor pins located in the ends of each tube. This feature will be apparent from a study of Plates 5.9, 5.20, 10.13 and 10.14. Both groups of link are examined in more detail in Chapter 7 in connection with the building of the Cornwall span.

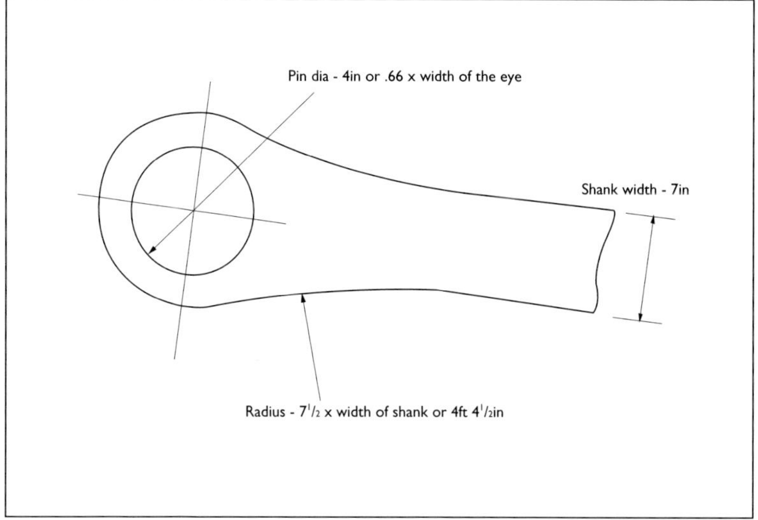

5.11 *An extract from one of Brunel's original drawings, showing the development of the profile of the second batch of one piece chain links, to provide a more generous radius from the shank to the eye.* RTGW

The Roadway

The main roadway incorporated a rise from each end of the Bridge to the centre pier of three feet, which will be apparent from the view of the structure in Plate 5.12. Indicative of Brunel's meticulous attention to detail, each span also embodied its own camber so as to produce a smooth profile to the roadway from each land pier to the centre pier. This feature emerges from the contour of the roadway as measured at the time of testing of the complete structure, as shown in Plate 8.10.

The girders were fabricated from ¼ inch thick wrought iron plates, 8 feet deep and incorporated single stiffened web plates. The upper flange in ½ inch plate, connected by 3½ inch angle irons ⅜ inch thick to the web, was of semi circular cross section, 2 feet wide, with the ends pointing downwards - an arrangement so often favoured by Brunel. The lower flange, 3 feet wide, also in ½ inch plate with 3½ x 3½ x ⅜ inch connecting angles, was dished slightly downwards. Cross girders, 16 feet 10 inches in length, and 13 inches in depth, fabricated from ¼ inch thick plate,

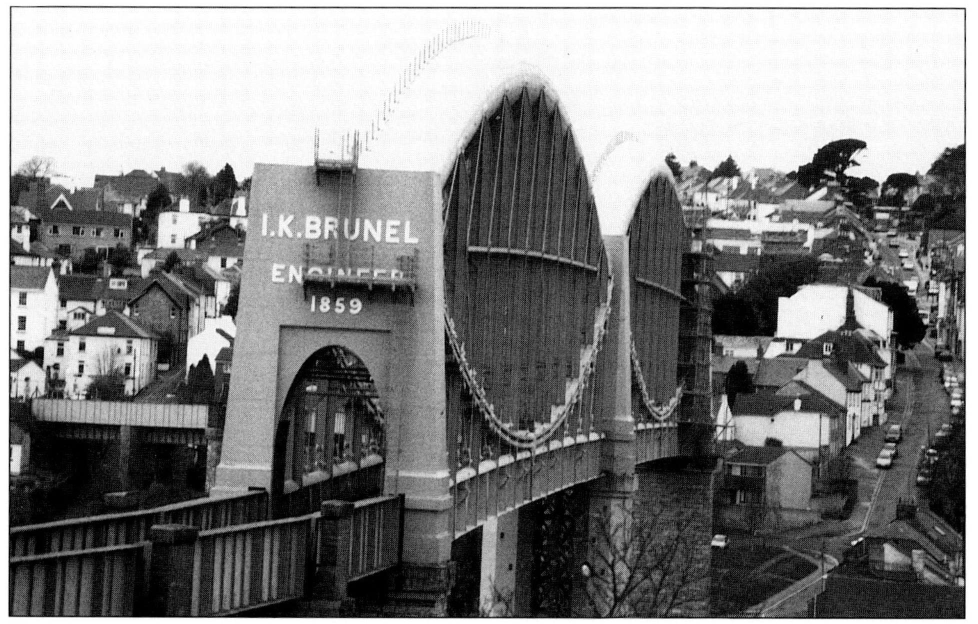

5.12 *This north east aspect of the Bridge clearly shows the three feet rise of the roadway to the centre support, followed by a corresponding drop to the approach spans from Saltash station in the left background. The tower of the Parish Church of SS Nicholas and Faith (a simple and rather unimposing structure) can just be distinguished above the trees behind the large white building on the slope of the hill. Note also the seven platform scaffolding complex, temporarily attached to the northern face of the Cornwall span for maintenance.* AUTHOR

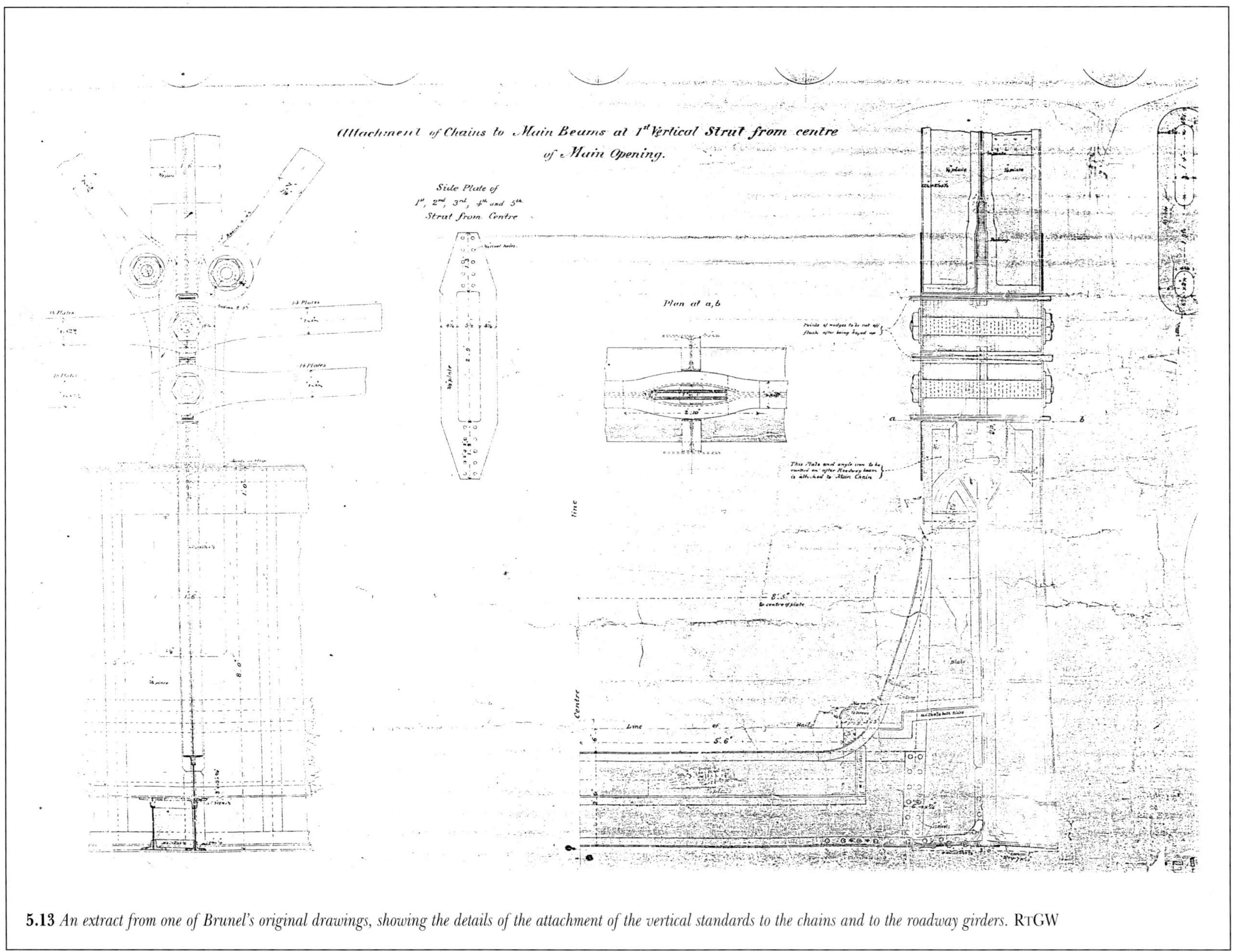

5.13 *An extract from one of Brunel's original drawings, showing the details of the attachment of the vertical standards to the chains and to the roadway girders.* RtGW

stiffened with 3 x $2\frac{1}{2}$ x $\frac{1}{2}$ inch angle irons and seated on the lower flange of the main girders, supported the 4 inch thick timber decking which carried the ballast and permanent way; see Fig. 1 of Plate 5.6 and the section of Plate 5.13. An overall view of the track and roadway will be appreciated from Plate 5.23A which shows the formation at the time of the broad gauge.

SUSPENSION STANDARDS

This roadway was suspended within the structure by means of eleven pairs of vertical wrought iron members, often called 'standards', which were attached at their upper ends to the main tube and extended down to link and bridge the suspension chains, with a further extension then connected to the upper flange of the roadway girders (see Plate 5.13). Plate 5.10 includes details of the series of wedges which were inserted between the two tiers of each suspension chain to ensure that the standards bore equally on each tier.

Each standard was fabricated as a cruciform, Fig.3, Plate 5.6. The main centre plate, running parallel to the centre line of the chains, comprised two plates which together were 1 foot 6 inches wide by $\frac{3}{8}$ inch thick; the other plate, set at right angles to this, was 2 feet 6 inches wide by $\frac{1}{4}$ inch thick. These plates were united at their intersection by four $2\frac{1}{2}$ x $\frac{3}{8}$ inch thick angle irons while there were also two $2\frac{1}{4}$ x $\frac{1}{4}$ inch thick angle irons at each edge of the $\frac{1}{4}$ inch plate.

For the attachment of each standard to the main tube the $\frac{3}{8}$ inch plate formed a tangent therewith and was bolted through a lapped extension of the tube. The $\frac{1}{4}$ inch plate on the outer edge of the standard was tapered to meet the tube at this junction while at the

5.14 *This extract from another of Brunel's original drawings gives details of the intermediate suspension links, between the chains and the roadway.* RTGW

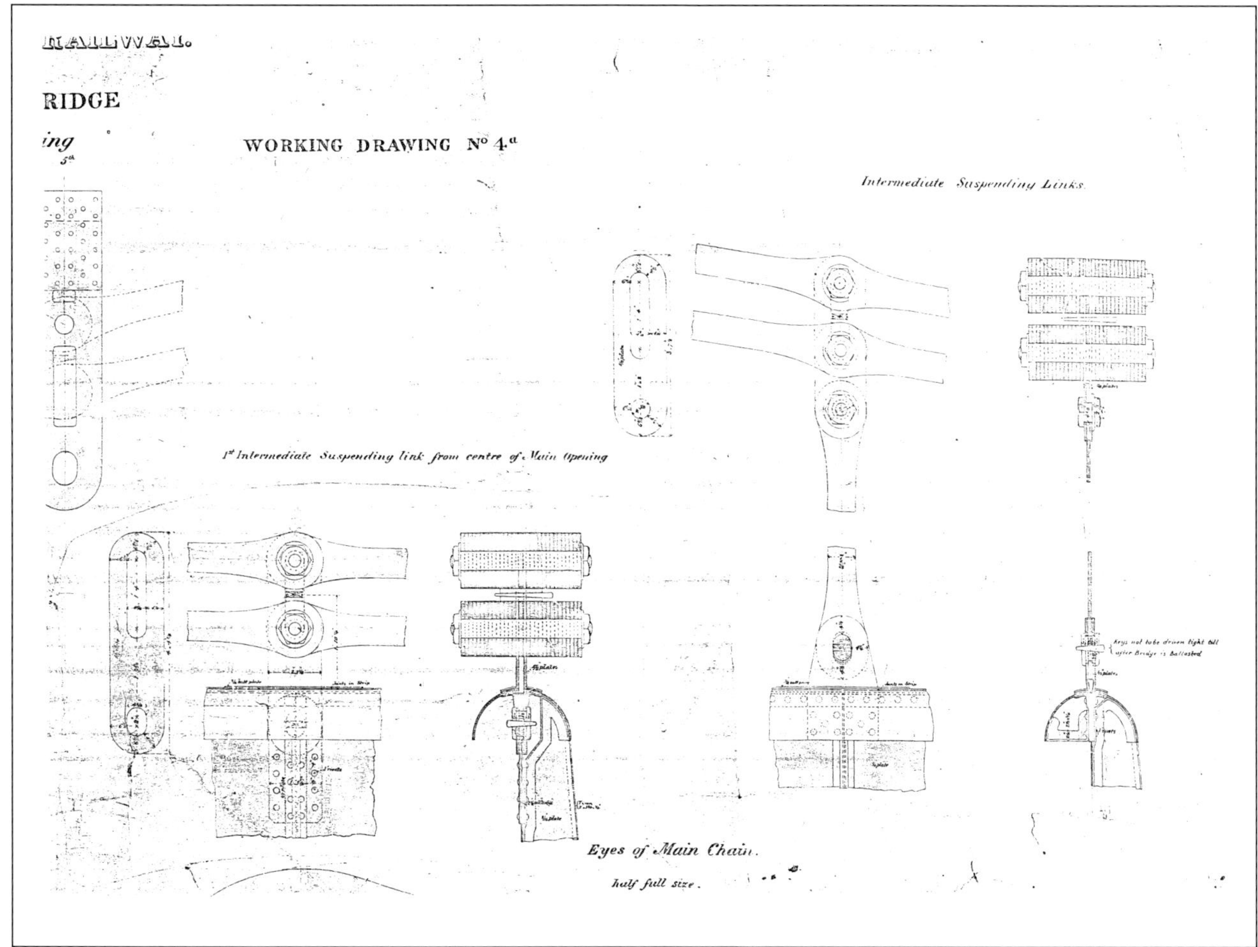

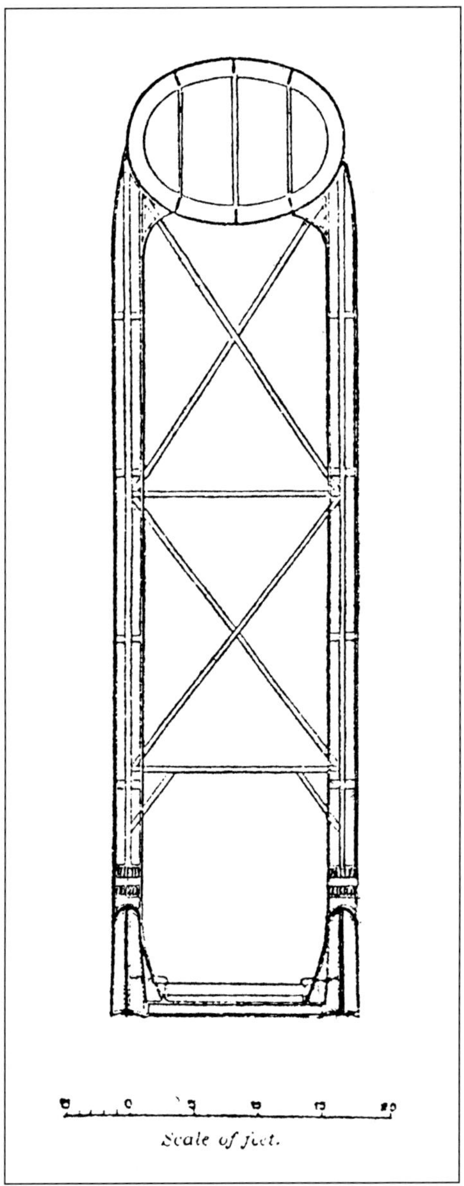

5.14A *A centre cross section of a main span showing the transverse cross bracing and diagonal stays between the standards.* BRUNEL 1870

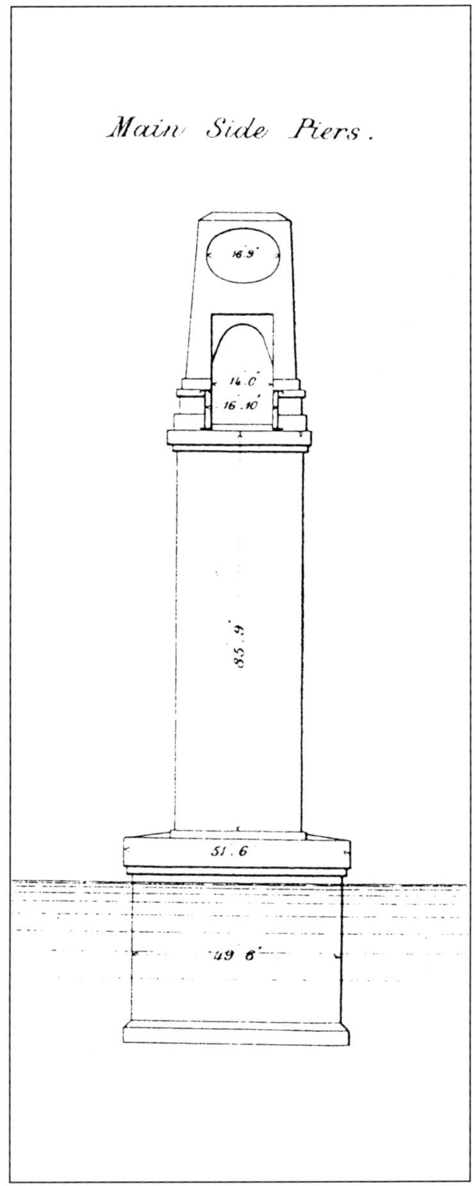

5.15 (right) *An outline drawing of one of the two massive landward masonry piers, which support the outer ends of the two main trusses.*

inner edge, an additional plate was attached through a cover plate, 5 inches wide x $^3/_{16}$ inch thick, the inner plate being radiused to form a smooth connection to the tube: see Fig.1 Plate 5.6. The standards passed through the suspension chains at varying distances from their junction with the roadway girders. Here the cruciform section was cut, and only the centre $^3/_8$ inch thick plate continued through the chains, with cheek plates riveted on either side. Through these passed the 4 inch diameter main pins of the chains, which were retained in position vertically by wedges. Below the chains and through the cheek plates a short pin passed to connect the bottom (and separate) $^3/_8$ inch centre plate of the standard. This continued downwards, again in cruciform section, to a connection with the track girders; see Figs. 2, 5, 6 and 12 of Plate 5.7. and the details of Plate 5.13.

Between each standard was an intermediate suspension link or hanger, of section 7 inches wide x $^7/_8$ inch thick, having its upper end attached to the chains and its lower end to the flange of the roadway girders, as shown in Plate 5.14.

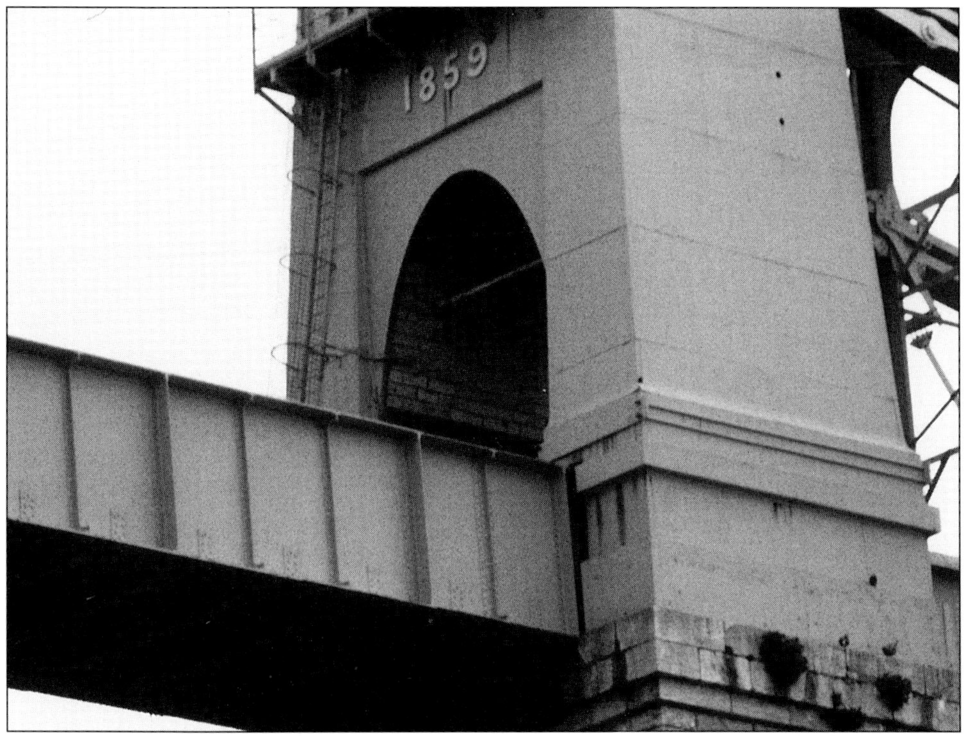

5.16 *A close up view of the western portal, set on top of its massive masonry pier, showing the masonry and brickwork lining within the cast iron shell. The expansion bearings that support the end of the Cornwall span are located at the top of this portal. Note the chain links in the top righthand corner which are of the pattern shown in Plate 5.11.* AUTHOR

5.17 *A view of the Devon portal, before the fitting of the permanent access ladders and platforms. Unfortunately, this photograph is undated but as it shows the trackwork carried on baulk timbers it probably dates from soon after the gauge conversion. Again, the masonry and brickwork arch can be clearly seen. Note also how the ends of the bridge girders are concealed within the cast iron shrouding, thus making painting difficult.* RTGW

THE DIAGONAL BRACING

The locations where the standards were intersected by the main chains, were braced to the main tube by wrought iron ties, 7 inch wide and of varying thickness, 1¼ inch at the centre and 1 inch at each end of the span. Each brace comprised four ties, which met between two ¾ inch formed plates, to which they were firmly keyed, the plates being connected through a 1½ inch diameter bolt. The lower extremity of each lower tie was bolted to lugs on its respective standard while the upper end of each upper tie was bolted to the side of the main tube, being covered by the same plate which overlapped the top of each standard. See Figs. 2, 5, 7, 8 and 9 of Plate 5.7.

A curious feature of this linkage was that the main connection pins were apparently intentionally made of a diameter about ⅛ inch smaller than the holes in which they fitted. While this lapse from good engineering practice may be explained by Brunel, in failing health, being preoccupied with other projects (Berridge 1969), inevitably with a pin bearing on a small area instead of a total diameter, the connection was bound to work loose in a relatively short time. This fault

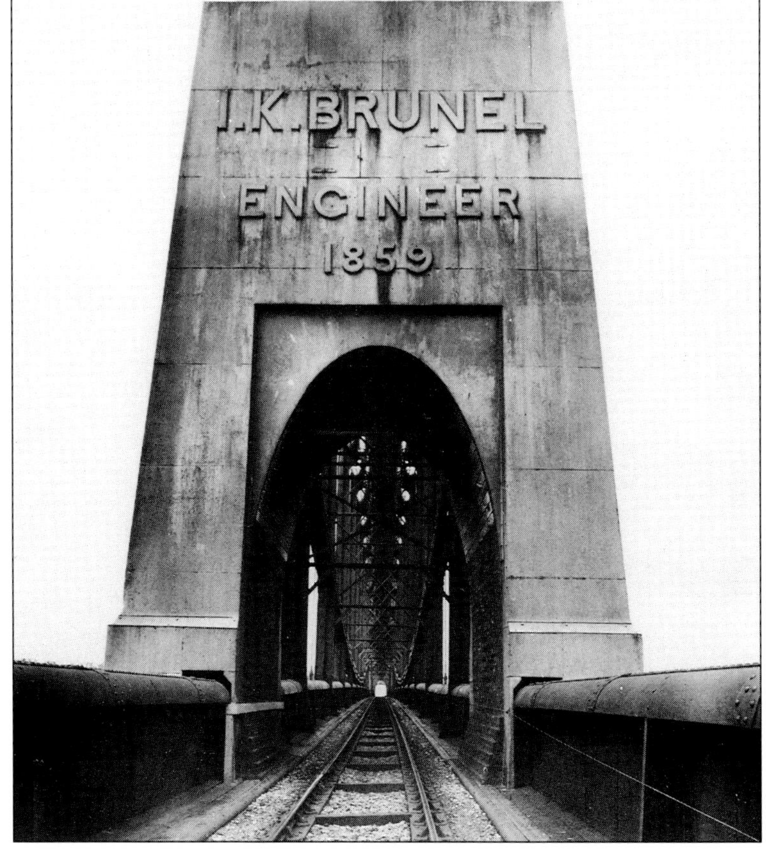

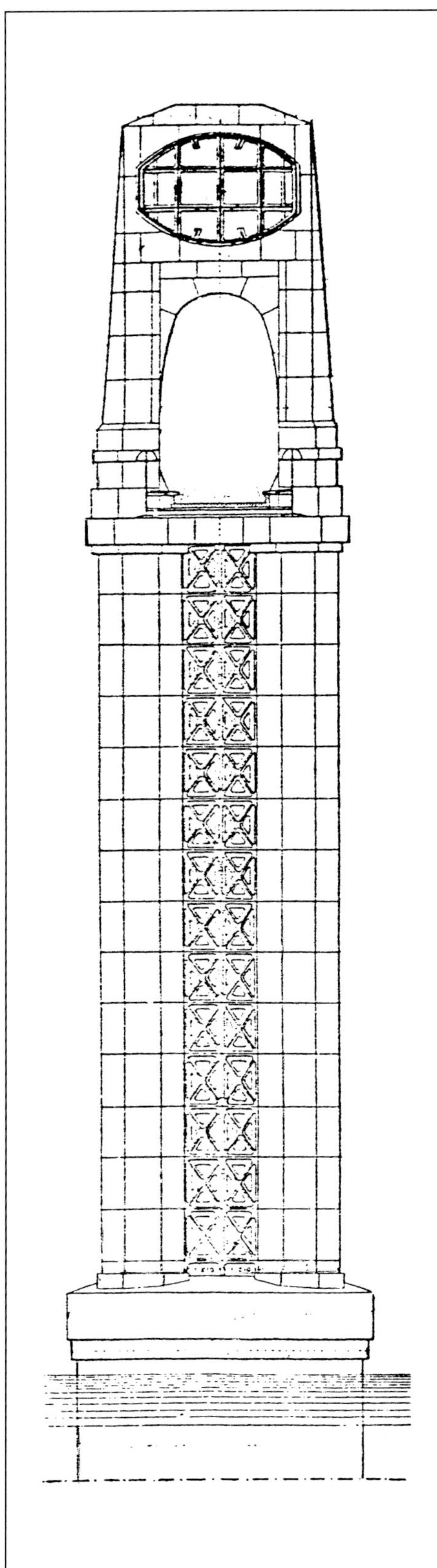

5.18 *A sketch drawing of the centre pier with its four cast iron columns, showing their formation, with the transverse cross bracing and the cast iron standards set on top of these columns forming the portal and fixed support for the inner end of each tube.* H. RESAL, PARIS

appears to have proved an ongoing problem over the years.

In addition, the standards incorporated transverse bracing from 4 x 2 x 3/8 inch T sections, together with diagonal stays, as shown in Plate 5.14A.

The copy of Brunel's original working drawing, Plate 5.10, showing the chains and associated details at the vertical intermediates intersections, and the copy of working drawing No 4a shown in Plate 5.14, illustrate his unique design for these important features.

AFFECT OF TEMPERATURE VARIATION ON MAIN SPANS

It will be appreciated that each complete main span may be considered as a double bow, the tensile action of the chains upon the bed plates being counteracted by the thrust exerted on them by the arched tube. The inner end of each span was fixed above the portal of the centre pier, while the overall depth of each span, measured from the centre of the tube to the chain centre, at mid span, was about one-eighth of the clear span.

The effects of temperature variation on the length of each of these spans was catered for by locating the outer frames of each main tube upon 48 wrought iron rollers. These were 3 feet 3 inches in length and 3½ inches diameter, set in a double cast iron framework or bed plate located on the portal of each landward pier. While a possible change in length of six inches was catered for, in practice the greatest change initially observed amounted to only three inches in the entire length of both spans.

THE MAIN LAND PIERS

The main spans were supported on each foreshore on massive granite piers, 29 feet wide by 17 feet thick, and 130 feet in height from the foundation to the level of the rails (Plate 5.15). Above that height, substantial portals of brick with courses of stone, all encased in cast iron (Plate 5.16) formed the outer support for the above expansion bearings for each span. Plate 5.17, an early photograph of the Devon portal reflecting its clean architectural style before the addition of the access ladder and platform, also shows the brick and masonry lining of the portal as well

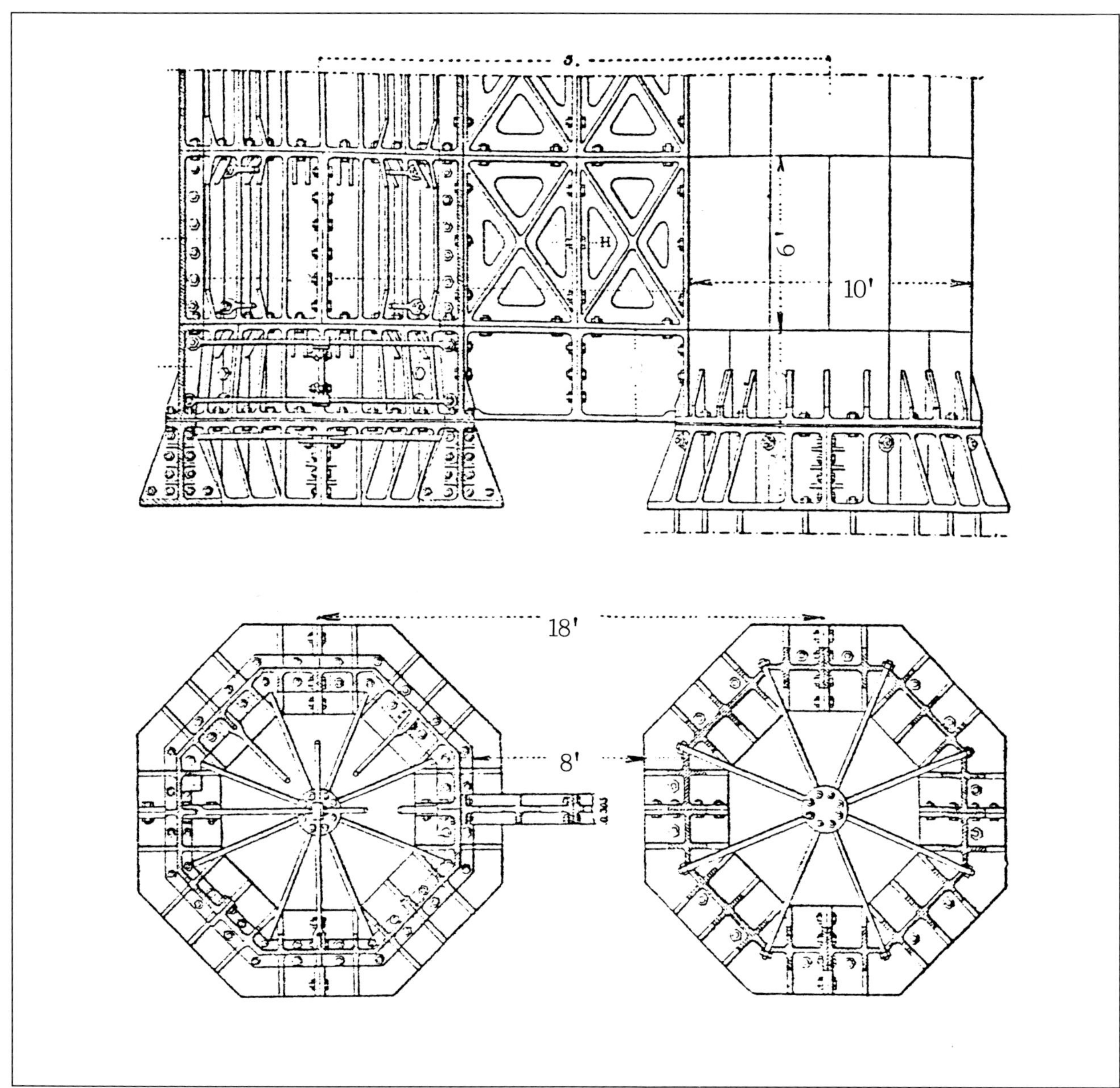

as the 'concealment' of the ends of the approach girders within the cast iron casing of the structure.

The Centre Pier

The centre support (Plate 5.18) was formed as a circular column of solid masonry, 35 feet in diameter and 96 feet high from its foundation on bedrock to its upper surface, some 12 feet above high water level. Rising from that masonry plinth, the pier comprised a series of cast iron sections, as shown, extending to the location of the fixed bearing support of the main tubes. The initial support was built up as four octagonal cast iron columns, set in a square, each column being ten feet wide and eight feet apart from its neighbours. This arrangement placed the columns at 18 feet centres. Transverse cast iron cross bracing linked each pair of columns but there was no longitudinal bracing between the pairs. Each column was formed from 6 feet sections, having thickness of 2 inches, with substantial internal stiffening, flanged and bolted together, as shown in Plate 5.19, and

5.19 *A detail drawing of the cast iron columns, set on the central masonry pier, showing their internal stiffening ribs, the bolting flanges and transverse cross bracing between them.*
H. Resal, Paris

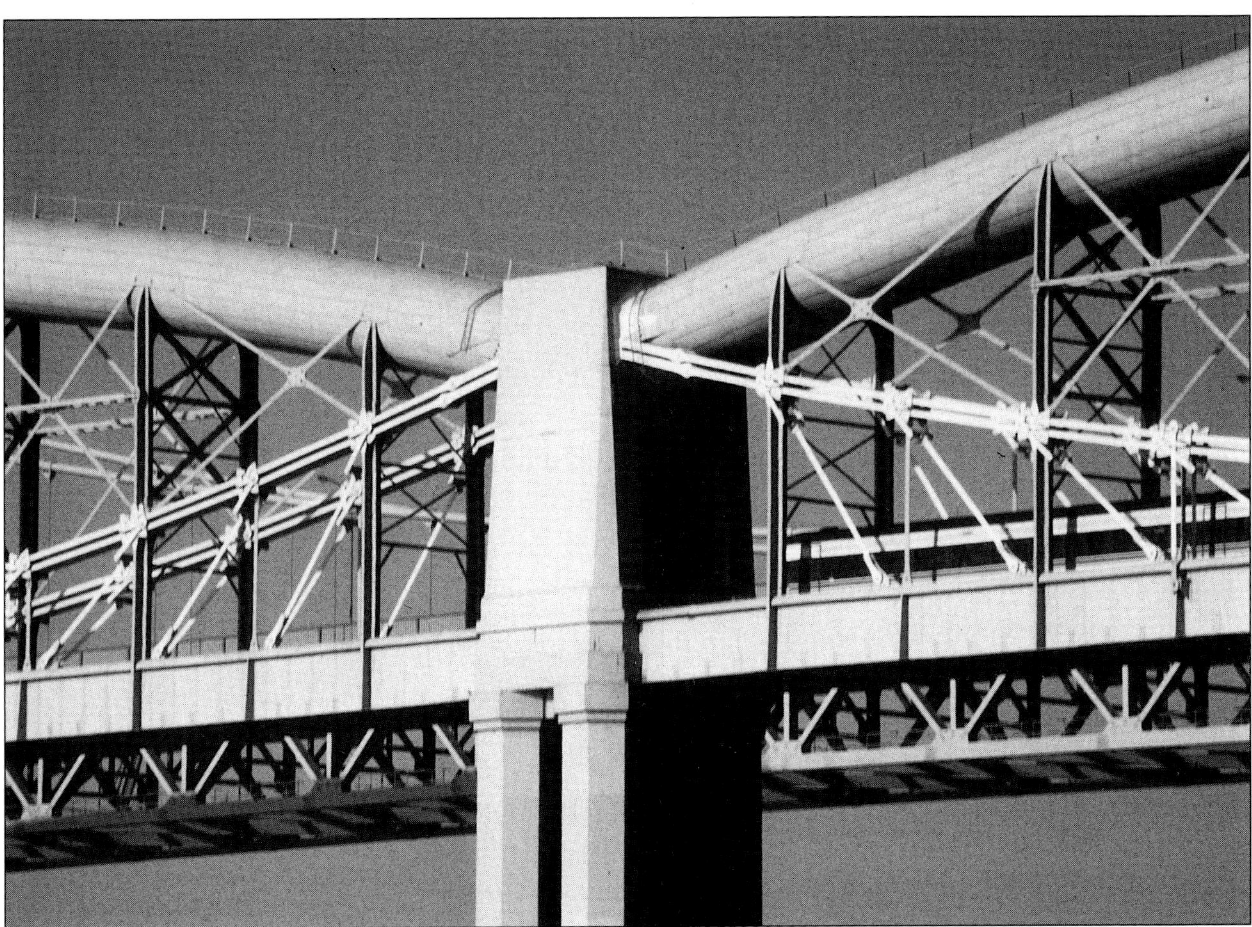

5.20 *A view of the all cast iron centre portal, forming the location for the inner ends of the two tubes. A pity the decking of the 1961 roadbridge in the background confuses an otherwise clear view of this important central support.* AUTHOR

extended to a height of 88 feet 9 inches at rail level, and weighed 150 tons.

Located on their tops was the central portal, formed from four massive cast iron frameworks, often also referred to as 'standards' and not to be confused with the vertical supports discussed above. They were of construction similar to the octagonal columns, each standard, in a series of six feet planed and flanged sections bolted together, weighed 50 tons and extended to a height of some 50 feet above the top of the octagonal columns. This portal (Plate 5.20) incorporated the seating and location which supported the ends of each tube, and thus provided the fixed centre bearing of both spans. This bearing arrangement[5] comprised a wrought iron framework, on which the ends of the tubes were seated, with 4 inch thick oak packings between the framework and the tops of the columns. A non structural cast iron shroud, extending above the top of the standards served to cover in and roof over the ends of the tubes and chains. Taking account of the total weight imposed on this centre pier, Brunel had estimated that the loading at the bottom of the masonry foundation would be about 9 $^1/_2$ tons/ft^2, increasing to about 10 tons/ft^2 when a train crossed the Bridge; a level of loading which was considered acceptable.

Plate 5.21 is a view from within the centre portal, taken in 1927 and looking towards the Devon end of the Bridge, showing its cast iron formation compared with the brick and masonry lining of the two land piers. In recent years access ladders have been fitted within the cast iron standards, so that the inside of the columns can be inspected and painted as necessary. Over the years the cast iron appears to have adequately withstood any corrosion from the salt laden air.

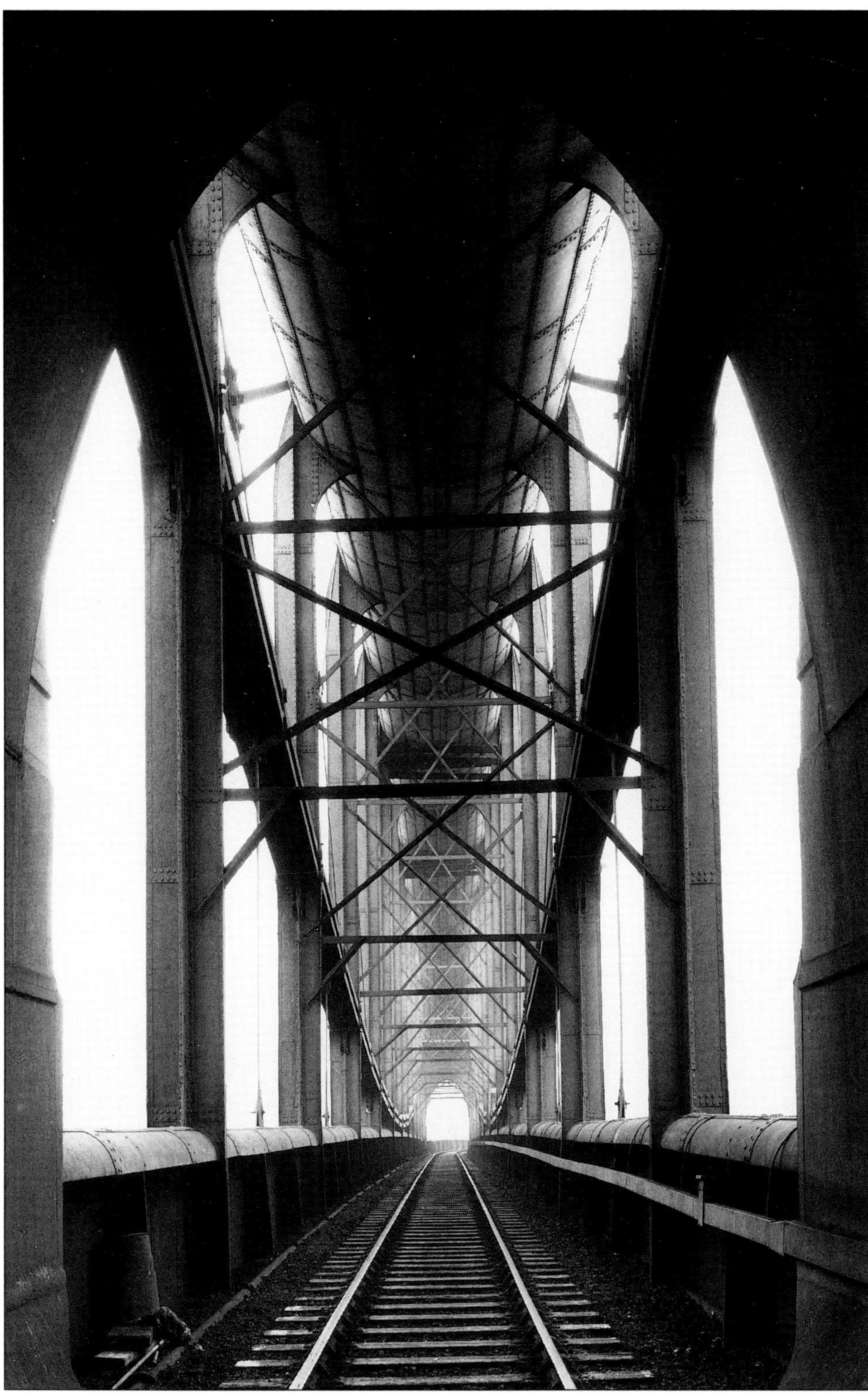

5.21 *A 1927 view from the centre portal, showing its cast iron formation, looking towards the Devon shore. This photo also well illustrates the standards linking the tube, main chains and roadway girders with their associated cross bracing, the formation of the roadway girders and the excellent fabrication details of the tube itself.* RTGW

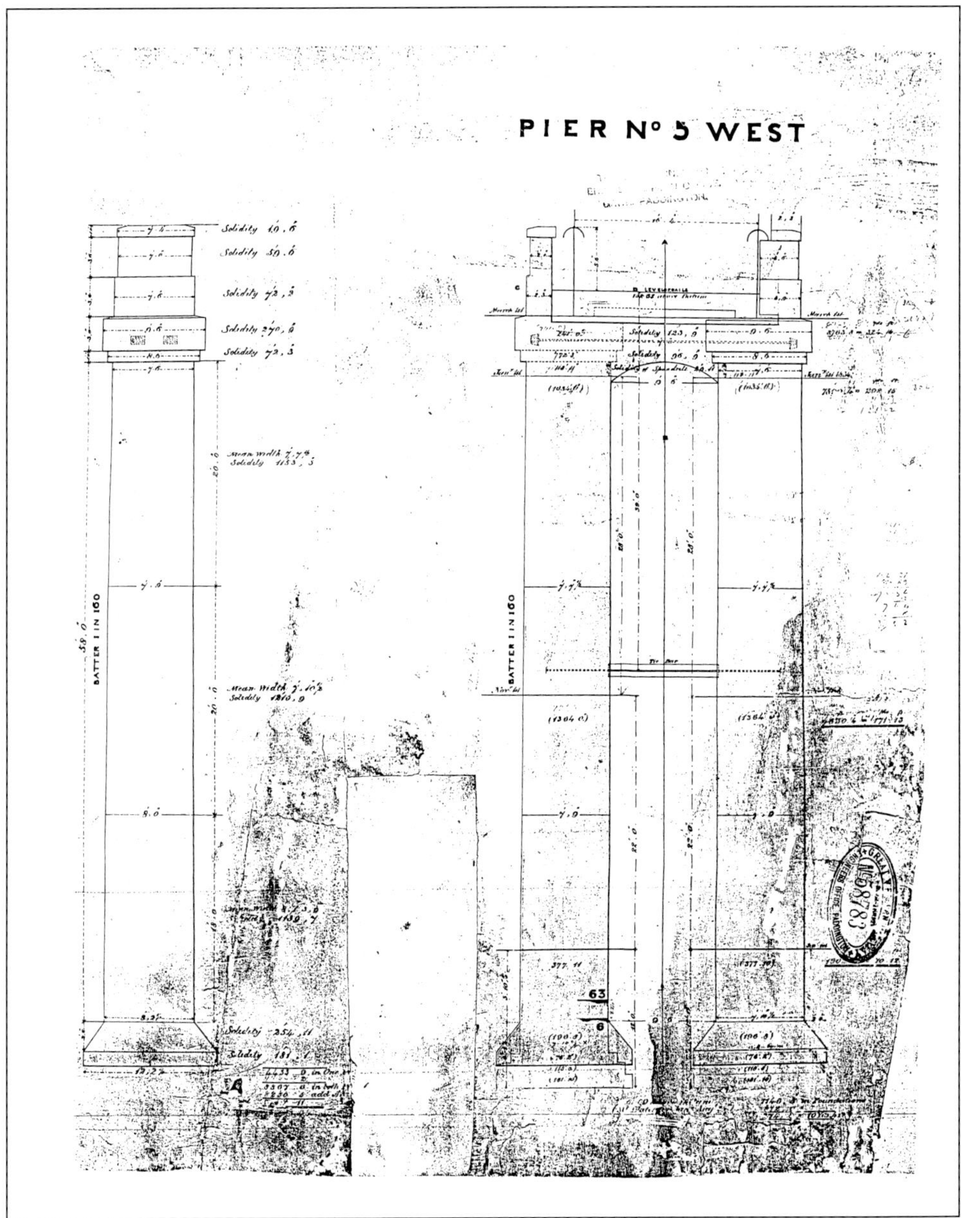

5.22 *A copy of one of Brunel's original drawings showing the typical details of one of the masonry land span piers, No 5 West.* RTGW

THE APPROACH SPANS

The approach spans on each shore were carried on massive double columns of solid masonry, 11 feet square, of which Plate 5.22, a copy of one of Brunel's original drawings, shows a typical construction. Each span was built up from wrought iron plate girders, generally similar to the bridge girders of the two main spans; 8 feet deep x 3/4 inch thick, incorporating a semi circular top flange, 1/2 inch thick and 2 feet in diameter, attached to the web by means of 3 1/2 x 3/8 inch angle irons, with 7/8 inch rivets. The slightly curved bottom flange, of 1/2 inch plate 3 feet wide, was also attached to the web by similar angle irons; the 4 inch thick timber platform being carried by cross girders made of plate and angle irons, 13 inches in depth and 16 feet 10 inches in length.

Plate 5.23 shows a typical cross section of one of these wrought iron 'through girders', following conversion from broad to narrow

5.23A *A rare view of the broad gauge roadway on the Cornwall main span showing the longitudinal and transom timbers, ballast and adjacent timber walkway, giving a striking appreciation of the considerable width of Brunel's gauge compared with the standard trackwork of today.*
COLLECTION - STEPHEN ROWSON

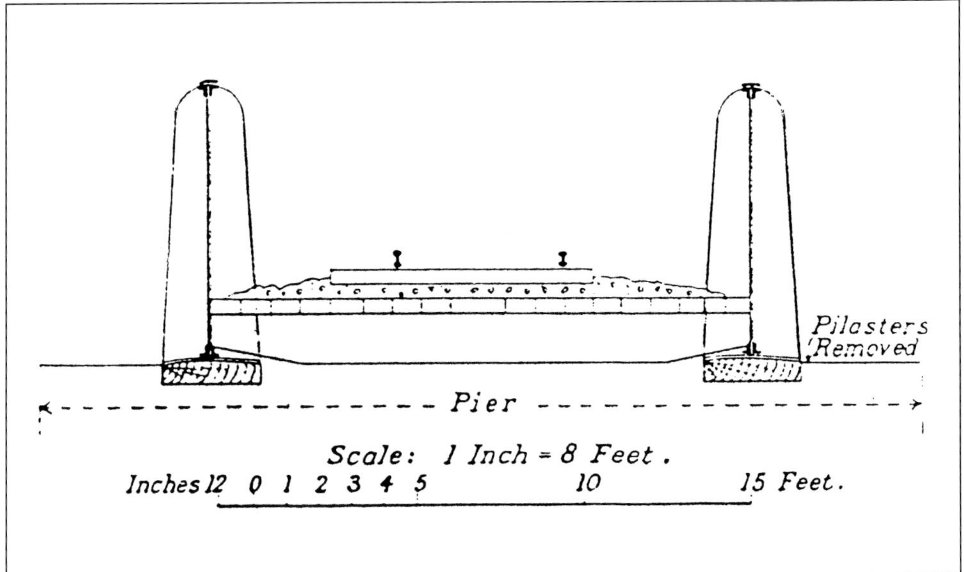

5.23 *A typical section through the girders of one of the approach spans, following conversion from broad to standard gauge and before the replacement of Brunel's wrought iron girders.* PROC ICE

5.24 *An early 1900s view of the Bridge as Brunel had built it, other than the change of track gauge in 1892, and before the start of the several modifications introduced from the early 1900s onwards. The* MOUNT EDGCUMBE *training ship is moored to the right of the structure which is presumably painted dark brown, perpetuating earlier colour schemes.* RIC

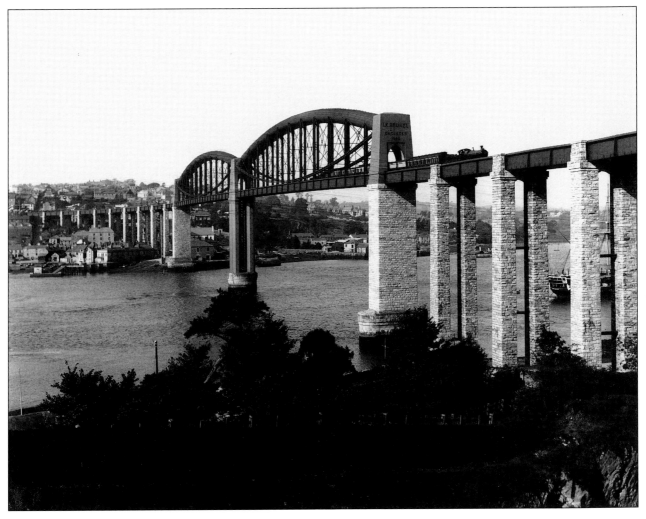

gauge and prior to replacement by steel girders. Surprisingly, the spans were not of uniform length but comprised two of 93 feet, two of 83 feet 6 inches, two of 78 feet, two of 72 feet 6 inches and nine of 69 feet 6 inches; such relatively small variations in the length of these approach spans would not be acceptable for fabrication today. It would seem that the economics of repetition were secondary to Brunel's aesthetic consideration of the overall Bridge design; these openings were progressively shorter from that of 93 feet immediately adjacent to each of the main land piers, through 83 feet 6 inches, 78 feet and 72 feet 6 inches on either side to the 69 feet 6 inches spans of the remaining openings.

Together with the two main spans, the overall length of the structure was nearly 2,200 feet, which was over 670 feet longer than Stephenson's Britannia Bridge across the Menai Straits. Ballast extended throughout the length of the plate girder roadway and initially supported the longitudinal timbers and bridge rails which formed the usual broad gauge track, as shown in Plate 5.23A. Because of the sharp curvature of both sets of approach spans a speed limit of 15 m.p.h. has always applied for trains crossing the Bridge.

Apart from the conversion from broad to narrow gauge in 1892, it would appear that the structure continued in service substantially in its original form, as shown in Plate 5.24, into the early 1900s.

Brunel's Contractual Position

Since the majority of the detail drawings and calculations had been completed by late October 1852, Brunel was then able to consider his own position in relation to the overall contract and in particular, for all the work he had carried out on the Saltash Bridge. He submitted his suggestions in a letter to the Cornwall Railway Finance Committee at their meeting in Truro on 17 June 1853. This is reproduced in full on page 60 since it reveals a clear insight into Brunel's dedication to his work, his relationship with his client (the Directors and Shareholders of the Cornwall Railway) and his support for his hardworking assistants.

The Committee then considered the Accounts as submitted, which were identified in the Minutes as shown below.

The Committee having examined and considered these accounts reported that, as the sum of £5,000 for Mr Brunel's past professional services 'included the designs & plans of the Bridge' did not appear to be unreasonable, they recommended that his arrangement be accepted. A total of 308 shares were accordingly allotted to him.

With regard to the other items involved, the Committee felt that, apart from the scale of travelling expenses, they were reasonable. However, they recommended that in future these expenses should be covered by a fixed sum, particularly in the case of the resident engineer, Mr Glennie, who will be in receipt of the recommended increase in salary which the

1. Mr Brunel's account of personal services including design of the plans of the Albert Bridge		£5,000.0.0
2. Mr Brunel's professional services and travelling expenses for one year ending Mar 1853		£1,200.0.3
3. Salaries & Expenses of Assistants & Surveyors during the setting out of the line to Dec /52	£2,132.13.9	
Travelling expenses during the same period	480.14.2	2,613.7.11
2. Assistants' time Clerks, draftsmen & Office expenses from April 1852 to April 1853		1,271.14.0
4. Assistants Salaries & Expenses		
Quarter ending March 1853	682.10.0	
On Surveys & setting out the line	197. 8.0	
Assistants Travelling expenses	232. 8.1	
Do on Surveys	42. 7.3	1,154.13.4
		11,239.15.6

18 Duke St Westminster
2nd June 1853
My Dear Sir

I now send you to lay before the Directors to morrow, the Engineering Accounts for the half year ending December 1852 and also for the first quarter of 1853.

The former as you will perceive includes what I propose to allow Mr Glennie for the last three years, during which time he has been actively and most usefully engaged, as it is proved by the result of our letting of contracts, in working up every detail for me so as to enable me to diminish the amount of Work and consequent cost of construction to a minimum. In the second account the salaries of Mr Glennie and his several assistants are carried out at the amounts at which I propose they should be fixed since the more active progress of the Works commencing 1st January last.

I have endeavoured and shall continue to do so to study economy in the expenditure upon engineering superintendence, at the same time it must constantly be borne in mind that great economy in the much larger amounts expended in the execution of Works can only be obtained by considerable labor [*sic*] and skill in the original setting out of the works, dependant upon the correct info [*sic*] of detail obtained from assistants and by great and zealous attention on the part of all those assistants during the progress of the works to insure their execution according to the instructions and terms of the Contracts, so that they may be sufficient and no extra quantities be required and such service cannot be obtained except by the employment of a sufficient number of trustworthy and competent Assistants reasonably but sufficiently paid.

As regards my own professional charges, I have been somewhat at a loss to know how to make them - I should wish to be governed by the same spirit of economy which is essential throughout this undertaking at the same time I cannot, nor of course could it be desired, that I should deal with the Company otherwise than as a professional man, - and in this case there has been a great deal of thought and time devoted to the undertaking generally, while in one single Work, namely, the Saltash Bridge, the result of the thought and consideration of some years is concentrated. What I propose is under the circumstances and in consideration especially of the labour and responsibility attending this particular work, to make a fixed charge of £5,000 (which I will take in paid up shares of the Company) and that I should receive also a salary of £1,000 a year with £200 a year for travelling expenses making £1,200 a year during the construction of the railway from April 1852 since which date I have not made any charge.

The charges for copies of drawings, contracts &c and for other office expenses actually incurred by me or payments made to surveyors or draftsmen are of course exclusive of this - these have been rather heavy during the last 12 months, but will henceforth be lighter as the principal part of the work is done.

I trust these arrangements will be satisfactory to the Directors.
I am, Dear Sir
Yours truly
(Signed) I K Brunel

W H Bond esq

Committee considered he was fairly entitled. They also felt that some estimate should be given of the likely level of future office expenses.

Thus, seven years after the granting of the Cornwall Railway Act, the design of the major work on the line had at last been finalised and Brunel had established his fee for this particular part of the overall contract in the sum of £5,000. It is interesting to relate this figure to the corresponding value today which, based on the relative RPI figures for 1853 and 1993, indicate a fee of around £240,000.

In the meanwhile, as we shall see in the next chapter, with the fortunes of the Company improving, he had been able to seek tenders for its construction and a contract was eventually let for this project early in 1853.

CHAPTER SIX

THE CONTRACT LET CONSTRUCTION: THE CENTRE PIER

1853 to 1856

With some improvement in the overall market conditions, and following the reorganisation of the Company's capital in April 1852, the financial situation of the Company under the guidance of the new Chairman had sufficiently recovered during the year to enable the gradual resumption of the work of construction. This commenced with the letting of a contract for about 15 miles eastward from the West Cornwall Junction at Penwithers (MacDermot) and, before the end of the year, for its extension to Liskeard. Furthermore, with the design of the Saltash Bridge finally completed by October of that year, Brunel was in a position to seek tenders for its construction.

These he diligently pursued, and at the Board Meeting of 14 January 1853 he laid before the Directors the following Tenders for the work of building the Bridge[1], and the viaducts connected therewith, comprised in Contracts No 1 and No 2:

Mr Finch	No 2 Contract	£129,858
Lowest Contract for No 1		£ 42,000
Mr Hennett	Both Contracts	£173,000
Mr Mare	Both Contracts	£162,000

All these contractors were considered by Brunel to be responsible men and equal to the

6.1 *An extract from Johnston's site survey showing the land purchased for the establishment of the fabrication facility on the Devon shore. It is interesting to note that the inn, identified as '50' on the plan, was not required; that building is still in use today as the 'Royal Albert'.* RtGW

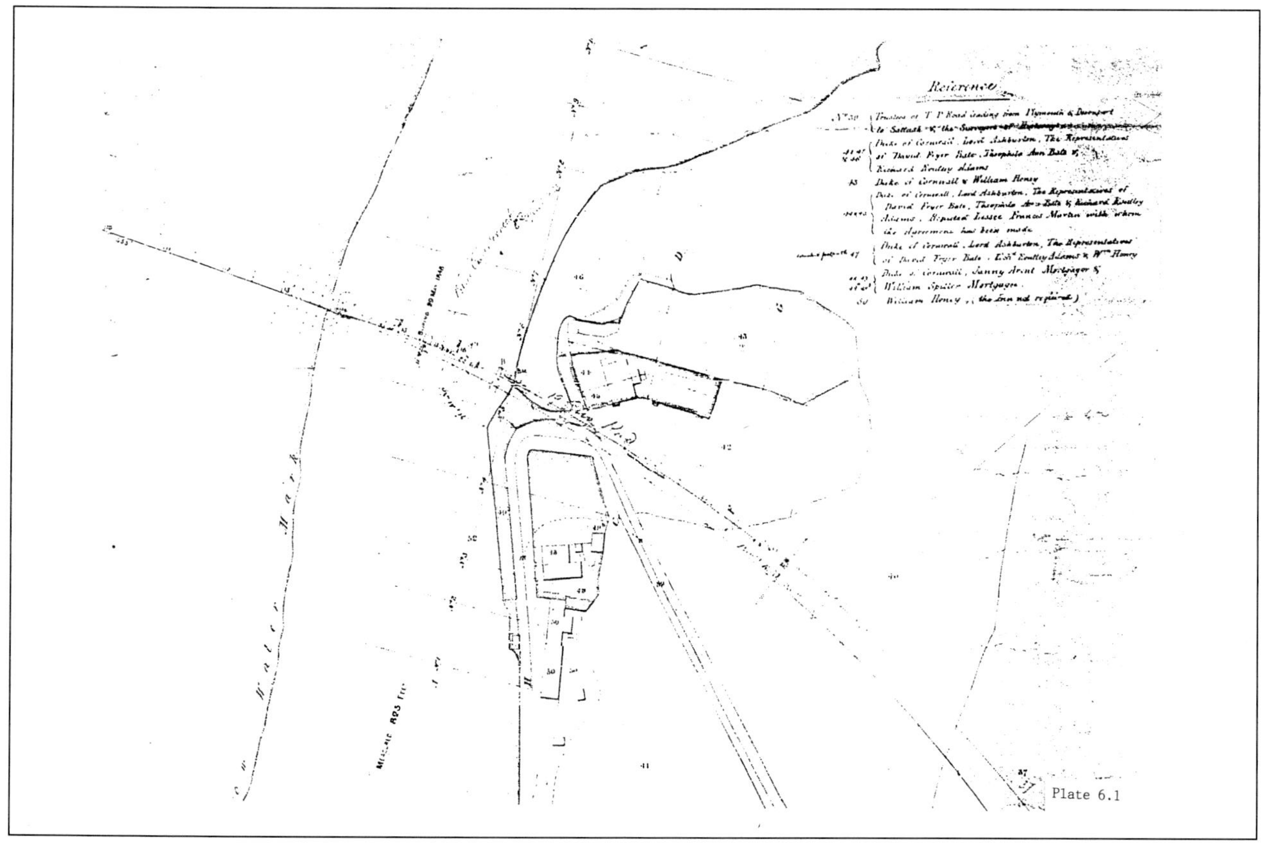

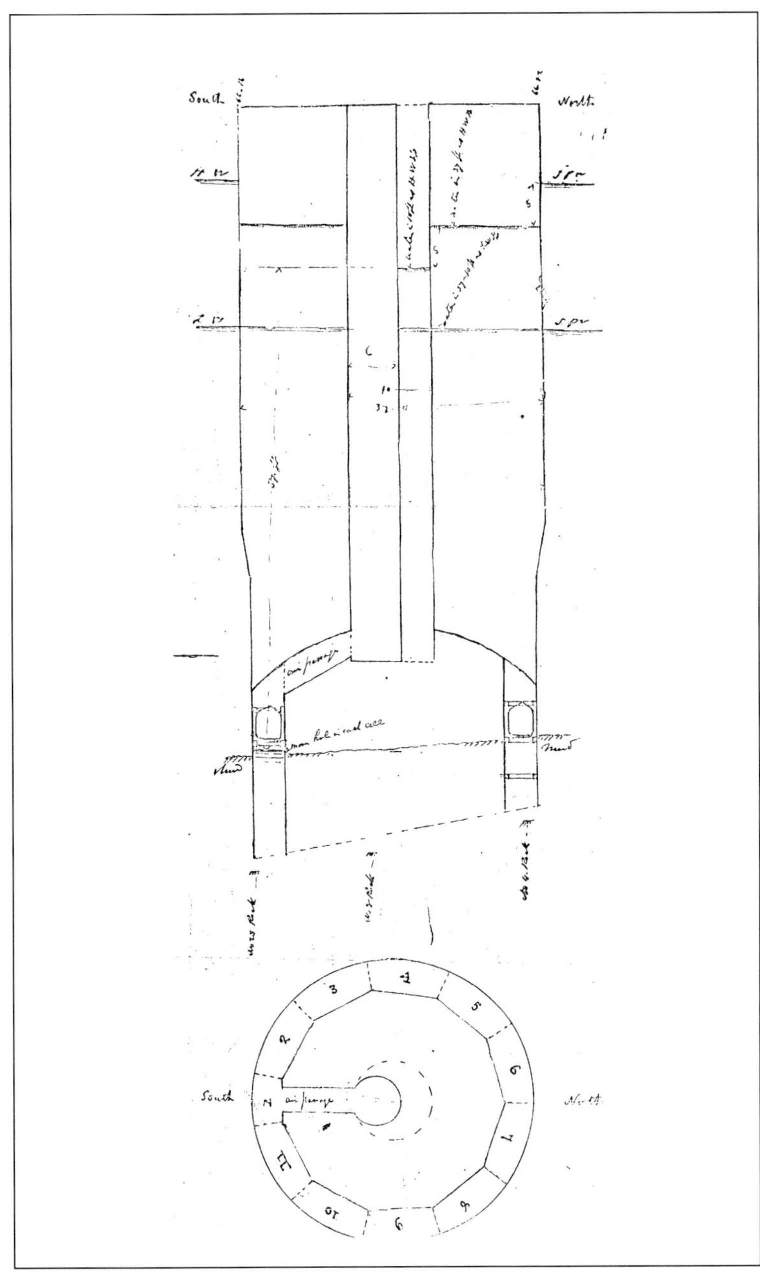

6.2 *Believed to be a copy of one of Brunel's original sketches of his concept of the great cylinder to be used in constructing the central pier. It shows the arrangement of the annular chambers in the base, connected by the air passage to the central pneumatic cylinder, to be used as required either as a coffer dam or a pressurised working chamber.* RTGW

task of completing the works 'in the most satisfactory manner'.

After due deliberation, he was authorised by the Board to let the contract for the construction of the Saltash Bridge to the firm of Mr C. J. Mare, 'under such arrangements and stipulations as he Mr Brunel may be able to effect'. In this respect, the subsequent indenture[2] dated 1 October 1853, relating to the Contract (apparently agreed to by Mr Mare some nine months after the original terms had been established) was to be of significant benefit to the Company in connection with the eventual completion of the Bridge. Under the terms of this indenture, in the event of Mare's bankruptcy, the Company was empowered to take over the works out of the hands of the receiver or his assignee in bankruptcy.

Accordingly, at long last, on the occasion of the fourteenth half yearly meeting of the Cornwall Company[3] at the end of February 1853, Brunel was able officially to report that the Contract for the building of the Saltash Bridge had been let during January to Mr C. J. Mare, the eminent iron ship-builder of Blackwall. He was well known as the principal contractor for the iron work of the Britannia Bridge across the Menai Straits, completed in 1850 by Robert Stephenson.

Mare's contract price for the Saltash Bridge was a fixed sum of £162,000, which covered the entire execution and completion of the whole work, including the founding of the centre pier through to the erection and finishing of the superstructure. With Board approval, Mr Mare had agreed to take 1,000 shares at £3.15s.0d. discount in part payment of the sum stipulated to be paid.

Brunel further reported that although a sudden rise in the price of iron, coupled with a demand for other work of a similar nature, had caused some tenderers to withdraw, a number of 'highly respectable and responsible parties' had submitted prices which showed a remarkable similarity, unusual in large contracts of this nature. Consequently, in selecting Mare the Directors had been able to make a 'safe and satisfactory' choice.

That the scope and size of the works involved in the construction of the Saltash Bridge had led many to entertain doubts regarding its feasibility was apparent from Brunel's remarks to the shareholders at this meeting. He pointed out that he was not disposed to underrate the difficulties but, equally, he would not propose plans which could not be executed for a moderate sum; he was confident that the design as proposed was capable of satisfactory completion under the direction of himself and his engineering assistants.

Following an approach by the Chairman to the Consort, Prince Albert had consented to the Bridge being called the 'Royal Albert Bridge', and it is interesting to note an exchange of letters[4] in March 1853 between M. Williams (Chairman) and W. H. Bond (Secretary) recorded that steps should be taken to see that this information was published 'in a proper manner by the newspapers and if possible to get it also stated in *The Times* - Prince Albert having consented to the Bridge being called the Albert Bridge'. Furthermore, Brunel was to prepare a drawing of the Bridge for presentation to the Prince.

The Site Fabricating Facilities - known as Saltash Bridge Works

Meanwhile, the contractor was proceeding[5] to make the necessary arrangements to start work without delay and these 'indicate every desire and every ability to do substantial justice to the work'. They involved setting up all the facilities necessary for the construction, which were sited on the Devon shore on land and existing buildings purchased by the Company as shown in Plate 6.1. These comprised a jetty for the landing of materials and workshops built to house the fabricating machinery, furnaces and stores. It is interesting to note that the adjoining inn, which today is known as the 'Royal Albert', was not acquired.

While we have no specific details of the machinery involved at this initial stage, it is reasonable to conjecture that, having regard to the need to shear, punch and roll wrought iron plates to form the great cylinder required for the construction of the centre pier and, later, to prepare the massive oval tubes of the main spans, it would probably have included a range of plant similar to that used by Mare for the construction of the Britannia Bridge. This in turn had evolved from then current British shipbuilding practice.

In that respect, we do have a report[6] produced in December 1842, by Monsieur Dupuy de Lome of the French Navy, covering the results of his survey of British shipbuilding operations at that time. It will be recalled that during the 1830s a number of vessels had been constructed of wrought iron but the most significant progress was initiated when, in 1839, the steamship *Great Britain* was laid down in Bristol. Following the deliberations of a technical committee, which included Brunel, the hull was to be built of wrought iron.

At that time methods of fabrication and construction were primitive, being tried out very much on an experimental basis; a particular limitation being the small size of plate then available. However, the builders were practical men who pursued ship construction with diligence and application, such that British shipbuilding in iron led the world.

Conversely, it is interesting to note that in the early 19th century, compared with Great Britain, France was probably in the forefront in the application of scientific principles to the solution of practical problems. Nevertheless, thanks to the work of engineers such as Brunel and Stephenson, who with a practical turn of mind had successfully developed the use of wrought iron in engineering structures, Great Britain was pre-eminent insofar as actual achievement was concerned.

In his report, de Lome included descriptions and illustrations of then typical shipyard machinery, as probably used in the construction of the *Great Britain*. All this plant was sold in 1850 on the liquidation of the Great Western Steamship Company. It would be reasonable to assume that Mare would have required a similar range of plant at Saltash to carry out the fabrication of the centre pier cylinder and the oval tubes of the Bridge. The following descriptions of the machinery probably involved has been compiled from the details of de Lome's report.

SET OF SHEARS - hand or belt driven, where the moving cutter was uppermost.

COMBINED PIERCING AND SHEARING MACHINE - with a movable lower jaw, hand or belt driven. It would appear that for cutting plate or strip this would have been a difficult machine to use, since the work would have moved with the lower jaw. Such use must be assumed

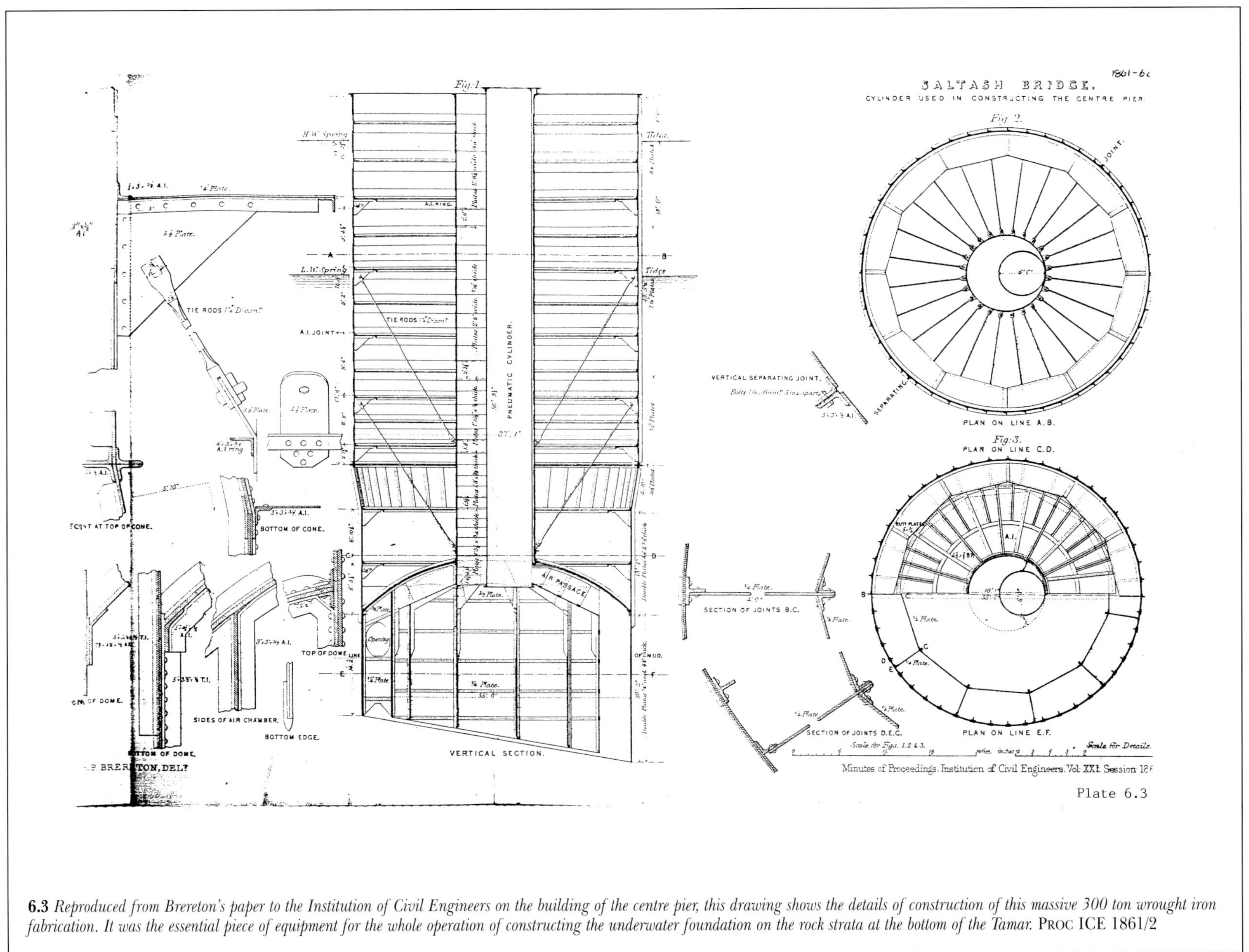

6.3 *Reproduced from Brereton's paper to the Institution of Civil Engineers on the building of the centre pier, this drawing shows the details of construction of this massive 300 ton wrought iron fabrication. It was the essential piece of equipment for the whole operation of constructing the underwater foundation on the rock strata at the bottom of the Tamar.* PROC ICE 1861/2

incidental to the main one, that of piercing the work for rivets, using a conventional punch. This machine was approximately 12 feet in length, while a smaller version, 8 feet in length, was available as a portable unit.

HAND ROLLS - similar in principle to those in use today except that the latter are larger and incorporate mechanical drive and adjustment. De Lome's report indicated that they could accept a maximum plate width of 5 feet 6 inches and a maximum thickness of $^{3}/_{8}$ inch on plates of narrow widths. However, larger capacity rolls had probably been developed by the time Mare was rolling plates at Saltash.

RADIAL DRILLS - While lighter examples would have been hand powered, larger examples would have been power driven from one of many steam engines installed at this site.

BENDING PRESS - De Lome specifies a press for holding the heavy plates required to form the trough sections involved in the keel of the Great Britain. A similar press could have been involved at Saltash in forming the heavier sections of the centre pier cylinder and the oval tubes.

HAND TOOLS - De Lome illustrates a hand ratchet-drill which would have been used for drilling holes in place and also for reaming out rivet holes; he also shows a hand riveting hammer - perhaps an indication of how far French engineering practice lagged behind that of Great Britain at that time.

This machinery would have been powered by a number of steam engines and as a local press report commented, 'engines of the most beautiful construction [were installed in the sheds and] soon the sounds of the hammer and the anvil, and the puffing of the steam engine, announced the progress of preparatory works'.

Furthermore, from the advertisement for the eventual sale[7] of these facilities in September 1859 (see Plate 10.1), we do know that the site incorporated a powerful overhead travelling crane, a 7 ton wharf crane, two portable 3 ton cranes on trollies, 13 smiths' forges, levelling plates and slabs and all the paraphernalia associated with an engineering construction facility. However, no details appear to have survived to indicate the type and extent, if any, of illumination on the site. While gas lighting was available in towns, no evidence has emerged of such outside lighting being installed. For working in the sheds it is probable that workmen depended on candles and one or other of the various oil burning lamps which had appeared in the early part of the nineteenth century, such as Holliday or Lucigen lamps. Information on this aspect of contemporary industrial activity appears scarce.

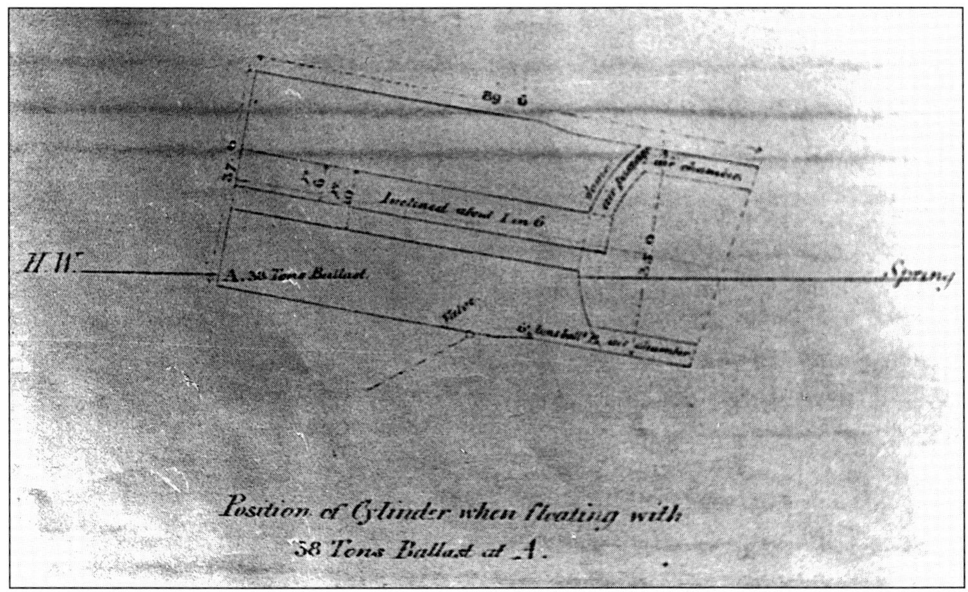

6.4 *A copy from one of Brunel's original drawings showing the attitude of the great cylinder following launch and as floated out to the four pontoons located over the proposed site of the central pier.* RTGW

6.5 *A reproduction from a lithograph of the great cylinder being floated out, showing the separate divisions around the base and the substantial reinforced construction.* DEVON LOCAL STUDIES LIBRARY

Without delay, Mare had also driven the piles required to support the platform which was to form the temporary site for the building of the main spans on the shore, before they were floated out into their final position within the Bridge formation. All these activities attracted press comment and an entry in the *West Briton & Cornwall Advertiser* of 2 September 1853 referred to that quiet location, known as Saltash Passage, having been converted into a

> ...place of bustle and business. Extensive workshops and smithies have been erected. Steam machinery of every description for planing, rolling into shape, cutting, drilling, and punching the masses of iron to form parts of the bridge, is in full operation. The smiths' shop contains eight forges, worked upon the principle of exhaustion, of what is commonly called fan bellows, driven by steam. A long slip, similar to that used for ship-building, has been laid down for the construction of the cylinders...

While the major activity of construction was settled on the Devon bank, it would appear that a small yard was also sited on the Cornish shore, since on the day that the first complete span was floated out, a report[8] referred to '...The Company's yards on either side of the river were enclosed, and admission to them was granted by tickets issued by Mr Bond, the Secretary of the Company'.

This yard would presumably have contained the materials required for the building of the masonry piers for the Cornwall landspans, as well as those for the main western pier. Although no evidence has so far come to light in confirmation, it is also possible that, following their cutting and punching on the Devon side, the plates and sections for these wrought iron landspans could have been shipped over and finally fabricated in the Cornwall yard, or adjacent to their respective piers. In that way they would have been more easily transportable.

It would appear that a revival in the prosperity of Saltash may be dated from the inauguration of Mare's contract, following which numerous new houses and villas were erected in the vicinity; a system of drainage adopted; two lines of steamers started and 'comodious [*sic*] landing stages erected'.

THE GREAT CYLINDER

Now, the key to the whole Saltash Bridge project was, of course, the building of the centre pier and with the manufacturing facilities thus established, the first task was to fabricate the massive cylinder which was required for its construction. In July 1852 Brunel had prepared a sketch (Plate 6.2) of his initial conception of this equipment while Plate 6.3 shows it in its final form[9]. The cylinder comprised a shell formed from wrought iron boiler plates, approximately 37 feet in diameter and 90 feet in overall length, open at the bottom and, including all its internal fittings, weighing some 300 tons. Plate thickness varied between 3/8 inch for the top sections, through 5/8 inch; with the lower, pressurised, sections in double 3/8 inch and 1/2 inch plates, rivetted and ribbed to form a strong shell, as will be seen from the illustration. The profile of the bottom was shaped to suit the contour of the rock formation, as determined from Glennie's original survey of 1848/49; consequently, one side was some six feet longer than the other.

A dome, or lower deck, was incorporated within the cylinder at about the level at which the mud of the river bed was expected to be, when it was sunk in position. This dome was connected to the top, or upper deck, by an internal chamber, ten feet in diameter, which was open at top and bottom and, fixed eccentrically therein, Brunel positioned the 6 foot cylinder previously used by Glennie for his surveys. This formed a connection to an air jacket, some four feet in width, which extended as an annulus around the lower portion of the main cylinder, and was in turn divided into eleven separate compartments or cells. Thus, in the event that the cylinder was not effective as a coffer dam, Brunel had made provision to use it as a diving bell, with the facility to introduce air pressure at the lower working face should it be found to be necessary.

It was intended that the lower part of the cylinder, within the level of the mud bank, should be filled in with masonry and not removed. The upper part, 50 feet in length, however, was constructed in two pieces of larger diameter than the masonry, with vertical separating joints bolted together, so as to be capable of being removed after the completion of the pier.

Work on this fabrication commenced on the Devon shore in the spring of 1853, with its lower end towards the water and its axis at an inclination of about 1 in 6. Brunel had produced a general arrangement drawing showing the details of the cylinder, its location between the pontoons over the proposed site of the centre pier and the related mooring chains. An extract from that drawing is shown in Plate 6.4, which indicates that when empty, it was designed to float at the above attitude and to draw about 15 feet of water forward.

CONTRACTUAL PROBLEMS

From such records that still exist[10], there now begin to appear the usual contractor's claims for interim payments, with corresponding questioning of the amounts involved; particularly relevant since Brunel reported[11] on 23 February 1854 that 'the sinking of the cylinder for the centre pier, has been delayed beyond the time fixed in the Contract'. However, he expressed himself generally satisfied with progress, reporting the masonry piers within the town of Saltash to be nearly completed and considerable progress with the arrangements for the erection of the ironwork for the first of the main spans. It is interesting to note his comment that 'very great delays are caused by the great difficulty experienced at the present time in obtaining materials'.

Meanwhile, four wrought iron pontoons, eventually intended for the floating of the main spans of the bridge into their positions,

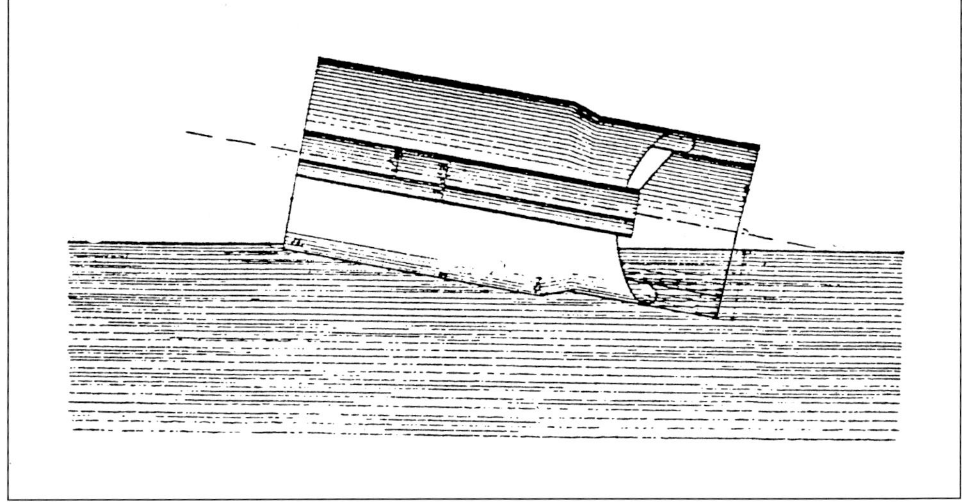

6.6 *One of a series of drawings depicting the floating out of the great cylinder, which should be studied in conjunction with Plates 6.7, 6.8, and 6.9.*
H. RESAL, PARIS

were moored in the middle of the river, around the intended site of the centre pier, while four mooring anchors and cables were laid out ready to receive the cylinder.

All this work was being carried out at a time when the Company was very short of funds. To alleviate this situation, the Secretary reported[12] on 28 April 1854, that he had visited their bankers in London, Messrs Glyn & Co, to establish the terms on which they would agree an additional facility of £40,000 in conjunction with the Company's local banker, Messrs Tweedy & Co. It was agreed that they would advance 'a sum not exceeding £30,000 to be repaid in four months in such amounts as the Directors might fortnightly require'; in addition, they consented to the Directors overdrawing the Company's account to the extent of £10,000 'on like terms'. So work was able to proceed.

THE CYLINDER LAUNCH

By early May 1854 the massive fabrication for the centre pier was nearing completion and on 9 May Glennie wrote to Bond[19] to advise him that it would shortly be floated off. He informed him that

> ...it will not be a launch like a ship launch, but it will be eased down on the ways by tackles at low water and will remain for the tide to lift it at high water. I suppose we shall begin to lower it out about noon and it will be near to in the evening before it floats - of course if the weather is very boisterous we shall not float until the next springtides.

A further letter of 11 May confirmed that 'the Contractor proposes to commence lowering the Cylinder between 6 and 7 in the morning on Monday' and asked Bond to advise the Directors in case any should wish to be present.

Following its launch, the cylinder was towed out (Plate 6.5) and placed between the pontoons. Water was admitted to bring it into its proper position, with the upper deck well out of the water. The mooring chains were secured between the attachments on the cylinder and the pontoons. Water was then gradually admitted until it floated in a vertical position. This progressive series of operations, occupying a period of several weeks, is illustrated in Plates 6.6 to 6.9 inclusive.

On 24 May Brunel reported[14] to Bond that the floating off and sinking of this massive fabrication had been satisfactorily completed, 'with the help of a remarkably quiet state of wind and tide'. The tone of his letter reflects his obvious delight and satisfaction of completing this difficult operation with the placing of the cylinder 'within $^{4}/_{10}$ of an inch [*sic*] of its intended location' - he admits more by accident than design. However, with justification he reports 'it amounts to this that we pitched the bottom edge of this large cylinder at 60 feet under water exactly where we intended'.

The cylinder was allowed to settle under its own weight and in so doing adopted a position slightly out of perpendicular. With a further 6 feet of mud to be penetrated before reaching the rock foundation, Brunel was not concerned; 'once forced to the solid ground as it is - we are preparing to get into it and dress the base to a level when it will be returned to its perpendicular'.

However, the results and optimistic tone of Brunel's letter (24 May 1854) should be considered in relation to the extensive details given by Brereton[15] in his excellent and detailed paper of 1861, describing the building of the centre pier. The illustration in Plate 6.10 is taken from that paper and shows the progressive settlement of the great cylinder over the ensuing months. Brereton reports that while the cylinder was launched in May, it was not sunk at its intended site until early June. As it then settled through about 13 feet of mud at the bottom of the river it landed on some irregularities on the rock and heeled over from the vertical by approximately 7 feet 6 inches towards the east.

In order to correct this position it was necessary to make preparations for men to enter and reach the bottom edge of the cylinder. To that end, air locks were assembled at the top of the 6 foot cylinder, the air pumps and associated apparatus which had been used on the Chepstow Bridge were brought down and fixed to the top of this chamber; two steam engines of 10 h.p. being located on the upper deck to work these pumps. In addition, two 13 inch water pumps were fixed within the 10 foot cylinder.

While these arrangements were being put in hand, it was hoped that the combination of water pressure on the lower deck level or dome, together with the loading of the high side of the upper deck with iron ballast, would help to correct the lean. In addition, gravel was thrown down around the outside of the cylinder to help secure the mud from scour but the quantity involved was too small to have any affect on the 'righting' operation.

By the end of June, the cylinder had forced its way through the obstruction at the bottom edge, to sink a further three feet and take up an almost vertical stance. Early in July the air and water pumps were set to work, so that men were able to go down under compressed air, through the 6 foot chamber and the air passage below the dome to excavate the compartments of the annular ring. Two separate 2 foot diameter bucket ways were provided for bringing out the spoil.

In a letter[16] dated 24 July, Glennie advised Bond that

> ...two compartments of the air chamber at the bottom of the Cylinder have been excavated down to the lower edge which is found to be resting on a bed of clay and oyster shells. The rock has not yet been uncovered - the excavations are on opposite sides of the Cylinder.

It is interesting to note that this same report referred to

> ...a length of 394 feet of the first tube is being framed and rivetted - 6 girders are ready to go up on their Piers on the West shore and 4 more are being framed in the yard.

Obviously, there was great activity on the site, not only in connection with work on the centre pier, but also in the preparation of the superstructure.

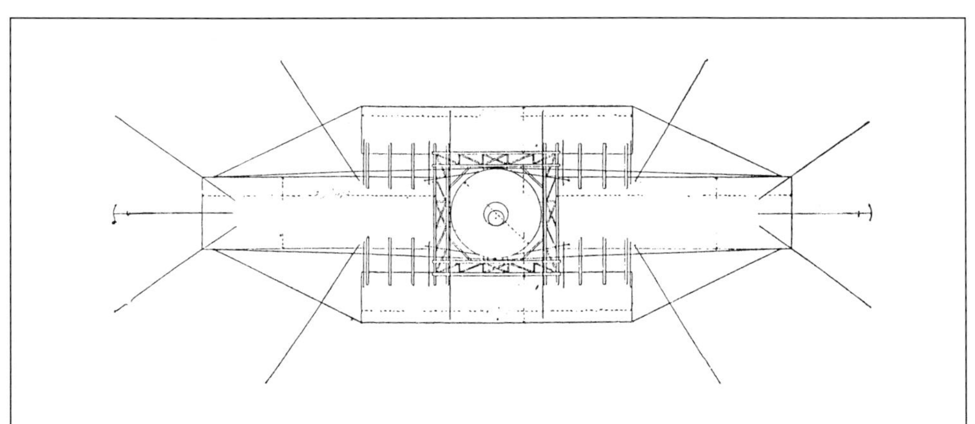

6.7 *A plan view of the centre pier site, showing the four pontoons located in position, the warps and anchors laid out to keep them steady at all stages of the tide, and with the great cylinder located in position, being prepared for lowering to the bottom of the river.*
H. RESAL, PARIS

This is, perhaps, best illustrated by the October 1854 view from the Cornish side of the Tamar shown in Plate 6.11. The Cornwall truss, encased in scaffolding, is under construction on the Devon foreshore; in mid stream, the top of the cylinder can be seen, surrounded by the pontoons marking the site of the centre pier, with its attendant engines and pumping equipment; and the partially completed approach spans sit astride the piers high above the slopes of Saltash.

THE CENTRE PIER FOUNDATION

At this stage of building the centre pier, the bottom edge of the cylinder was about 82 feet below high water level, which meant that the men were working under an air pressure of some 35lb/in^2. Although this level was reduced by pumping out some of the water in the 10 foot cylinder, it was found that the seven hour shifts then being worked were far too long, as many of the men suffered from 'the bends' or temporary paralysis. At that time little was known of the effects of working in such an environment; however, the situation could apparently be ameliorated by reducing the shifts to three hours.

Work continued during the following weeks and through August the majority of the mud and oyster shells which filled the bottom of the compartments of the air jacket had been removed, eventually to reveal the irregular surface of the rock. This could then be dressed to suit the cylinder profile.

The work was further complicated by a leak having been exposed through a fissure in the north east or higher edge of the rock formation; great difficulty was experienced in maintaining sufficient pressure with the air pumps, to keep the water down and the bottom dry for the men to work. Eventually, the leak was curtailed to some extent by driving close sheet piling into the fissure. We can but admire the stamina of the men working with only simple hand tools in these almost intolerable conditions.

Brunel set this overall position in context in his report to the shareholders at their meeting in September 1854, commenting[17] on the fact that even at low water, neap tides, there was over 50 feet of depth with a strong current, except at the time of the turn of the tide. Accordingly, to have set the bottom edge of this great cylinder 'within three or four inches of the exact point required' (a more realistic figure than that previously quoted) was due to the readiness with which the contractor supplied all the equipment required, the dedication of Brunel's assistants in their preparatory work and the skill of the men involved in this operation.

He went on to comment on the hardship endured by the workmen engaged in preparing the rock surface. They were working in darkness under wet and cold conditions, their only illumination being miners' tallow candles (or possibly Holliday or Lucigen type lamps) under an air pressure which many could not tolerate, and in an environment not entirely free from risk. He paid particular tribute to Brereton who had moved to Plymouth to be in constant attendance during this important stage of the contract, as he had 'been obliged to prohibit Mr Glennie from exposing himself to what I know he could not safely bear'.

ANXIETY OVER RISING COSTS

While Brunel was able to give these relatively encouraging reports regarding the technical progress of the Contract, the Board had become increasingly exercised by the mounting cost of the overall project. At a Board Meeting held at Truro on 27 October 1854, arising from the report of the Finance Committee, the following resolution had been agreed:

> ...That the large amount of expenditure on Engineering and inspection of works is such as to require their submitting to the Board the propriety of making some enquiry as to the necessity of continuing so large an expenditure in the present state of the works.

Having considered this recommendation, on the basis of charges of about £8,300 per annum for Engineering expenses and inspection, a Committee consisting of Messrs Tweedy, Smith and Carne was appointed to examine the details of these charges and, following consultation with the Engineer, to report to the Board regarding the feasibility or otherwise of reducing the level of this expenditure without prejudicing an efficient oversight of the works.

Siting the Great Cylinder

Meanwhile, by February 1855 the cylinder had been sunk to its proper depth in an upright position, its bottom everywhere sitting on rock. The step by step procedures by which this final position was achieved can be visualised from the drawings included in Plate 6.10; the lowest point of the cylinder then being 87 feet 6 inches below high water. In order to assist in making the bottom seal watertight, a hemp gasket was worked under the edge of the cylinder, all around the outside. The bottom edge, both on the up and down stream sides, was also secured to the rock by means of lewis bolts, so as to steady it against the action of the current and tides.

Through March the rock was levelled in all the compartments of the air jacket, and its surface cemented over. This preparation of the rock was a tedious operation as in some instances as much as 6 feet in depth had to be

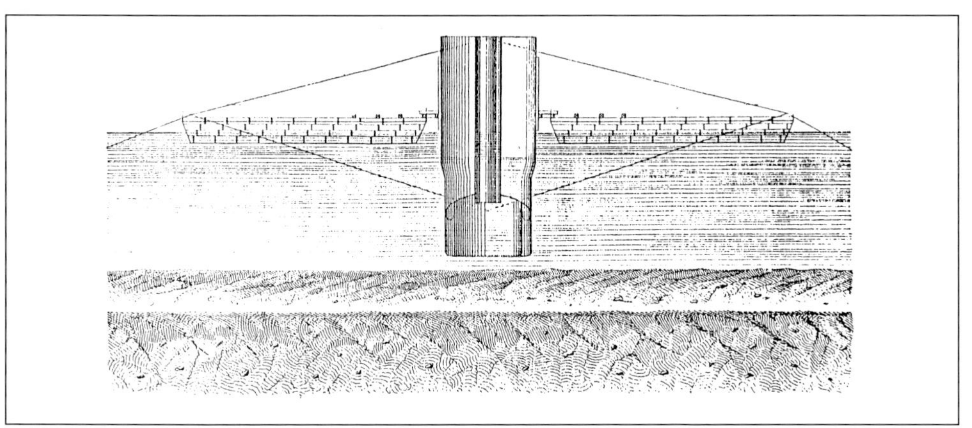

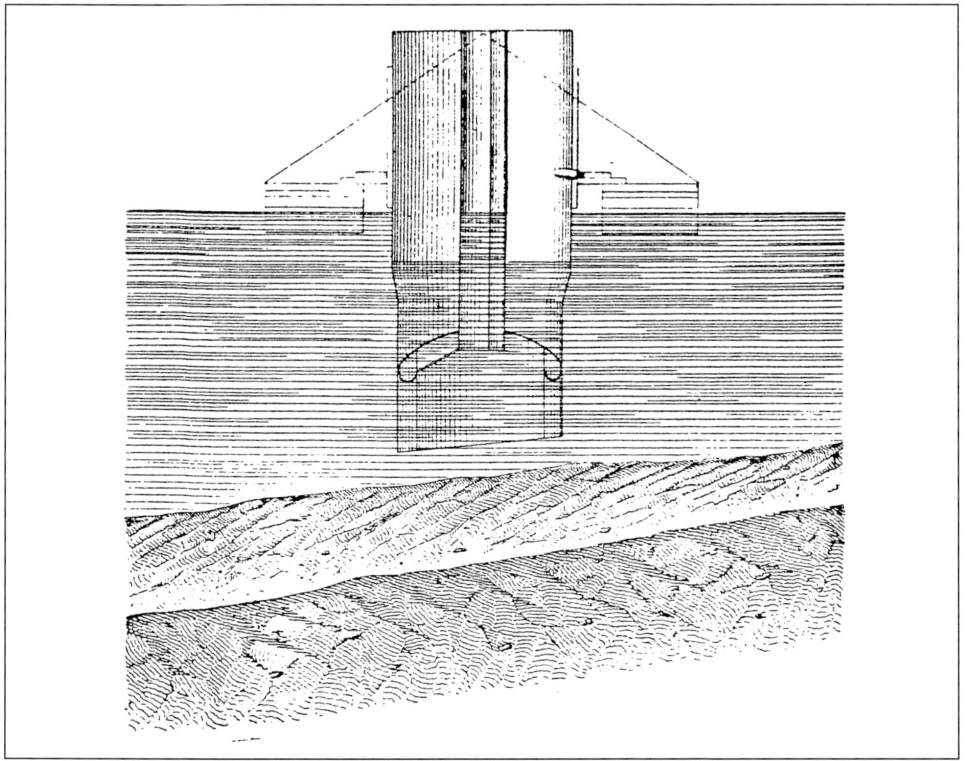

6.8 *and* **6.9** *Two further views of the great cylinder with its supporting pontoons, showing how it was located and adjusted in position, prior to lowering.* H. Resal, Paris

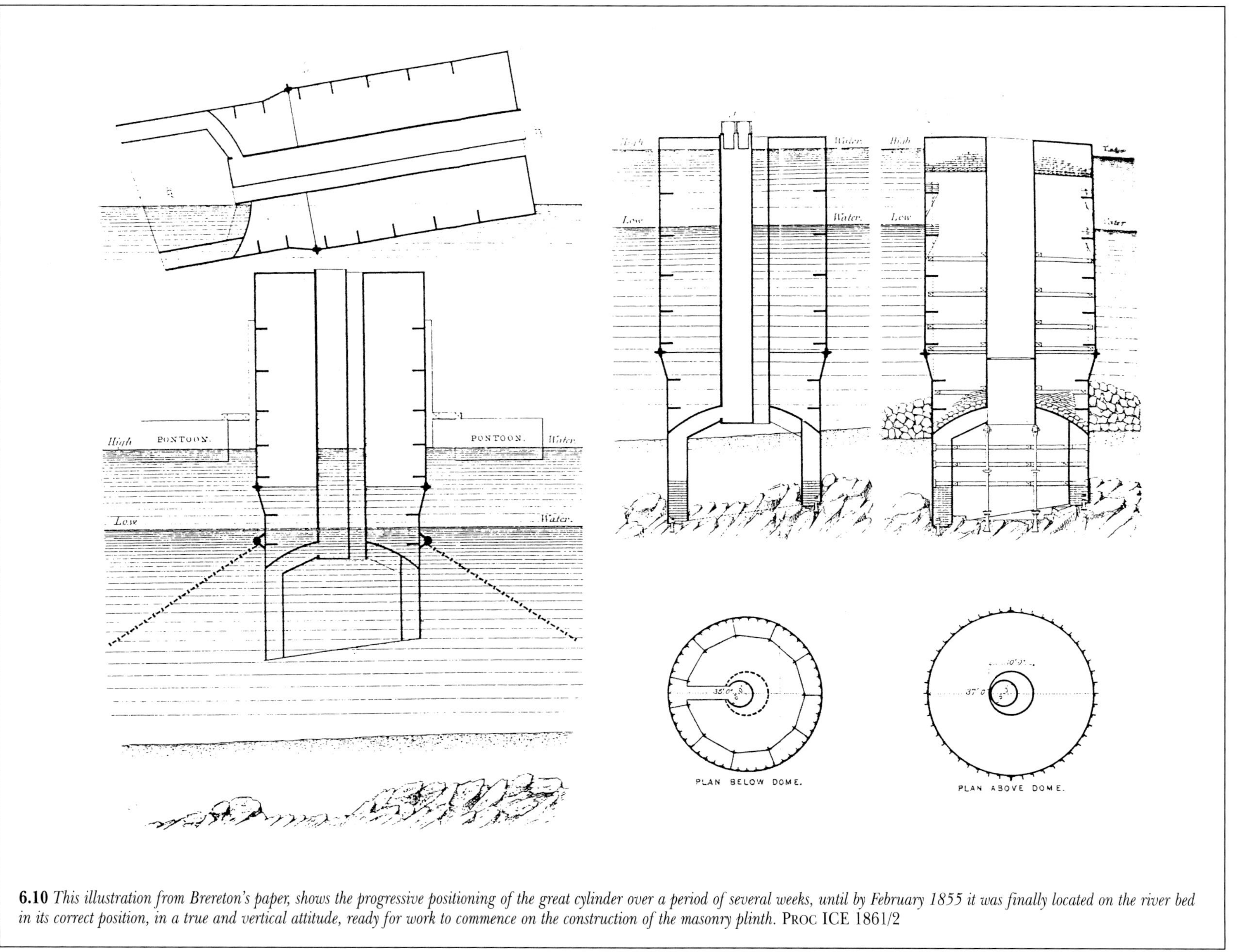

6.10 *This illustration from Brereton's paper, shows the progressive positioning of the great cylinder over a period of several weeks, until by February 1855 it was finally located on the river bed in its correct position, in a true and vertical attitude, ready for work to commence on the construction of the masonry plinth.* PROC ICE 1861/2

removed from the extremely hard dyke, using hand chisels. Work then proceeded through April and May with the employment of some thirty to forty men, working at times under a head of 86 feet of water, in building within the air jacket a complete ring of masonry, 35 feet in outside diameter, and varying from six feet to nine feet in height. This formed the foundation of the pier. While this work was in hand, a bank of slag and sand was thrown around the outside of the cylinder to assist in compressing the mud.

Early in June 1855 the air extraction equipment was removed from the 6 foot chamber, the water was pumped out of the main body of the cylinder below the dome and excavation of the mud commenced. Unfortunately, at the end of the month a leak broke out and the available pumping equipment was unable to stem the flow. Two additional 13 inch pumps with their associated engines were provided and during the following weeks, through to October, attempts to control the leakage, including throwing additional material around the outside of the cylinder, were not successful.

In his report[18] of 2 August 1855, Brunel had recounted these difficulties in some detail and emphasised the importance of proceeding with caution:

> ...the principal difficulties have been overcome, and, without hoping to avoid all casualties or causes of delay, the progress of the work, if slow, may be considered sure.

The completion of the Bridge depended only on the progress of the centre pier and, provided due caution was exercised, he believed the Bridge may be completed as soon as the rest of the line east of Liskeard. 'By any undue or imprudent haste, a delay of six months might easily be caused'.

MARE'S CONTRACT

We must now pause to consider the overall contractual position of Mare at this time in relation to all the work which he had so far completed. There are on record numerous letters between the parties in relation to the certification of work and its payment, while by the autumn of 1854 the correspondence[19] between Mare and Bond was becoming more pressing as will be seen from the following copy letters:

Letter of 2 October from Morris, one of C. J. Mare's staff, to Bond;

> ...I am instructed by Mr Mare to inform you that he has not received your order for £10,000 - the amount certified by Mr Brunel on a/c Saltash Bridge Contract and...he had anticipated this amount in his financial arrangements.

Again, on 4 November:

> ...Mr Brunel last week informed me that he had certified for £10,000 on account of Saltash Bridge.

And a strong letter of 20 November from Mare himself to Bond:

> ...I certainly was much surprised to find that, the liberal offer I had made through Mr Brunel to the Company, that, as they were not in a position to make the payments to us in Cash, we were prepared to take their acceptance on 3 months date for the amount of the Certificate, in addition to which you were advised by Mr Morris fourteen days ago prior to this Certificate being issued, that the amount would be £10,000. No reply was made to this communication, we therefore concluded the amount would be paid in due course. We therefore think we have much cause for complaint that this subject has not been as yet attended to. We rely on receiving either the acceptance or cash on Friday next.

By 24 November Morris was again writing to Bond, this time from the Royal Hotel, Truro, to the effect that:

> ...The resolution of the Finance will I am sure be very unsatisfactory to Mr Mare, as I know he depended upon having the Bill accepted, or a cheque for the amount.
>
> Mr Mare will consider that a sufficient time has elapsed to have enabled the directors to decide what way they propose paying the amount certified on a/c of Work done at Saltash Bridge and he was confirmed in this assumption from Mr Tweedy's letter...that the matter would be arranged this day at the Board Meeting.
>
> I trust therefore you will not fail in doing so next week, as any further delay will I know seriously inconvenience Mr Mare.

Evidently there was some response from the Company, since Mare himself wrote to Bond on 2 December to say:

> ... Your reply to my letter is most unsatisfactory; in order to meet the difficulty in which the Company is now placed, I volunteered to take the Company's acceptance in lieu of Cash and which acceptance I engaged to return either at [instantly] or at any time the Company required it after they had made their financial arrangements. The Contract is anything but a remunerative one and unless satisfactory arrangements can be made with me by Tuesday next, I shall not only stop the works but I shall abandon the Contract.

While the Minutes of the Finance Committee Meeting[20] of 22 December report the consideration of various Bills submitted by Mr Mare, there is no specific reference to the problems of payment which were obviously of great concern to the Contractor. However, it would appear that in this unhappy situation some reconciliation must have taken place, since Mare was writing to Bond on 26 December:

> ...Agreeably to your letter I now beg to enclose you a Bill for £5,000 which I shall be obliged by your returning to me accepted by return of post. Mr Brunel's Certificate should have been for £12,000 and as he has promised to certify for the balance next week I shall be obliged by your informing me whether it is the intention of the Company to pay this amount in cash or by acceptance.

However, it would appear that the Company was, apparently, not beyond taking delaying tactics; a further letter from Mare on 30 December complained that

> ...Before I can make the enclosed acceptance of any value to me, it is necessary it should bear the Corporate Seal of the Company. I shall therefore be obliged by your affixing the seal and enclose it to me by return of post.

There the record of this unhappy correspondence ceases so we do not know how matters developed during the ensuing months, but in February 1855 Brunel expressed[21] his anxiety to Bond regarding Mare's inability to satisfy his creditors; 'I believe myself that he cannot fail to become bankrupt - in which case we must take possession of the works and carry them on'. However, it appears that he was able to soldier on with the support of his creditors and from January through to July 1855, further substantial payments were due to Mare, which the Company was in some difficulty in meeting. Eventually, they were only settled from the proceeds of a Debenture of £375,000, negotiated with the other broad gauge companies in return for a seven year lease of the line, effective from its date of opening between Plymouth and Truro.

Nevertheless, it is apparent that the overall situation must have continued to deteriorate, since the Finance Committee, meeting[22] on 29 July 1855, resolved:

> ...That the Secretary write to Mr Brunel that the Board feel it is of great importance that he should acquaint Mr Mare that no further new accommodations will be granted until the centre pier of the Bridge is in a course of satisfactory progress.

Mare's Bankruptcy

Sadly, for all his efforts in connection with the building of the centre pier, Mare must have been fighting a losing financial battle, for on 21 September 1855, trading under the name of Charles John Mare & Co, he filed[23] a Petition for bankruptcy. On 25 September 1855 he was duly adjudged and declared bankrupt; throughout the period to 24 December 1857 he attended meetings with his creditors, including that of 7 July when he made 'an offer of composition' which was accepted by 90% of his creditors. However, by order of the Court of Bankruptcy, dated 24 December 1857, his Petition was annulled and the Petition for arrangement dismissed. He now disappears from our story as we hear nothing further of his activities in relation to the Bridge.

Insofar as his contract at Saltash was concerned, matters were formalised for the Company to take over the works, by means of a resolution[24] of the Board, dated 2 October 1855, to the effect that

> ...inasmuch as Charles John Mare who by

an indenture dated the 1st day of October 1853 contracted with this Company for the construction and maintenance of a Bridge over the valley and the river Tamar at Saltash and the other work referred to in the said indenture has been declared Bankrupt, this Company do forthwith in pursuance of the provisions of the said indenture in this behalf and without any previous notice take the works by the said indenture contracted for entirely out of the Receiver of the said Charles John Mare and of his Assignee or Assignees in bankruptcy.

That Mr William Henry Bond the Secretary of the Company be and he is hereby directed to take the necessary steps for carrying the foregoing resolution into effect.

Thus, the way was clear for the Company to continue the ongoing operation of the contract. At a subsequent Board meeting on 16 October 1855, Brunel reported[25] that, having regard to the 'peculiar circumstances in which the works have been left by the late Contractor', there was no alternative but for the Company themselves to proceed with the work on the centre pier, and also to continue for the time being with the construction of the iron work of the Cornwall span. He was hopeful that in due course tenders could be obtained from other contractors for the completion of the outstanding masonry work and also for the work involved on the remaining iron work. The Board resolved to adopt these arrangements.

While Mare was undoubtedly widely experienced with regard to the costing of the wrought iron work of the contract, the cost of the on going saga of the centre pier must have far exceeded his original estimate. This factor, combined with the apparent difficulty he experienced in obtaining payment for the work he had completed, compounded an already difficult situation, leading eventually to his failure.

This unhappy state of affairs was reported[26] in the local press:

...The unfortunate bankruptcy of Messrs Mare and Co. the contractors for the erection of the Saltash Bridge has again drawn attention to the prospects of the Cornwall Railway Company, and in numerous quarters we hear a strong desire expressed that as the possibility of completing the line still seems to be remote, an effort should immediately be made by the Company to open it for traffic at least as far as Liskeard. We do not happen to know whether the breaking of the contract may occasion any prolonged stoppage of the works. But...it is well known that the most serious difficulties have occurred in the attempt to obtain a foundation for the Bridge, and opinion is prevalent among persons who are well competent to judge, that four or five years may yet elapse before the concluding portion of the line can be completed.

The editorial went on to emphasise the importance of the Company taking action to bring part of the line into operation, otherwise 'public patience...will be entirely exhausted long before there is the smallest possibility of the line being completed throughout'. But, no such action was implemented and nearly a further four years were to elapse before the line was completed between Plymouth and Truro.

In the meanwhile, Brunel reported to the shareholders at their March 1856 meeting[27], that Mare's failure had caused the works to be unavoidably suspended. In all the circumstances, he had no alternative but to recommend the Company take over the contract under the direct supervision of Brereton, assisted by Gainsford, the resident engineer, and foreman George Whitting. He paid warm tribute to the efforts of his staff in the face of the physical difficulties under which they toiled, in order to progress the work on the centre pier. Later, the completion of the upper masonry was let to Messrs Willcocks, the sub contractor who had built the land piers.

THE WORKS CONTINUE

Returning to the sequence of events relating to the foundations of the centre pier, by November 1855, in spite of continual pumping, the four pumps could not reduce the water level below 54 feet. The decision was, therefore, made to resort to using air pressure within the body of the cylinder below the dome, Brunel having already anticipated that this alternative method would have to be adopted. Since the 10 foot cylinder for much of its upper length was of insufficient strength to accept air pressure, an additional 9 foot cylinder some 50 feet in length, and of sufficient strength, had to be fabricated to fit inside and secured at its bottom to the 10 foot cylinder shell through a rivetted shelf, the original 6 foot air supply cylinder being removed. It was considered that the existing four pumps were adequate to keep the water level down to 50 feet. Air locks were fitted to the top of the 9 foot cylinder, while, in addition to the air pumps already at site, two pairs of new 12 inch units were provided.

To counter the buoyancy or upward air pressure against the dome arising from this arrangement, over and above its own weight of 290 tons, it was necessary to load the cylinder with some 750 tons of ballast. This was arranged as 350 tons of pig iron and kentledge stacked upon the shelves of the 37 foot cylinder, near the top, and upon cross girders under the upper deck; 100 tons of sand in bags lowered through the water and uniformly distributed over the top of the dome, and 300 tons of pig iron afterwards thrown down on to these bags on top of the dome.

All this preparatory work was not completed until the middle of December, when the pumps were brought into operation and the water level kept down to a level sufficient to enable the mud and shells to be extracted from the centre of the cylinder. It was then stiffened by suitable cross shores, and the exposed rock levelled.

A contemporary report on the state of these works is given in a letter from Mr J. Allen[28] dated 12 December 1855, addressed 'My Dear Friend' (Brunel?) in which he comments that 'the work does not seem to be proceeding vigorously. I heard that altogether 170 men are employed, and that at one time Mare had 300'. He commented that;

6.11 *A general view of the site from Saltash, in the autumn of 1854, with the four pontoons and great cylinder in position, complete with pumping machinery and steam engines on board, indicating considerable activity. On the Devon shore the Cornwall truss, encased in timber scaffolding, is taking shape while the girders for the Cornwall approach spans are being positioned on top of their piers.* GREAT WESTERN MUSEUM, SWINDON

> ...The large tube, the roadway beneath, the supports and the iron work for the upper parts of the central pier, seem to be very nearly completed, especially the first. Many parts are prepared for the next tube, but they cannot be joined together till the central pier is built and the other tube removed into its place.

His letter gives an overall impression of a general lack of activity -'nothing is doing on the viaducts; on the other side for a mile or more there seems nothing doing'. Of course, this may well have been due to the fact that the project was no longer under the control of a contractor. However, in connection with the works for the centre pier he was able to report that the 6 foot cylinder had been removed and the 9 foot cylinder which was to replace it was nearly finished. Notwithstanding this rather depressing report, early in January 1856, according to Brereton, the granite masonry within the shell was started and although there was a further leak through the original fissure, adequate measures were taken to contain it; including arrangements to collect the water and convey it to two cast iron wells set around the sections of the water pumps and built into the masonry.

Continual pumping kept the water level down so that the masonry could be progressively built up through the following months; at the same time, the ingress of water was gradually reduced and a number of pumps taken out of use. By the middle of June the masonry level had reached 46 feet, sufficient to stop the influx of water altogether so that the remaining pump well could be filled in with cement and closed off.

Brunel reported[29] on these achievements to the shareholders at their meeting in September but also recounted how, in trying to expedite the work, the hitherto cautious approach in the building of the masonry was no longer considered mandatory. However, the need for such caution was proved almost at once since

> ...a high tide caused the Cylinder to collapse at points where it was not properly supported and, the joints being broken, the water was admitted, but the masonry being then nearly at the level of half-tide, little, if any delay has been caused. The work is now within a few feet of high water mark, and all risk is passed.

At that meeting, the Directors considered the position regarding the shares which had been allocated to Mare in connection with his remuneration for the bridge contract. His bankruptcy, of course, rendered it necessary that the Company should take back the shares reserved for him. A similar situation prevailed with regard to another contractor, Garrett, who was engaged on the construction of the line and who had also gone bankrupt.

By the end of October the masonry had been completed to the top of the plinth, or cap of the pier, including the fixing of the bolts for securing the cast iron columns which were to form the central support of the main spans. Then, in the middle of November, the remaining upper part of the original cylinder was unbolted at the separating joints, and floated ashore with the pontoons.

The Centre Pier Foundation Completed

Hence, at long last, by November 1856, nearly 2 1/2 years after this great cylinder had first been floated out and work started on its building, the massive granite centre pier was completed, representing, as Brunel believed, 'the deepest foundation which has yet been built under water'. Sadly, the price for this great achievement had involved the failure of an eminent contractor.

Meanwhile, in order to finish the complete structure, the two main spans remained yet to be finally fabricated and then progressively raised, to be fixed in position on the tops of the three main piers, some 100 feet above high water level, and the approach spans on either bank duly completed. As we shall see, to conclude all this work would involve Brunel and his engineering staff, together with the new contractors who were now employed on the site, in many more months of dedicated effort.

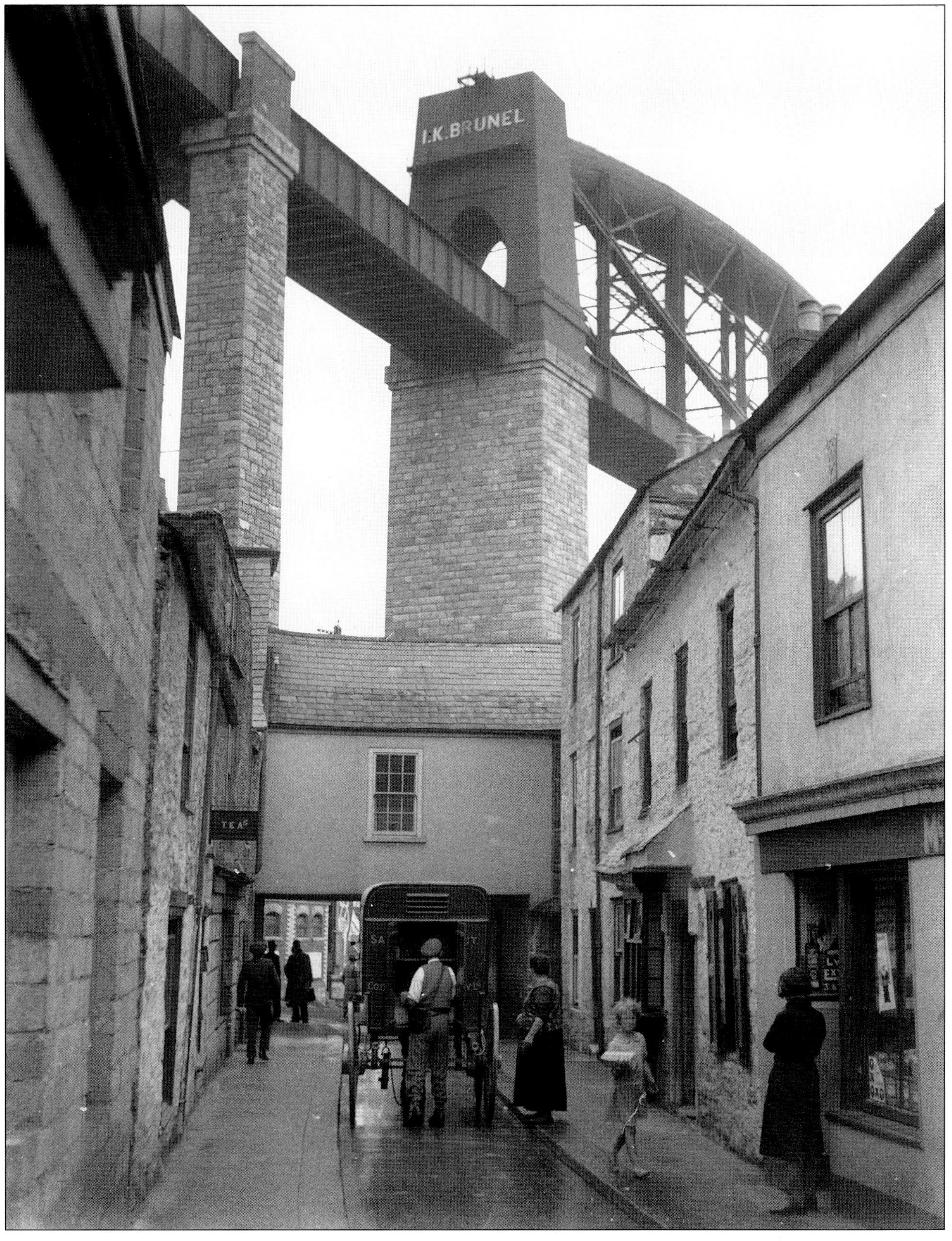
I.K.BRUNEL
TEAS

CHAPTER SEVEN

CONSTRUCTION: THE CORNWALL SPAN

1854 to 1858

We now revert to the position of the overall contract as it was in June 1854, following the launch of the great cylinder in preparation for the building of the centre pier. Work could then start on erecting the first of the main spans on the piled and prepared slipway site. Having chosen Mare as the main contractor, Brunel was well aware of the considerable involvement he had in the fabrication of the wrought iron tubular spans for the Britannia Bridge across the Menai Straits for the Chester & Holyhead Railway, working with his friend and rival, Robert Stephenson. Such experience should stand him in good stead with regard to the spans for Saltash.

Meanwhile, we should review the other work involved in the project. Following the inception of the contract in January 1853, Brunel had reported[1] in his letter of 22 August 1853 to the Directors that the masonry piers for the approach spans on the Saltash side of the river had been commenced, the first foundation being laid on 4 July. In general, each pier comprised twin columns each of nominal section about eight feet square, spaced nine feet apart with a batter of 1/160, terminating at their tops with a spandrel to support a plinth approximately 27 feet x 10 feet 6 inches wide. The wrought iron girders of these spans were to be seated on these plinths at 16 feet 4 inch centres. Plate 5.22 is a reproduction of one of the original drawings showing the layout of Pier No 5 West.

In February 1854, he reported[2] these piers had been nearly completed, adding at that same time, 'considerable progress had been made with all the preliminary works' for the ironwork involved in the bridge itself. This included the wrought iron main girders for the approach spans, each of which weighed between 12½ and 16½ tons, depending on the relevant span, exclusive of cross girders and timber decking.

We have little information on this latter aspect of the contract, but following their fabrication, presumably each main girder would have been floated across from the Devon side on pontoons and landed on the Saltash shore. Alternatively, their component parts could have been shipped over piecemeal to the small yard on the Cornwall shore, there to be finally assembled into complete girders. Whichever method was followed, their eventual manoeuvring through the narrow and picturesque streets of Saltash (Plate 7.1) and up the hillside, to their locations adjacent to the relevant piers, must have been fraught with difficulties. From Plate 6.11 it would appear that each was then hoisted up into position using the sheer legs shown on top of the piers. The fitting of the crossmembers and timber decking would have followed, to complete this part of the Bridge.

Because of the location of the fabricating facilities and slipway on the Devon shore, the corresponding masonry piers and spans could not be completed at that time, which is apparent from Plate 6.11. As already described, this illustration reflects the situation at the Tamar crossing as it probably was in late 1854, showing the four pontoons around the great cylinder at its location over the site of the centre pier, complete with the engines and pumping apparatus relating to that work.

Constructing the Cornwall Span

That illustration also shows the tubular span under construction on the Devon shore, enveloped in supporting scaffolding. While surviving records give little information on this important aspect of the contract, we can conjecture the contemporary scene and the procedures involved, as outlined in the following paragraphs. On the piled site, substantial timber scaffolding was erected to

7.1 (opposite page) *An impressive view of the western portal and the Cornwall approach spans reaching high across the narrow streets and houses of Saltash, taken on 15 July 1936. This illustrates the limited space and cramped working conditions under which this part of the Bridge was built.* Reece Winstone Collection

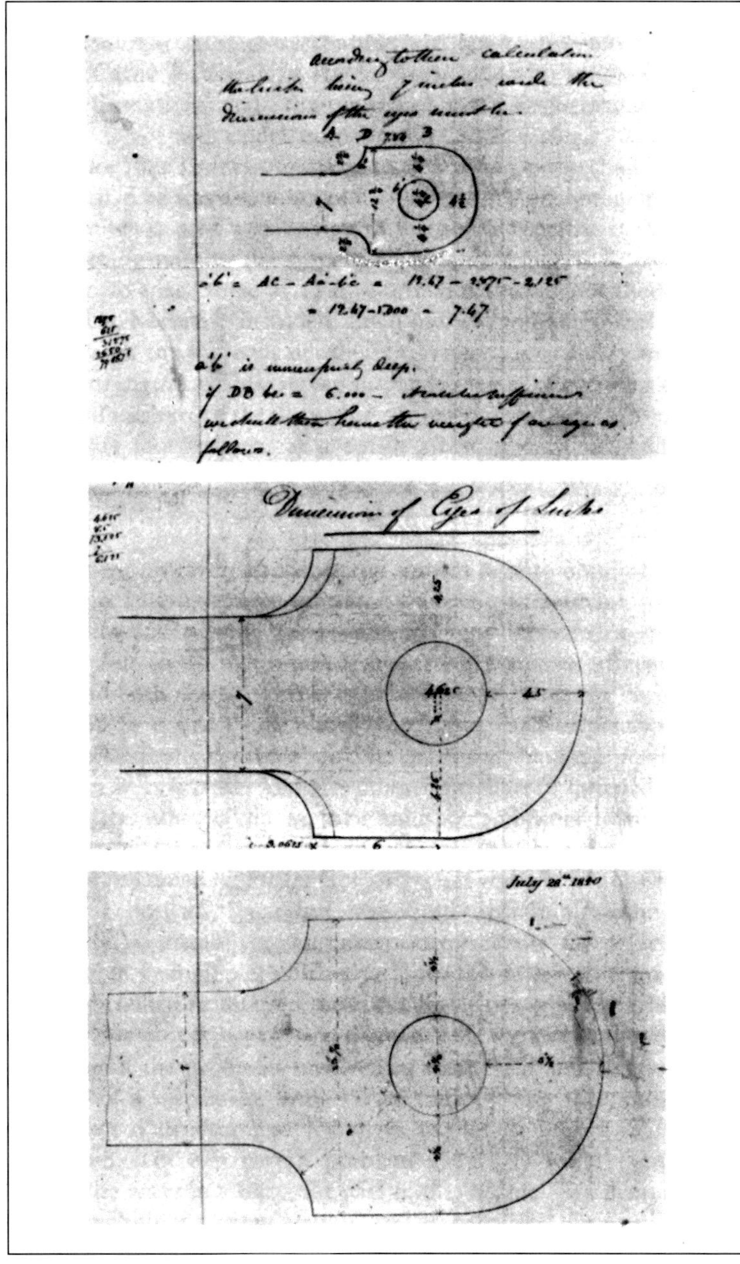

7.2 *Brunel had earlier spent some time in developing a suitable profile for the eye of the ends of the suspension chains, particularly in connection with the chains intended for the Clifton Suspension Bridge, which were eventually incorporated in the Saltash Bridge. This composite drawing taken from one of his sketch books illustrates this development.* PUGSLEY

form the support for the elliptical main tube, with its parabolic elevation. It was hoped that the extensive piling would resist any tendency for the span to settle under its own weight; a situation which had developed with the Britannia spans. Alongside this structure a railtrack would have carried a crane for transporting the plates from the nearby Punching Shop to their position within the scaffolding complex of the main span.

With regard to contemporary fabricating practice, Clark (1850) gives extensive details of the techniques current at the time the spans for the Britannia and Conway Bridges were under construction in the late 1840s. The wrought iron plates were not always flat when delivered from the supplier, and required 'hammering' to prepare them for shearing and punching. For this latter operation the rivet holes were marked out from a wooden or iron template, and then punched out by an ordinary punching-press worked by a crank with a flywheel; the plates being moved by workmen to bring the marked places beneath the punch. These machines were capable of punching up to three holes at a time through $^3/_4$ inch thick plate, with a good punch lasting about three days to make some 8,500 holes.

While details of the general type of machinery thought to be currently available at Saltash in the early 1850s has been described in Chapter 6, in the meanwhile an improved steam driven punching machine had been developed by Messrs Roberts and Evans, of Manchester, based on the principle of the 1801 Jacquard loom. It was used for the punching of the plates intended for the Conway bridge, and enabled two or more rows of holes to be punched automatically, as the plates were fed through the machine, with an accuracy and speed far superior to the original marking out and hand fed operation. In all probability this type of equipment was subsequently available at Saltash, which could account for the excellent quality of the platework in the tubes.

The rivets used in both the Britannia and Conway bridges were on average made from $^3/_4$ inch diameter iron rod, sheared into about four inch lengths and heated red hot before being dropped into a mould, about $1^1/_2$ inches shorter than the rod. A few blows from a heavy hammer reduced the projection to a flat head; and similar techniques could have continued at Saltash. While we have no information regarding the riveting methods used at Saltash, it would be reasonable to assume that they probably followed the techniques thus developed by Mare.

There the men worked in gangs or sets; a

set comprised two 'riveters', one 'holder-up' and two boys. One of the boys would be stationed at the furnace, either a portable forge with bellows, or a reverberatory furnace, to attend to the heating of the rivets. When ready, he would cast a rivet up to the second boy who, with pincers, would thrust it into the hole destined to receive it, with about 1½ to 2 inches protruding through the hole. The 'holder-up', with his large hammer, would then maintain a pressure behind the rivet so that the two riveters could assail it in front, striking alternately. Two or three blows given around the rivet would bring the plates into close contact, with the rivet then driven back into the hole so as to completely fill it, and lastly form the head by means of a cup shaped tool known as a 'snap', which when struck by the riveter gave the head a hemispherical form. These operations were all performed very quickly, usually in less than half a minute, with an overall average of a rivet being closed at the rate of one per minute. However, it is believed that alternative riveting techniques were developed during this time, hand operations being superseded in some instances by machine riveting - not always with the complete accord of the workmen involved.

Obviously, extensive precautions must have been taken to protect the scaffolding from the risk of fire, due to the red hot rivets being constantly thrown about. A major fire within the scaffolding could have caused the collapse and destruction of the tube. Thus, over the ensuing months work progressed on the platework for the fabrication of the first, or Cornwall span of the Bridge, and as work proceeded on this aspect of the contract, nearly all the materials for both main spans were reported as being on site[3] by August 1855.

The Chain Links

Among these materials were included a total of 1,150 chain links[4], dating from 1843, when Brunel had spent some time in evolving the most suitable proportions for the lug end of these links, as depicted in Plate 7.2. (Pugsley 1976). They had been intended for the Clifton Suspension Bridge but when, due to lack of funds, that concern stopped work in 1853, they were purchased from the Clifton Bridge Company. Manufactured by Messrs Carne & Vivian of the Copperhouse Foundry, Hayle, (Pugsley 1976) at a cost of £19.10s.0d per ton, the eye ends were welded to the 7 inch width bars.

Obviously, there were insufficient to complete both spans and the balance, amounting to some 1,630 links, was supplied by Messrs Howard, Ravenhill & Co from its King and Queen Iron Works, Rotherhithe. That company had in the meanwhile developed a process[5] for rolling the chain links, including the heads, in one piece thereby avoiding the welding of the lugs to the 7 inch bars - thus providing a more satisfactory product.

Some doubt seems to exist regarding their date of manufacture; Berridge (1969) quotes 1857 while Pugsley (1976) gives a date of 1858. As the first truss was completed and tested during 1857 (and would have required some links additional to the original Clifton ones) they may well have been forged during 1856. Brunel considered that the method of rolling in one piece was obviously a great improvement. However, with moderate care he believed the welded links to be equally strong. Nearly all the rolled links had clamping cheeks at one end to provide a grip for handling (Pugsley 1976) while every link was inspected and tested by Brunel's representatives during manufacture.

Brereton later recalled[6] that in evolving the final design of the Saltash links Brunel had carried out further experiments to determine the optimum proportions for the head and eye; arriving at a pin diameter 0.66 of the width of the body and the curve of the shoulder being substantially increased to 7½ times the width of the shank (see Plate 5.11). This had

> ...the object of deflecting the lines of strain along the shank as gradually as possible, before passing through the eye and round the pin, which was essential when strains were suddenly applied.

Tests had also been carried out to determine whether the links exhibited any permanent set when stressed to 8 tons/inch^2

About three quarters of the number tested retained a permanent set of approximately 1/32 inch, and it was established that this arose, in some measure, from the thorough straightening of the link and the perfect bearing that ensued at the eye when the strain was first put on. No further permanent set took place on a second test and this result was not to be considered as impairing the strength of the link.

Reference has already been made (Chapter 5) to the problem of assembling the chain links, with their nominal 20 feet centres, cascading in the form of a catenary, to the suspension standards. According to Humber's (1864) drawings (Fig.1, Plate 5.7) the latter were spaced at regular intervals across the span, that varied between 39.26 feet and 39.54 feet. This key dimension also determined the straight profile of the main tube between each standard; see Plate 5.8A. Consequently, the arrangement of tube profile, suspension standard location and suspension chain centres involved the most meticulous attention to detail, so characteristic of Brunel's designs, both in the preparation and calculation of the detail drawings and in the ultimate fabrication of the component parts and their assembly. It will be seen from the copies of Brunel's original drawings (Plates 5.13 and 5.14) that the inevitable variations were accommodated by the careful introduction of elongated holes and half pins secured by taper wedge or keys. It could not have been an easy task to complete this work on the scaffolding set high above the bank of the Tamar, exposed to all winds and weathers. We can but admire the skill and fortitude of those Victorian craftsmen, who produced such excellent workmanship.

The Contract Delayed

Unfortunately, as reported in the previous chapter, the timely completion of this major fabrication was delayed by the failure of the contractor in September 1855. Subsequently, Brunel advised[7] the shareholders, in March 1856, that a contract had been arranged for labour to complete the work on the first span, so that by September of that year he was able to indicate that preparations were being made for its testing. However, in his letter[8] of 23 February 1857 the span was 'all but completed'; although it was in a forward state at the start of the half year, apparently, 'the completion has been a very tedious process'. Obviously, Mare's extensive fabrication experience was sadly missed and it would appear that his business failure could have cost a 12 months' delay in the completion of the Bridge.

By this time he was also able to confirm that the pier base for the western support of the main span, at a location known as Ash Torr Rock, had been completed to the plinth above water level and the masonry commenced, in readiness to receive the end of the main span. It was a massive granite construction, 29 feet wide by 17 feet thick, which was eventually to reach some 190 feet in height[9] from foundation to summit (see Plates 5.15 and 5.16).

Testing the Span

During the summer of 1857 the necessary steps were now put in hand for this first span to be 'severely tested' by the engineers before it was floated to its final position between the piers on the Cornwall side of the river. This involved freely supporting each end of the truss on substantial, deep piled timber piers located at the ends of the slipway site, the intermediate scaffolding being removed. The span was then subjected to test loading.

In the report[10] of his inspection of the Cornwall Railway, dated 25 April 1859, Colonel Yolland comments that he had been favoured by Mr Brereton 'with certain particulars that show the nature and strength of the structure', to the affect that

> ...By the specification under which they were constructed that the strain per square inch of section, with a load of 1¼ tons per foot lineal should not exceed 4 tons: and with a load of 2¾ tons per foot lineal it was not to exceed 5.5 tons per square inch.

His report then states that the 'West or first tube was accordingly severely tested by the Engineers, before it was floated to its proper position between the piers'. The following is a verbatim extract from that report of the results:

> ...When the tube had to carry itself, and

its portion of the Bridge, the deflection observed at the centre was under 2¼ inch on the east side and 2½ inch on the west side, with a load of 1¼ tons per foot lineal uniformly laid on the roadway; the deflections were respectively 5.1 inches east and 5.25 inches west. With the load increased to 2¾ tons per foot lineal, the deflections were 7½ inches east side, and 7¾ inches west side, but it was noted that during the last two experiments, the supports on which the Tube rested had sunk about half an inch, which quantity must therefore be deducted from the preceding deflections observed with the loads on. After the load of 2¾ tons per foot had been taken off, a permanent set of 1.2 inch on the east side, and 1.25 inch on the west side was observed, beyond that resulting from its own weight, and caused by the heavy weights that had been applied on the roadway.

According to Pugsley (1976) a deflection at the centre amounting to 5 inches, indicated a maximum stress in the tube and chains of 10 tons/inch², or nearly double the level of the original specification as quoted by Brereton to Yolland. Nevertheless, Pugsley states that these results were considered 'very satisfactory'.

Berridge[11] makes the interesting point that with 1,190 tons spread evenly over 455 feet of bridge decking, to give the above deflection of 7¼ inches, such test loading was two and three quarter times heavier than the trains then running on the Cornwall Railway, and about 14% greater than the heaviest operating on BR in 1973.

Floating out the Span

The testwork completed, elaborate preparations were put in hand for the floating out of this first main span, which comprised a weight of wrought ironwork in the superstructure of 1,060 tons (Brunel 1870). An extract of Brunel's original analysis of the scope of this operation, as he calculated it in one of his notebooks, is given in Plate 7.3 while in a corresponding sketchbook (No 10 folio 21) is included an outline sketch of 'Timbering for Saltash Bridge'. Although it is believed that copies of a number of Brunel's drawings of this site working were retained in the Great Western Railway archives for a number of years[12], sadly the only ones to come to light have been one of the pontoons and the framing structure shown in Plate 7.3A.

Firstly, docks were carefully excavated close to the piers supporting each end of the truss, of sufficient size to take a pair of pontoons, fabricated from ⅜ inch thick iron plates. These were identified[13] as the 'Saltash' pontoon (105 feet long x 20 feet wide x 10 feet

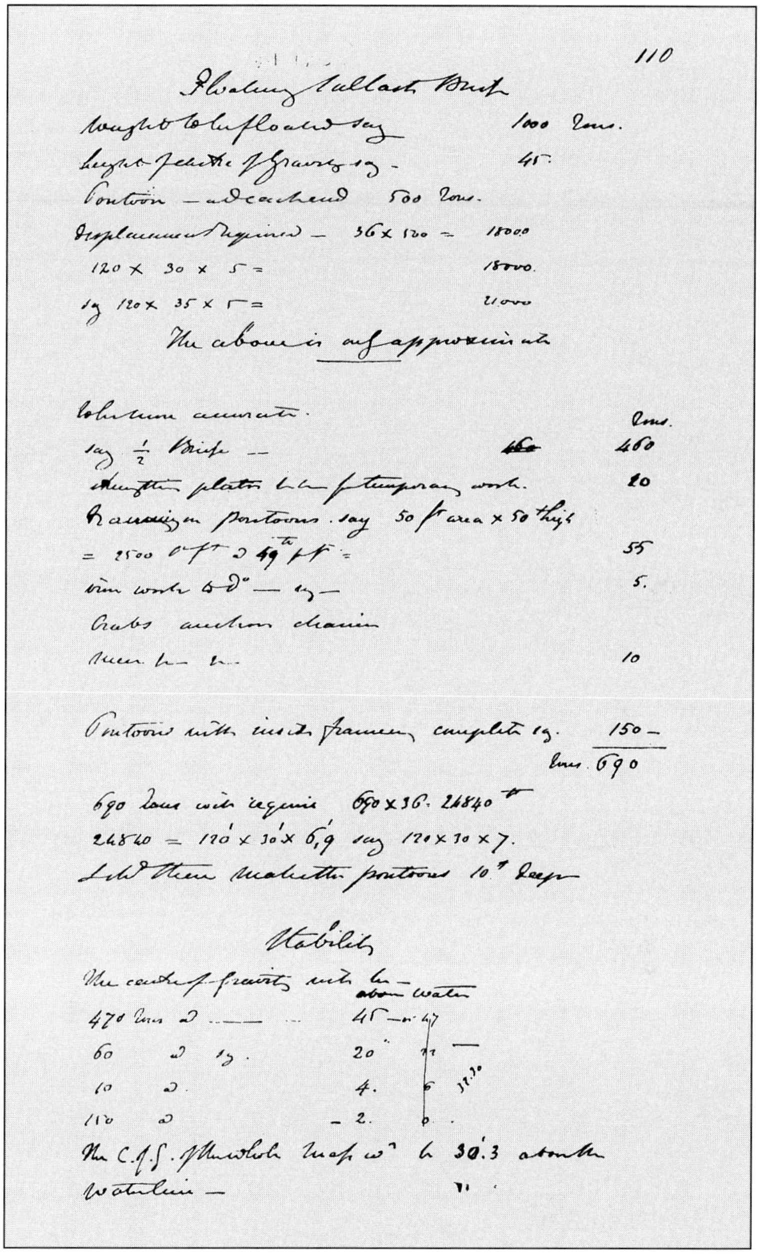

110

Floating Ballast Draft

Weight to be floated say 1000 Tons.

Weight of heads of girders say - 45

Pontoon — each end 500 Tons.

Displacement required — 36 x 500 = 18000

120 x 30 x 5 = 18000.

say 120 x 35 x 5 = 21000

The above is only approximate

Calculation accurate. Tons.

say ½ Bridge — 460

strengthening plates [illegible] temporary work. 20

Bracing on pontoons. say 50 ft area x 50 [illegible]

= 2500 [illegible] 49 [illegible] = 55

iron work to do — say — 5.

Crabs anchors chains

[illegible] 10

Pontoons with inside framing complete say 150 —

Tons 690

690 Tons will require 690 x 36 = 24840 ft

24840 = 120' x 30' x 6,9 say 120 x 30 x 7.

[illegible] make the pontoons 10 ft deep

Stability

The centre of gravity will be — above water

470 Tons at — 45 — or 47

60 at say. 20

10 at. 4.

150 at — 2.

The C. of G. of the whole must be 30'.3 above the waterline —

7.3 *A copy of Brunel's initial calculations which he prepared to determine the number and dimensions of the pontoons required to float out one of the main spans; these same pontoons first being used to locate and moor the great cylinder when building the centre pier.*
University of Bristol

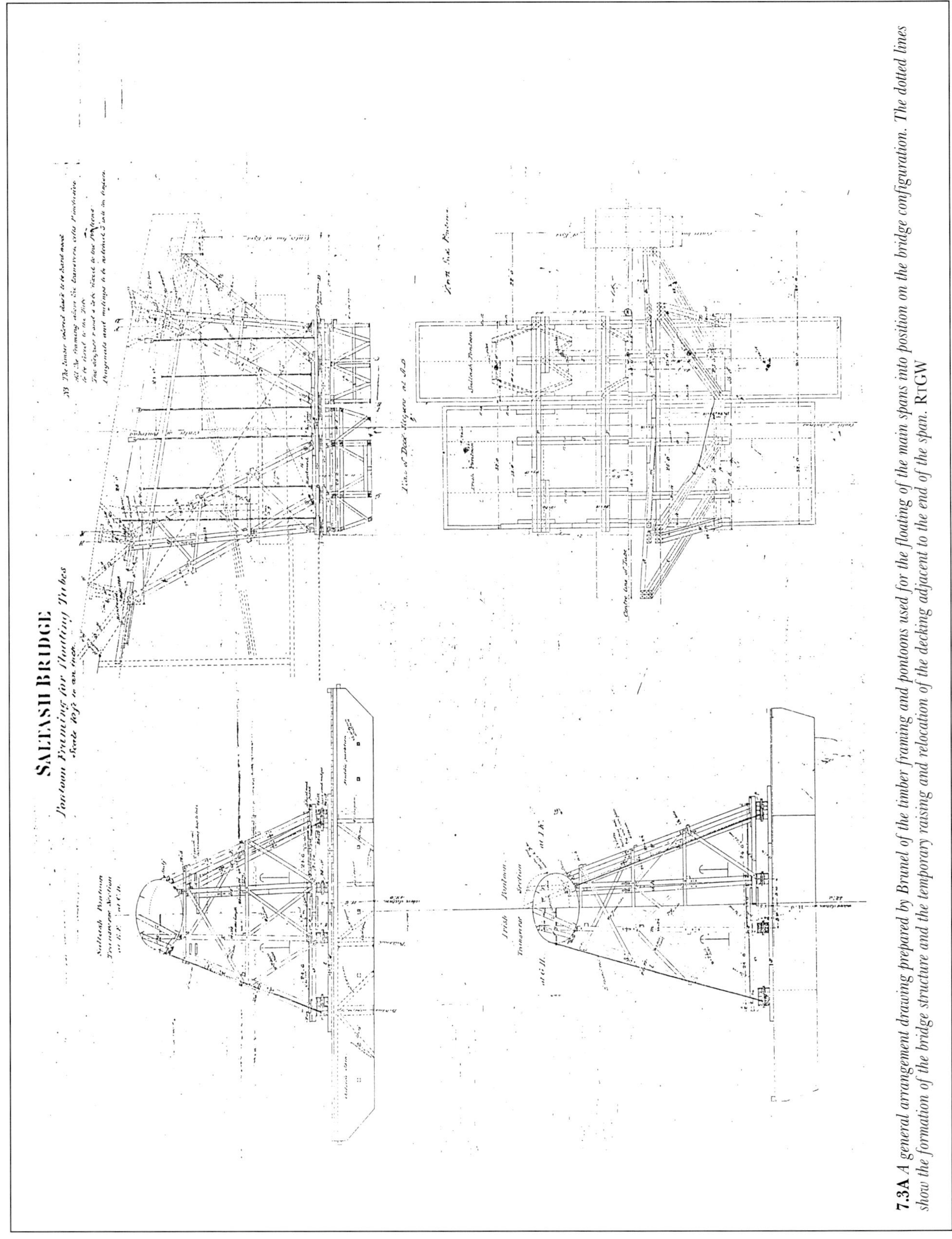

7.3A *A general arrangement drawing prepared by Brunel of the timber framing and pontoons used for the floating of the main spans into position on the bridge configuration. The dotted lines show the formation of the bridge structure and the temporary raising and relocation of the decking adjacent to the end of the span.* RTGW

TUBE OF THE ROYAL ALBERT BRIDGE, SALTASH, PREVIOUSLY TO ITS BEING FLOATED.—(FROM PHOTOGRAPHS BY EDMUNDS AND MARSHALL, DEVONPORT.—SEE PAGE 198.)

7.4 *An engraving taken from a stereoscopic photograph by Messrs Edmunds and Marshall, showing the Cornwall main span mounted on its two sets of pontoons, preparatory to being floated out on 1 September 1857. Note the massive timber structures supporting each end and the sheer size of the complete truss when compared with the surrounding craft. On the right hand side of the illustration can be seen the centre pier, with the first level of cast iron standards in place, which will form the centre support of the truss once it has been positioned, while in the background can be distinguished the various buildings of the Saltash Bridge Works.* ILLUSTRATED TIMES

deep) and the 'Irish' pontoon (95 feet long x 20 feet wide x 10 feet deep). Their decks were reinforced by 6 inch thick timber planking, bolted through massive 12 inch x 12 inch timber joists to the iron deck. In addition, a series of 8 inch x 10 inch timber props and struts in the hold provided additional reinforcement. Valves were fitted to control the filling and discharge of water ballast as required.

Each pair of pontoons was floated into their respective dock on the tide and when in position, the valves opened so that they filled and sunk on to timbers prepared to receive them on the dock bottom, at the appropriate datum relative to the position of the truss. The massive and elaborate timber framework shown in Plate 7.3A, was then erected upon each pair of pontoons, to carry the weight of half the truss. In order to facilitate the arrangement of this support, a temporary modification was introduced, to raise the roadway girders and decking immediately adjacent to the ends over the pontoons by about eight feet, and to move them a short distance towards the centre of the span. This arrangement was achieved by disconnecting the lengths of the standards below the chains and supporting the decking by a series of hawsers slung from the tube. Thus, the pontoons could be positioned at a higher relative level and so lower the height of the centre of gravity of the truss above the water.

It will be seen that these frameworks were constructed from a series of massive timber struts, each comprising four or more 12 inch square members, bolted together and suitably reinforced with diagonal bracing and walings. Each of these struts sprang from 12 inch x 24 inch timber cills, in turn seated on a series of individual support locations mounted on sleepers fixed to the pontoon decking. These locations incorporated hardwood timber wedges which thus enabled any slack to be taken up within the structure between the pontoons and the truss. The struts reached up to the arched oval tube, which they supported through a series of longitudinal timbers, while immediately adjacent to these supports, the tube itself incorporated temporary internal timber reinforcement. These frameworks were attached to the truss through a series of wrought iron suspension rods, extending from the cill timbers to the oval tube.

The arrangement of this first fabricated span on its pontoons is shown in Plate 7.4, an engraving made from a stereoscopic photograph taken by Messrs Edmunds and

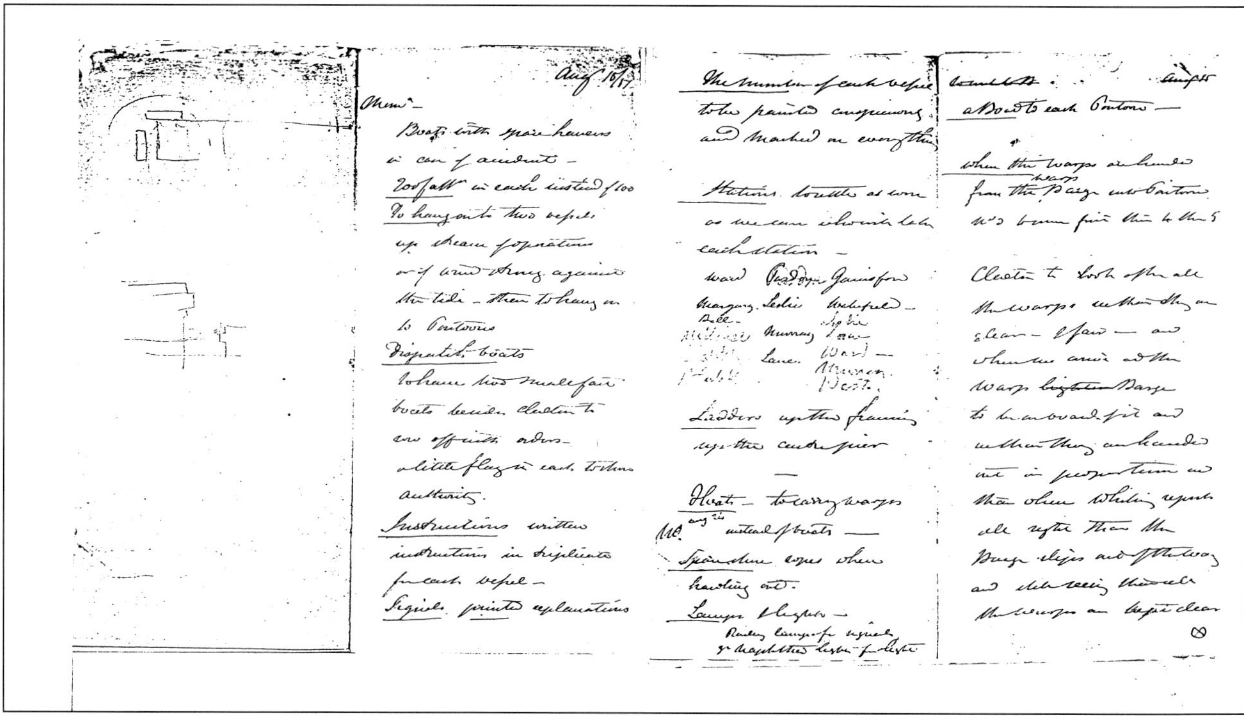

7.5 (above) *and* **7.6** (opposite page) *In preparation for this first floating out operation, Brunel recorded the details involved in his 'floating notebook', representative pages from which are reproduced here to illustrate his meticulous attention to detail. Other pages record the names of the personnel who were to occupy the various stations, his fertile mind trying to anticipate every difficulty which might arise during this critical operation.*
UNIVERSITY OF BRISTOL

Marshall, previously to it being floated. This clearly shows the substantial timber frameworks at each end, extending from the pontoon decks to the arched tube. Bearing in mind that each framework was required to support a weight of over 500 tons, it will be apparent from a study of the relevant details shown in Plates 7.3A, 7.4 and 7.8 that they were structural masterpieces in their own right.

Thus, once the truss had been correctly positioned within the Bridge configuration over the bases of the western and central piers, the pontoons would be free to float on the falling tide from underneath the truss, leaving its ends, complete with their support framework, resting on their respective main piers. In the right foreground of Plate 7.4 can be seen the plinth of the centre pier with the first cast iron standards in position, ready to receive the end of the truss, while the presence of the surrounding craft indicate the massive proportions of this splendid wrought iron fabrication. In the background, the various buildings of the site manufacturing facility can be discerned.

All these preparations took most of the summer of 1857 and, recalling his earlier experience in observing the movement and installation of the main spans of the Britannia bridge, which had apparently been subject to much delay and indecision, Brunel was determined to have this operation organised down to the last detail. Among his original papers are several charts of the tidal rise and fall in the Tamar estuary, prepared from records taken over the previous three years, from which he expected to make an accurate prediction of the timing and state of the tide when this first span was floated out.

In order to haul the truss from its dockside location, once it was afloat, five vessels were moored at strategic positions in the river; one being placed on the eastern side, another in the centre and a third at the western side, above the Bridge. The other two were moored lower down. On board each craft were powerful crabs for the purpose of warping the tube round to its final position. Much of the equipment used was borrowed from the Dockyard but Mr Canning, of Teats Hill, supplied the rope used in controlling the pontoons. To prevent the truss drifting under the influence of the current as it was being

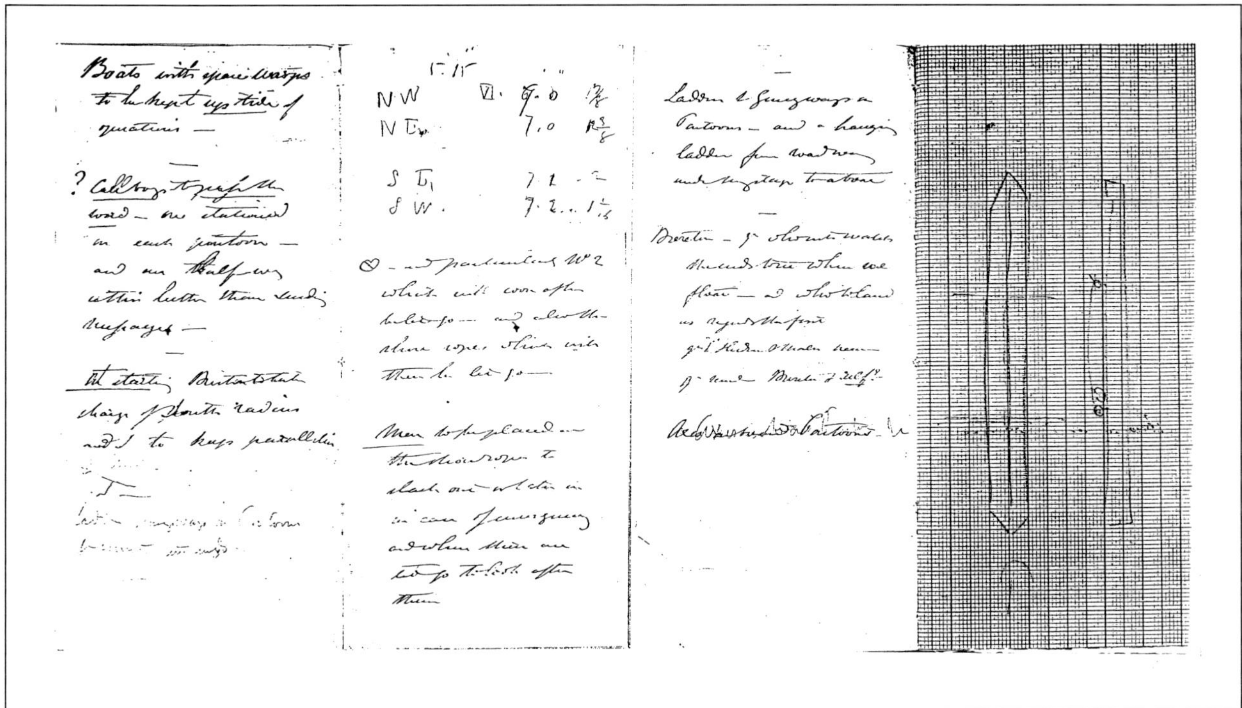

moved out, radius lines were laid from the pontoons to a series of separate moorings with facilities for shortening them if required. Extracts from a copy of Brunel's 'floating notebook', summarising the relevant details of this critical operation, as he conceived it at the time, are reproduced in Plates 7.5 and 7.6. Some of the pages list names of personnel and the allocation of their positions, typical of the detail with which Brunel concerned himself in the overall operation. His analysis was then formalised in printed instructions issued to all the staff engaged on this great operation, as detailed in Plate 7.7.

Altogether, about 500 men were directly employed for this movement, no separate contractor being involved. Within the records[14] is a list of the names of some 15 riggers, paid 7s. per day; in addition, the names of five 'men of war' men are quoted, to be charged at 5s.6d per day. These personnel probably represented the skilled element necessary to arrange the warps and tackle at each location, assisted by a number of unskilled labourers responsible for the actual manhandling of the ropes etc under their direction.

Captain Claxton, in one of two support tugs, was to be in command of the arrangements afloat, which comprised operation of the five naval vessels mentioned above. These had been borrowed from the Dockyard authorities and positioned in the river to facilitate the overall movement of the truss, One of Brunel's assistants was to be at each location, to act as 'Captain' of the hauling team, to superintend the men and implement the orders given by signal. One member of each crew had sole responsibility to watch out for these signals, to give the appropriate interpretation to the captain and to acknowledge the signal by a flag corresponding to that giving the instruction.

Brunel, assisted by Brereton, was to direct operations from a platform set in the centre of the truss, the relevant signals being given from a smaller stage immediately above, by means of red and white flags held in front of black boards, turned towards the vessel or location being addressed. All these operations and signals, together with the other actions involved in this movement, were carefully rehearsed beforehand which reflects the typical Brunellian attention to detail, by which the overall operation was to be assured of success.

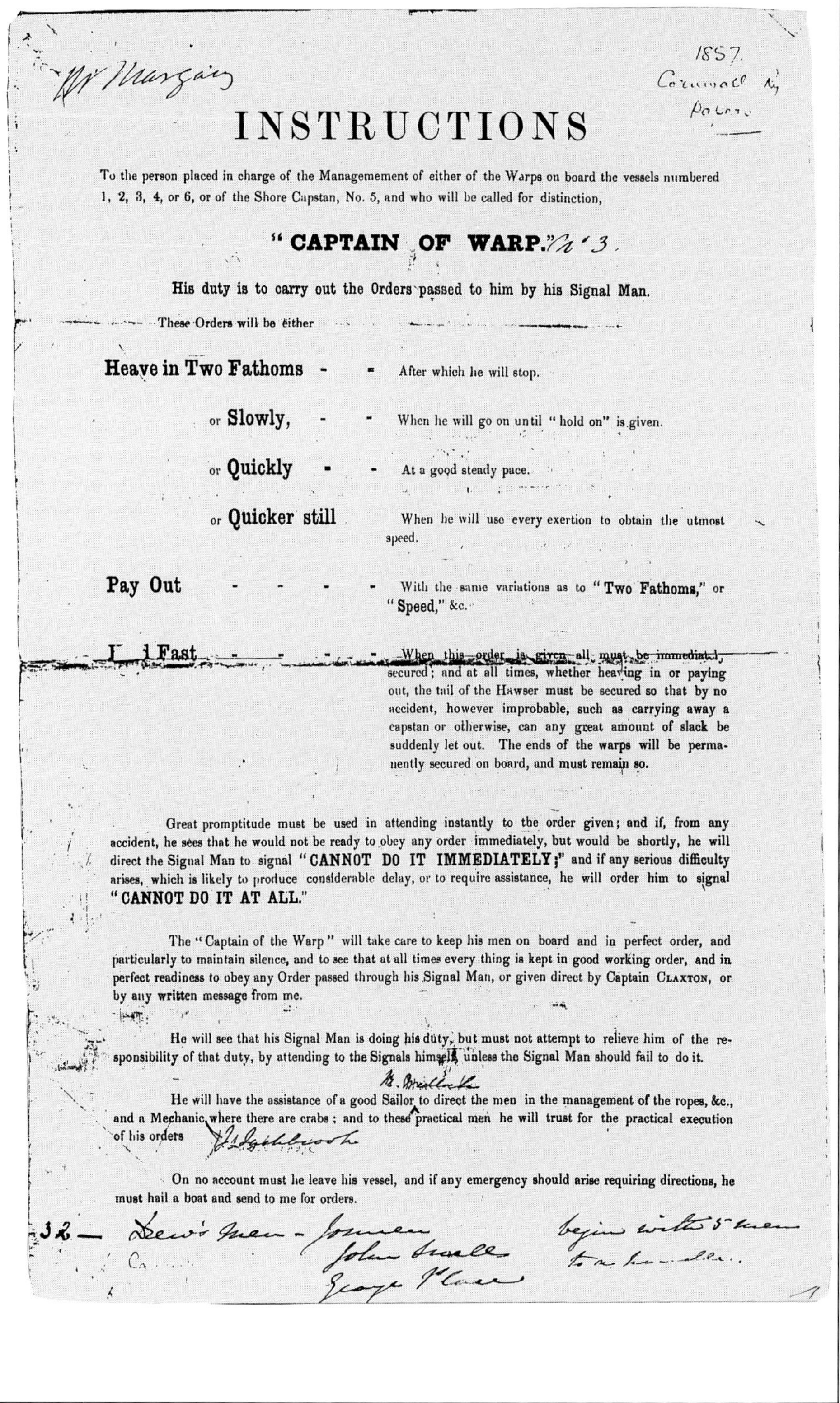

INSTRUCTIONS

To the person placed in charge of the Managemement of either of the Warps on board the vessels numbered 1, 2, 3, 4, or 6, or of the Shore Capstan, No. 5, and who will be called for distinction,

"CAPTAIN OF WARP."

His duty is to carry out the Orders passed to him by his Signal Man.

These Orders will be either

Heave in Two Fathoms - - After which he will stop.

or **Slowly,** - - When he will go on until "hold on" is given.

or **Quickly** - - At a good steady pace.

or **Quicker still** When he will use every exertion to obtain the utmost speed.

Pay Out - - - - With the same variations as to "**Two Fathoms,**" or "**Speed,**" &c.

Hold Fast - - - - When this order is given all must be immediately secured; and at all times, whether heaving in or paying out, the tail of the Hawser must be secured so that by no accident, however improbable, such as carrying away a capstan or otherwise, can any great amount of slack be suddenly let out. The ends of the warps will be permanently secured on board, and must remain so.

Great promptitude must be used in attending instantly to the order given; and if, from any accident, he sees that he would not be ready to obey any order immediately, but would be shortly, he will direct the Signal Man to signal "**CANNOT DO IT IMMEDIATELY;**" and if any serious difficulty arises, which is likely to produce considerable delay, or to require assistance, he will order him to signal "**CANNOT DO IT AT ALL.**"

The "Captain of the Warp" will take care to keep his men on board and in perfect order, and particularly to maintain silence, and to see that at all times every thing is kept in good working order, and in perfect readiness to obey any Order passed through his Signal Man, or given direct by Captain Claxton, or by any written message from me.

He will see that his Signal Man is doing his duty, but must not attempt to relieve him of the responsibility of that duty, by attending to the Signals himself, unless the Signal Man should fail to do it.

He will have the assistance of a good Sailor to direct the men in the management of the ropes, &c., and a Mechanic where there are crabs; and to these practical men he will trust for the practical execution of his orders

On no account must he leave his vessel, and if any emergency should arise requiring directions, he must hail a boat and send to me for orders.

7.7 *His draft notes were then formalised into printed instructions, issued to all the personnel engaged in the operation as reproduced in this illustration. The orders are quite clear as to whom they related, what was required and the procedures to be followed. Such attention to detail was rewarded by an operation which proceeded to a satisfactory conclusion without any mishap.*
PRO RAIL 134/19

7.8 *An engraving, again taken from an Edmunds and Marshall stereoscopic photograph, showing the Cornwall truss being inched into position between the western masonry pier on the right and the centre pier in the left hand distance. This critical operation is being watched by crowds of onlookers in the foreground, with the crews of the pontoons anxiously attending to the warps to ensure the correct positioning of this massive 1,100 ton structure. Again, the number and size of the supporting timbers mounted on the pontoons can be appreciated from this illustration, which also clearly shows the access entries into the great tubes.* ILLUSTRATED TIMES

Towards the end of August, invitations were extended to the Directors of the South Devon Railway to attend the manoeuvre; indeed they were even offered limited accommodation[15] on one of the support tugs engaged in the operation. At the same time, their Board had arranged for a short meeting to be held in rooms rented for that purpose at Saltash Passage, at the conclusion of the truss floating operation. Their Mr Carr wrote to Bond on 28 August in connection with these arrangements, and commented on the fact that Brunel was

> ...very hard at work here on your bridge. He went up to London by yesterday morning's train and this morning is again at Plymouth, and with the fly at the door ready I suppose for a start to Saltash.

Little wonder that his health was beginning to suffer; indeed, in spite of the importance of this floating of the first span of the Bridge, he had not had the time to prepare his usual report for the Directors for their half yearly meeting, held but a few days prior to this great event.

Meanwhile, Brereton reported to Bond[16] that during the last week of August (24 and 25) 'the bridge was floated off its bearings, to test the efficiency of the pontoons and framing; it is now ready for floating off'. Because of the suitability of the tides, Brunel had decided that this critical and all important operation should be carried out on Tuesday, 1 September 1857. The previous evening, as the tide ebbed, the valves on each pontoon were opened[17] to drain the water ballast and were then closed; all was thus set for this vital operation.

The great day dawned quietly with no wind - apparently one of those beautiful autumn days that come to Cornwall at that

7.9 *Viewed from the Devon shoreline, the tower of the ancient Parish Church of SS Nicholas and Faith on the hillside above Saltash can be seen in relation to the western face of the Bridge, indicating that it might have been used as a datum by Brunel in setting out the main spans.* AUTHOR

time of year - the flood moving silently up the Tamar and flowing into the numerous inlets along the banks, eventually reaching the docks holding the pontoons supporting the first great truss.

Brunel[18] reports that at about 1 p.m. signals from the tops of the temporary piers on which the truss rested, showed that the ends had been lifted three inches clear as the pontoons rose with the incoming tide. Signals were given for the men on the appropriate vessels moored in the tideway to haul on the warps and slowly the great structure glided out to the centre of the river. Here, warps were then attached to the vessel farthest from the centre pier which were to swing the truss around and set it across the Cornwall channel.

When all was ready, the different ropes were hauled upon in response to Brunel's overall direction and slowly the truss was swung around in a quarter circle, pivoting on the pontoon adjacent to the centre pier, until it spanned the whole of the western half of the river. Then, it was slowly inched into position between the centre and western piers, as shown in Plate 7.8; another engraving from a stereoscopic photograph by Messrs Edmunds and Marshall. It was finally adjusted to its exact position by strong tackles attached to the piers.

No details appear to have survived regarding the methods employed to set out the line of the structure or the procedure adopted to ensure that the truss was precisely positioned; knowing Brunel's reputation for meticulous attention to detail, these factors must have been scrupulously covered in the instructions issued to his staff stationed on the centre and western piers, so as to ensure the final line of the structure was correct.

However, site examination shows that the western faces of the three main piers of the Bridge appear to be in line with the north east corner of the tower of the ancient Parish Church of SS Nicholas and Faith, set on the hillside slope of Saltash. According to local opinion, this could indicate that Brunel may have used the corner of the tower as a datum for his layout. However, no evidence has emerged to support this theory, but its possibility will be apparent from the relative positions of the piers and the church tower shown in Plate 7.9.

By 3 p.m. water admitted into the

pontoons allowed each end of the truss to settle on its respective pier location - on the first six feet sections of the two iron columns on the centre pier and on the beginning of the masonry pier at the landward end. Plate 7.10 is a photograph taken from the Saltash shore, showing the massive span supported on the piers, the tide having turned and the pontoons floated away, leaving the great truss in position with the roadway girders and flooring a few feet above the water. Note the numbers '5' and '7' on the span which probably refer to the haulage locations identified in Plate 7.7, while the cradle and timber supports at the western end of the truss have already been removed. The corresponding cradle at the eastern end is still in position, awaiting dismantling.

The contemporary report[19] in the local press best captures the mood of the operation:

> ...The monster tube and its dependent roadway was seen to move from its native resting place, and obeying the impulse of unseen contrivances, quietly march across the channel at Saltash, nor scarcely for a moment stayed its slow, but certain progress, until as by the steering of some wondrous internal, but scarcely perceptible agency, without a mistake, without an accident, and almost without the sound of human voice to command, it reached its exact position, and without being a moment too soon or too late, just as the tide reached its height it remained suspended over its new resting place.

At three o'clock it was in its place, the event being marked by enthusiastic cheers of the multitude gathered on shore and water. The overall time for the movement had been one hour and twenty eight minutes, and 'it would be impossible to convey an idea of the ponderous grandeur of the floating mass as it moved majestically towards its destination'. At this distance in time we cannot but marvel at the successful execution of this critical operation, in floating into position without mishap this huge fabrication, which was subject to both significant tidal and wind forces, using the simple facilities, in combination, of the tide and manpower.

Once in position, it appears that a number of the visitors climbed over the main landpier and on to the roadway from the western shore; indeed, some even climbed on to the top of the tube. One unfortunate individual, not involved with the contract and therefore, not used to clambering over the structure, in displaying his bravery, missed his footing and fell from the tube into the river, injuring himself on the timber support structure. He was rescued but had received fatal injuries, and died the next morning. Sadly, this was the only accident throughout the day and marred an otherwise perfect occasion.

It had been a splendid day for Saltash, a public holiday being declared for the benefit of the vast crowd of onlookers who flocked to the water's edge to witness the scene - the village was bedecked with flags and church bells rang out in celebration. Not only was every area within the town which commanded a view of the Bridge packed solid with people, but the elevated grounds above it were also filled with sightseers. On the water, the Saltash Steam Packet Companies brought all their steamers into operation, to provide half-hourly trips to

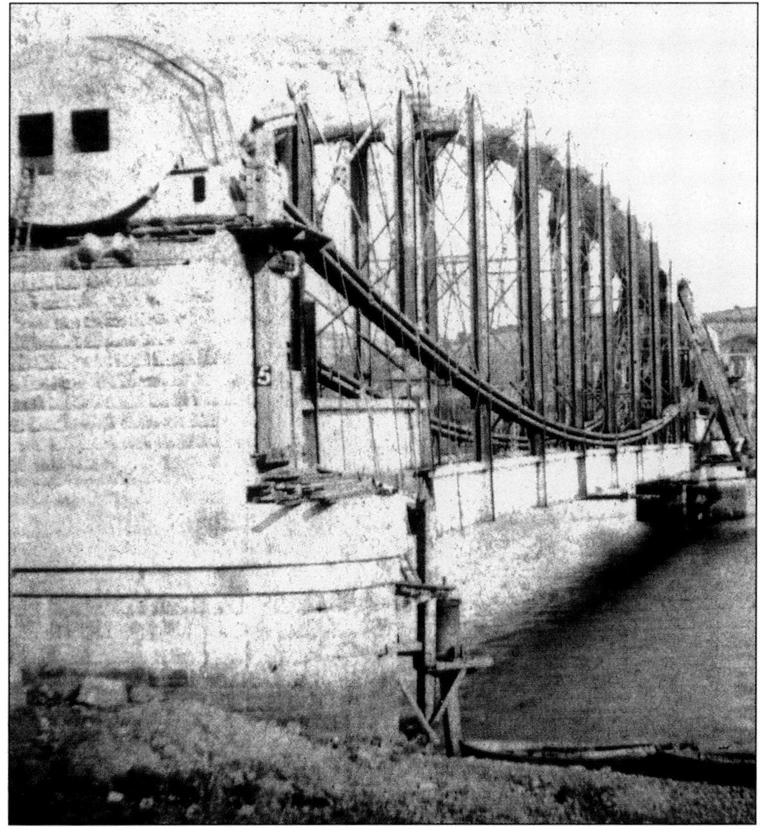

7.10 *A photograph taken from the shore at Saltash, probably soon after the Cornwall span had been positioned on the western and centre piers. Note the large numbers '5' and '7' attached to the truss, which presumably refer to the locations identified in Brunel's instructions, Plate 7.6. The timber supports have been removed from the span at the western end while those at the centre pier await attention.* RAILWAY STUDIES COLLECTION

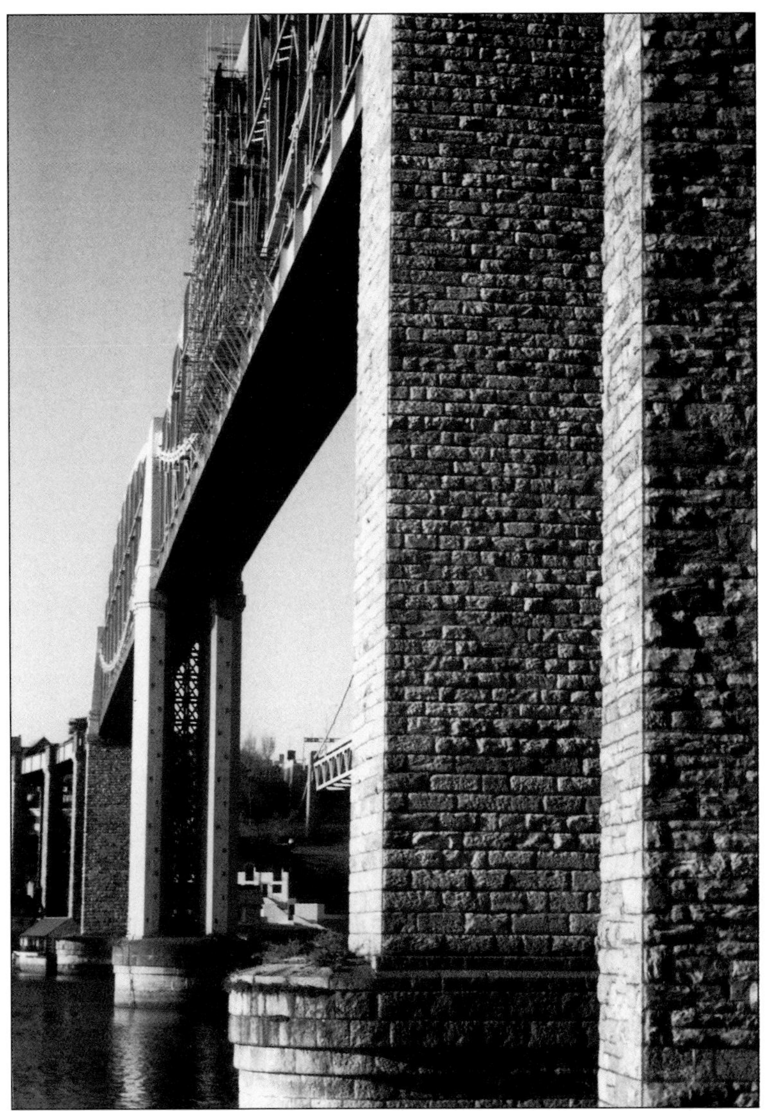

7.11 *An impression of the daunting task facing Brereton, in having to raise each main span from its floated out position, resting on the piers just above high water, to the level of the roadway 100 feet above. Each three feet lift of the truss added to the difficulty in raising and positioning the heavy cast iron standards of the centre pier, to ensure that they fitted together square and true, to form the centre support of the span.* AUTHOR

view the scene, being kept at a safe distance from operations by Captain Claxton's patrols. Tents and marquees were erected in private gardens to furnish accommodation for friends, while 'the various houses of entertainment' in the town, had laid in 'enormous stores of edibles and drinkables'. The provision, however, fell short of demand and by nightfall the town was bare of food. It was estimated that between 30,000 and 40,000 people were present to view the spectacle.

Throughout the whole manoeuvre, which had been completed with the 'most perfect order and regularity', the Chairman of the Cornwall Railway, Mr M. Williams MP, was present on the Bridge with Brunel. The success of the operation was a great tribute to the engineer and all his staff, which included Messrs Brereton, Gainsford, Murray, Wakefield, Burt and Blatchley, and resulted in a letter[20] of 2 September from the South Devon Superintendent to Brunel's assistant Gainsford:

> ...First let me congratulate you as I do most sincerely, on the wonderfully complete success of everything yesterday. Never was there anything done better.

RAISING THE SPAN

However, by far the most exacting operation now facing Brunel's engineers was to raise the Cornwall span from its off loaded location on the centre and western piers, to its full height of 100 feet above high water - a daunting task indeed, as will be apparent from the view of the Bridge in Plate 7.11. Surprisingly, this operation, extending over the period to May 1858, is not reported in the literature in any great detail. Yet, the work called for the exercise of great care and application; not only had the span itself, weighing nearly 1,100 tons, to be raised but that task involved progressively building up the western pier in masonry and the step by step construction of the twin octagonal cast iron pillars on the centre pier. In addition, once the truss had been raised to rail level, ie the tops of the piers, the portals which formed the final support structures for the tubes, in brickwork and masonry encased in cast iron on the western pier, and of cast iron standards for the centre pier, had to be constructed on top of their respective piers.

From the limited information that is available we can conjecture the scope of the work involved as identified in the following paragraphs, in connection with which, one of Brunel's assistant engineers, Charles Gainsford, was the resident engineer.

The lifting of the truss from its level a few feet clear of the water to its final location 98 feet up on the piers, was carried out using hydraulic jacks located under each end of the spans raising it one end at a time in three feet lifts. After each lift the ends had to be temporarily supported before the jacks were replaced and the next lift made; at the shore end, the masonry pier being built up beneath the end of the tube and the masonry allowed to set before the next lift. At the centre pier, the two octagonal cast iron pillars and the cross bracing between them, were built up six feet at a time so that the truss had to be temporarily supported between each lift.

Brereton had given careful consideration to this critical operation and on 31 January 1857 he had issued specifications[21] for the supply of two 22 inch and four 11 inch diameter hydraulic lifting presses, of capacity 600 tons and 300 tons respectively, which read as follows:

The main presses to be 22 inches diameter inside with a four feet extreme stroke, to be of cast iron 11 inches thick. The inside diameter to be bored perfectly true for its entire length. The end or cover to be in a separate piece bolted on with a faced joint and cup leather; the outer side of the cover to be faced to fit truly against the underside of a cast iron bed plate also to be faced.

The ram to be of cast iron 22 inches diameter at the upper end for 9 inches length turned perfectly true and with a cup leather attached. The remainder of the ram to have a screw or thread turned on it perfectly true $\frac{3}{4}$ inches deep with $2\frac{1}{4}$ pitch

MACHINERY FOR RAISING THE TUBES OF THE ROYAL ALBERT BRIDGE, AT SALTASH.

7.12 *One of the massive hydraulic cylinders located under the centre of one end of the truss, in the process of lifting; note the screw thread on the outside of the ram, the wrought iron 'follow up' nut and the massive timber packing, with inserts, supporting the truss as it was progressively inched upwards - three feet at a single lift.* ILLUSTRATED TIMES

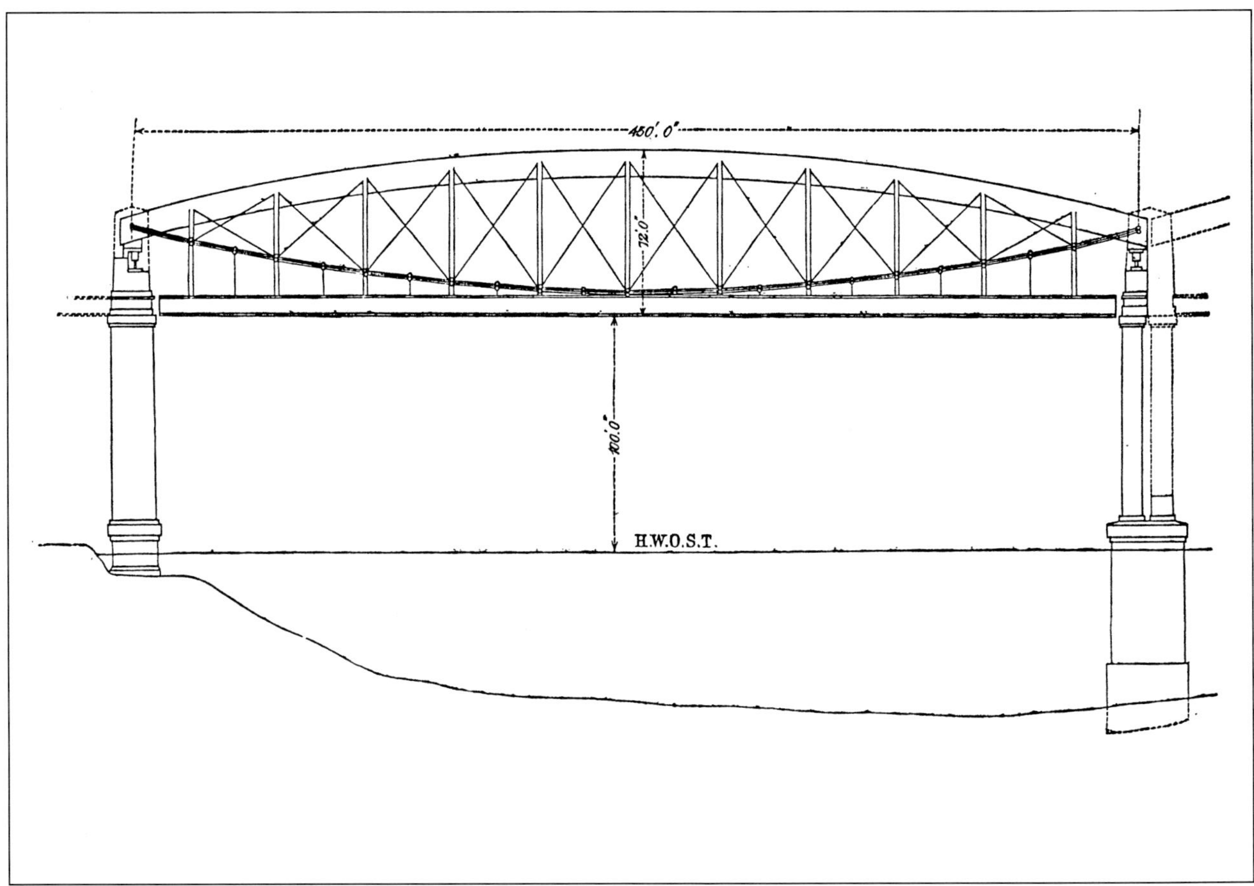

7.13 *A diagrammatic impression of the truss lifted to its final height but still supported by the hydraulic jacks at both ends while the portals were constructed over the western masonry pier and the central cast iron pier.*
PROC ICE VOL 69 1882

and 21½ inch extreme diameter, with a wrought iron nut 12 inches deep and 4 inches thick to follow up the press and working against a faced wrought iron collar attached to the bottom end of the press. This nut will be turned by a spur wheel keyed to it and worked by gearing. The bottom of the ram to be turned and faced to fit true into a cast iron bed plate also turned and faced to receive it.

The Ram is to be cast hollow and the lower end bored inside and fitted with a leather cup to receive a wrought iron secondary Ram or plunger 4 inches diameter turned perfectly true and passing through a hole in the bottom bed plan.

Except for modified dimensions, the specification for the smaller, 11 inch press was substantially similar. They were built by Messrs Easton & Amos and an estimate for their testing, issued on 6 August 1857, gave a total cost of £243. A note[22] dated 23 October 1857 confirmed the identification of the four small presses with large letters A.B.C.D. and the two large presses A. and B. A combination[23] of two 11 inch and one 22 inch press was set up in transverse line under each end of the arched tube, giving a base 18 feet wide. The central 22 inch jack by itself, or the outer two 11 inch side jacks together, were capable of lifting one end of the complete truss. Meanwhile, Gainsford had incurred Brunel's 'displeasure' (letter 17 October 1857) through his failure to have made arrangements to receive and unload this valuable equipment. He 'was instantly to remedy this neglect'.

The work programme was arranged so that twice each week the whole span was lifted three feet in one day, one end at a time, as shown in Plate 7.12, the large nut on the ram being screwed hard up to follow the outward movement of the ram and thus support the span in the event of hydraulic failure. An additional safeguard was provided by the insertion of timber packings, clear of the jack, between the underside of the span and the top of the pier.

On the western or Cornwall pier, the masonry was progressively built up after each lift, three feet each three days and, in the absence of evidence to the contrary, we must assume that this work was carried out by personnel working on top of the pier, without scaffolding, which then appeared to be the accepted procedure for this type of operation[24].

On the centre pier, the twin cast iron octagonal columns which formed the centre support for each truss, were made up in six feet high units. Each unit was cast in four separate flanged pieces, having a thickness of two inches, strengthened inside by stays and massive ribs (see Plate 5.19). When all four pieces of a section of a column had been cast, the flanges of each were planed true and square and the elements then 'fitted together with the neatness of joiner's work'. Thus finished, the sections were shipped piecemeal to the centre pier location, which probably included one or more pontoons, moored to the pier. These would have provided a working area at the site, accommodation for tools and equipment as well as storage area for the completed cast iron units. Lifting tackle erected on the pier itself would have been used to off load the cast iron units on to the pontoons, and later to lift them into position as required; no mean task having regard to the limited working area available on the centre plinth. There, as the truss was raised, the component parts of the cast iron units were bolted together and progressively built up to form the columns, to be capped on reaching their full height. Each column weighed about 150 tons. On average, therefore, it will be seen that during this stage of the operation, the span was lifted a total of six feet each week.

With the span positioned on the top of the western and central piers, arrangements then had to be made to raise it to its final height and temporarily support it while the portals were built under the ends of the tube. Plate 7.13 shows the hydraulic cylinders on suitable packing, supporting the truss at the appropriate height, for this work to be carried out.

On the western pier, the span was probably raised by the two outer, smaller jacks, so as to leave the central area free to enable the timber shuttering for the masonry portal to be set up, and the arch of the portal completed with brickwork and stone courses, as shown in Plates 5.16 and 5.17. The cast iron panels which formed the top of the pier, already

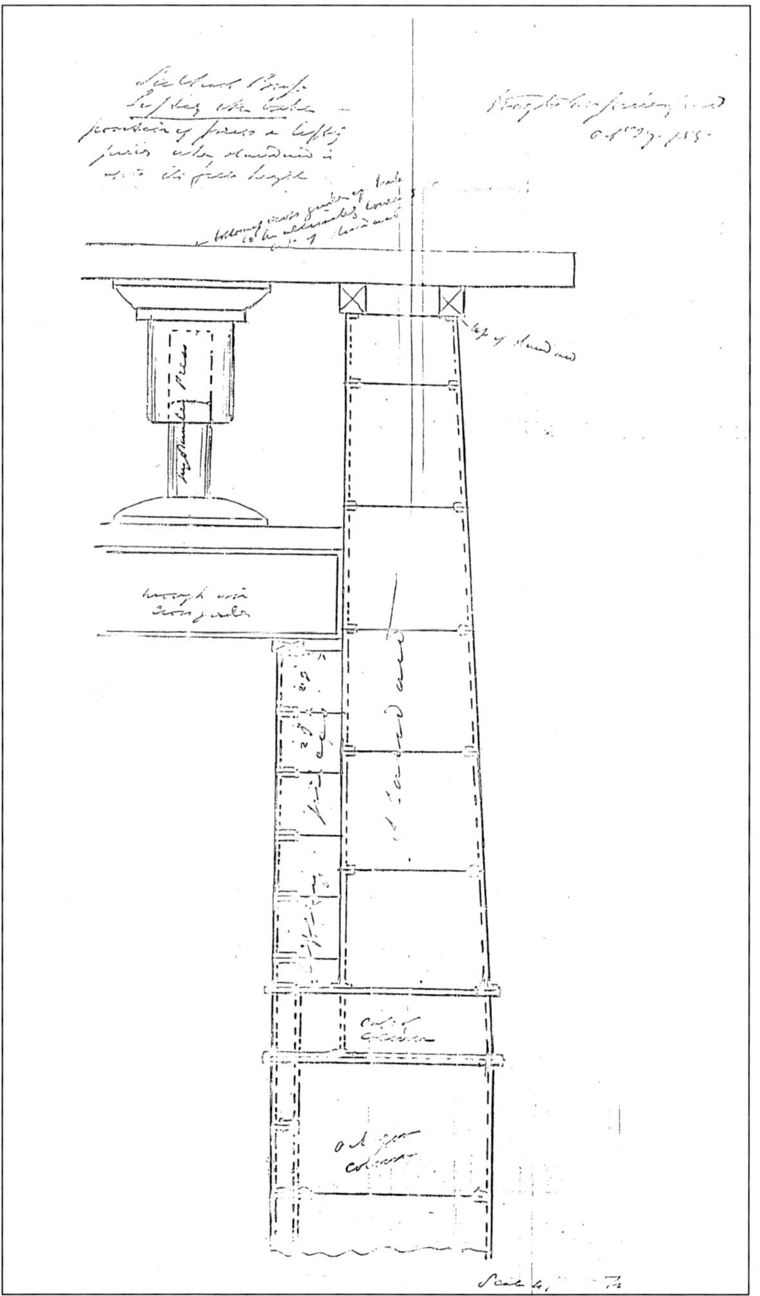

7.14 *Lifting the tube at the centre pier to its final height, with the cast iron 'standards' in position. This copy of the working drawing shows the location of the temporary supports for the wrought iron cross girder which carried the central hydraulic press during this critical final operation.* RTGW

prepared on the Devon shore and ferried across, were then hoisted into position and constructed on top of the pier. This then allowed the remainder to be infilled with brickwork and masonry to form the location and support for the expansion bearings of the outer end of the truss. In carrying out this work it will be seen from Plate 7.15 that a substantial temporary working platform had been built at the top of the pier in order to complete this important part of the construction.

On the centre pier, the cast iron fabrications (referred to as 'standards') which were to form the central portal seated on the capped octagonal columns, were shipped out to the centre pier in sections and hoisted to the top of the octagonal columns. They were then built up under the inner end of the truss, as shown in Plate 7.14, a reproduction of one of Brunel's original drawings issued during erection. Again, the positioning of these heavy cast iron sections, within the limited space available, called for care and application from the men involved. In turn, once it was finally positioned, this massive structure supported the fixed location and bearing seating for the inner end of the truss.

Under the direction of Brereton, the first lift of the Cornwall span was made on 25 November 1857, and the work proceeded steadily through the autumn and winter of that year. It is interesting to note that he later reported there were occasions when the lifting of the truss was carried out under most inclement weather conditions, with no interruption to the work due to the affect of lateral wind pressure on the tubes. He quoted one instance[25], when the tube had nearly reached its full height, the wind blew a very strong gale, such that men were scarcely able to stand, yet the work proceeded without interruption to a satisfactory conclusion.

In his report[26] of 23 February 1858, Brunel stated that:

> ...For some time past the Bridge has been lifted, and the piers built up, at the rate of six feet a week; and at this rate will be up to the level of the tops of the iron columns, or upwards of two-thirds of its intended height, in the course of a fortnight...The ironwork of the second span is advancing well, but I do not think it can be floated until the middle of the summer. There is reason to hope that, with favourable weather, the Bridge may be completed during the present year.

A report[27] by Gainsford dated 31 May 1858, spoke of the first tube having, during the month, been raised 'a few inches above its right height' for the purpose of fixing the four roller plates on the west pier to receive the rollers which allow for the expansion and contraction of the span. From this statement, it can be inferred that the Cornwall truss was completed in its final location during that month (MacDermot records the date as 19 May).

Brunel reported[28] this satisfactory state of affairs to the Directors on 27 July 1858, 'the western span of the bridge at Saltash has been raised to its full height and the piers built up, the roadway being 100 feet above high water spring tides'.

Great exertions were then being made to have the second span finished ready for floating out. The state of the works at that time will be apparent from Plate 7.15. This view, taken from Saltash in the Spring of 1858, shows the Cornwall span seated in solitary splendour astride its two piers, towering over the river and adjacent banks. The stub of the eastern masonry pier, seen on the far shore, appears ready to receive the landward end of the Devon span which, with all its support scaffolding, is nearing completion on the foreshore, prior to being prepared for floating out.

7.15 (opposite page) *A general view of the site in the spring of 1858. The Cornwall span has reached its final height, with the completion of its location and support on the western and central piers, evidenced by the platforms surrounding the top of each pier. Work is well in hand on the Devon span, here still shrouded in scaffolding, with the main chains in position awaiting attachment to the roadway girders. The plinth of the eastern masonry pier has been prepared, partially hidden by the top of the tree in the right foreground.* SM/SS

CHAPTER EIGHT

CONSTRUCTION: COMPLETION AND FINAL TESTING

1857 to 1859

From September 1857, with the Cornwall truss no longer occupying the slipway of the yard, Brunel was in a position to move forward the completion of the Bridge with all speed, by erecting the timber scaffolding ready for the framing and construction of the Devon span. As previously reported, the majority of the materials were already on site and this operation was contracted to Messrs Hudson & Male. To facilitate the work, coffer dams were built across the two docks to keep out the tide until it was finished and ready to be floated out on the pontoons. At the same time, the foundation and base for the masonry pier of the Devon span was put in hand, building it up initially to the requisite level to receive the truss when it was floated off into position. Work was also initiated for the completion of the remaining piers on the Devon side.

However, the winter had not been without its problems; during the autumn[1] the contractors had taken advantage of the fine weather so that the scaffolding was in an advanced stage of progress. Then a severe overnight storm reduced it to 'a total wreck'; many of the main beams and struts were splintered and broken. Fortunately, the storm occurred on a Sunday, with no personnel on site, so that no injury or loss of life was involved. However, Gainsford received another sharp reprimand from Brunel for his negligence and there was several weeks' delay in the overall construction programme while the structure was repaired. Nevertheless, the contractors were able to lay the first plate of this second truss on 20 November 1857[2].

They then worked assiduously through the winter months to recover the position. In a letter of 18 May 1858 to Bond, Gainsford commented 'the bad weather is sadly delaying our works', but by the end of the month he was able to confirm that 'all the main chains are suspended from the Tube and are being attached together by the Vertical trusses'. Also reported[3] during this period were problems with a number of the castings supplied by Bridgewater Iron Works, but the records do not give details of the faults.

Preparations for Floating Out the Truss

During the month, the coffer dams which had been built in the two docks were excavated and removed, ready to receive the pontoons for floating out the truss. The relevant preparatory work was completed by 30 June 1858, in time for the pontoons to be positioned and the truss supported thereon by means of timber frameworks similar to those used for the Cornwall span (see Plate 7.3A). This was the very day on which Messrs Hudson & Male's contract was due to expire[4]. The construction of this second span had been completed in some eight months, obviously benefitting from the experience gained in building the first unit.

The floating operation for this Devon span was not so straightforward as that of its predecessor since, in the meanwhile, the foundation and lower courses of the eastern pier had been built; occupying space immediately between the slipway and the river. This will be apparent from examination of Plate 8.1, a reproduction of one of Brunel's original drawings. This shows the positions he drew up for the line of the various moorings and warps which were to be used to manoeuvre the great truss from the dock to its final resting place on the piers.

Accordingly, he had to arrange for the brigs to be moored so that the pontoons could first be floated out from their respective docks,

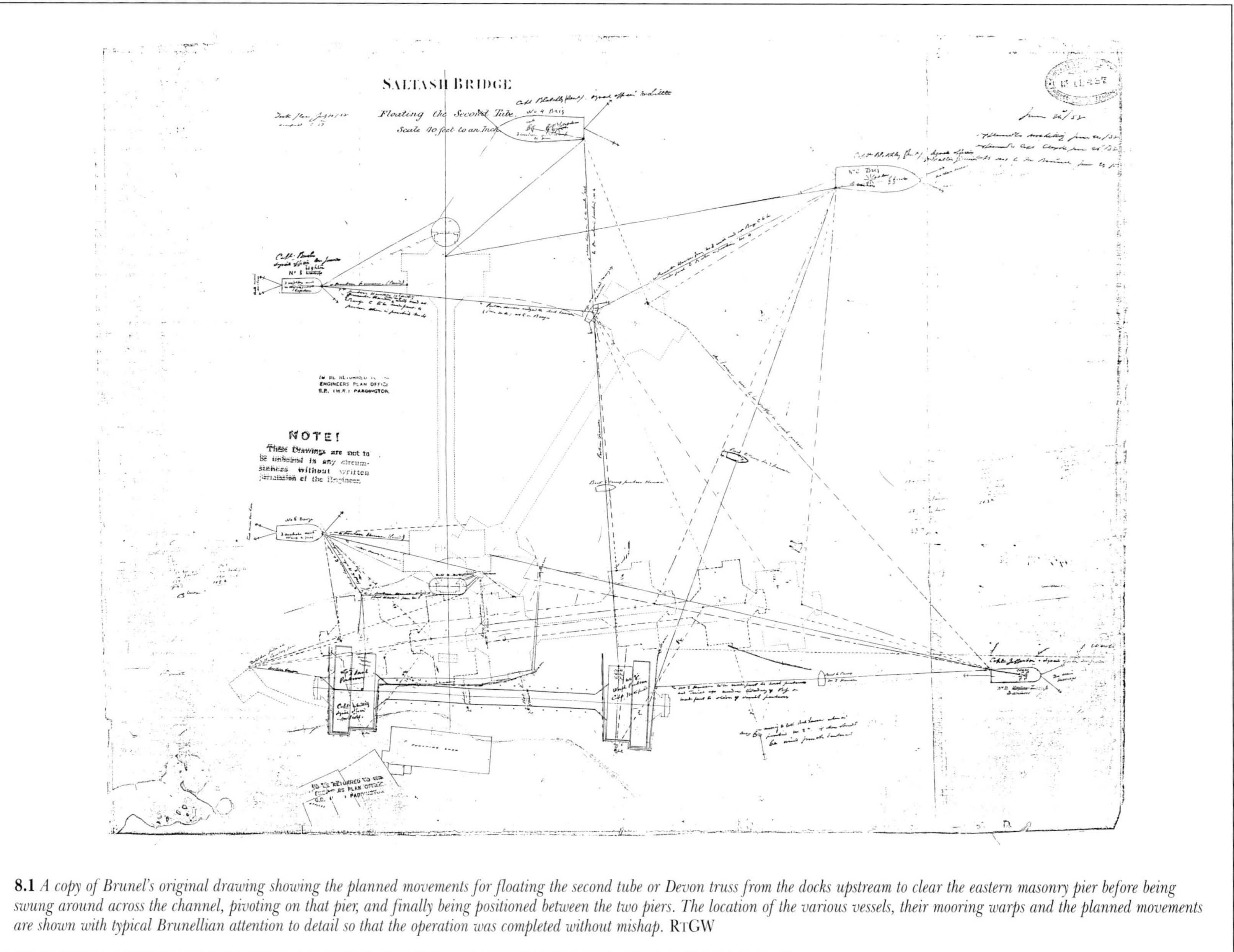

8.1 *A copy of Brunel's original drawing showing the planned movements for floating the second tube or Devon truss from the docks upstream to clear the eastern masonry pier before being swung around across the channel, pivoting on that pier, and finally being positioned between the two piers. The location of the various vessels, their mooring warps and the planned movements are shown with typical Brunellian attention to detail so that the operation was completed without mishap.* RTGW

8.2 *A diagrammatic appreciation of the Devon truss supported on its pontoons, shown firstly in the docks on the Devon shore, then located between the central and eastern piers and finally lifted into position on top of the piers.* RTGW

and then the complete truss moved upstream to clear the pier. These arrangements and progressive movements are shown in detail in Plate 8.1, from which it will be appreciated that this whole movement was indeed a critical operation, dependant as it was on a combination of tide and manpower.

Once the truss was in open water, then it could be manoeuvred across the Devon channel and inched between the centre and eastern piers, with the ends of the truss finally settling on their respective locations as the tide receded; the pontoons floating away as before. Plate 8.2 shows a schematic illustration of these movements, with the truss firstly, set in between the piers and then in its eventual final position astride its piers, at rail height.

The day chosen for the floating out was Saturday, 10 July 1858; his failing health kept Brunel overseas at that time and the whole operation was conducted, on the same basis as previously, by Brereton. He was assisted by Gainsford, Wakefield and other engineers of Brunel's staff, with the operations afloat under the active command of Captain Claxton. Although the weather that day was not favourable, with a high wind which added to the complexity of the operation, the whole movement proceeded smoothly to a satisfactory conclusion.

At about 2 p.m. the tube had come afloat and, shortly after, it was gradually drawn out from the stage where it had been built, then to be warped upstream to clear the eastern pier; all the necessary orders being given, as before, by means of signal flags. There followed the critical turning of the truss in the face of a strong north-easterly wind, which rendered the operation particularly difficult, as it was brought round to its place between the piers. Again, we have no details of how this second span was correctly positioned, to match the alignment of the Cornwall span, some 100 feet higher. However, as discussed in the previous chapter, the tower of the Parish Church of SS Nicholas and Faith on the hillside slope of Saltash, could have been used as a datum. It appears that the ends of the tube were finally located on their respective piers by about 5 p.m.; this feat being accompanied by hearty cheers from the workmen involved, to be echoed by the spectators gathered along the shores of the river.

The Directors had issued a number of tickets for persons to view the floating out from the yard, from where an excellent view of the whole operation could be obtained. Here the usual celebratory luncheon was provided by Mr Holmes, of George Street, Plymouth, which proved very acceptable to all the visitors, who included among others, the chairman, directors and staffs of the South

8.3 *A magnificent photograph taken from the Devon shore, shortly after the Devon truss had been floated out and positioned on its piers. At this stage it was, of course, dwarfed by the Cornwall span, now seen astride its two piers, with the cast iron standards of the centre portal clearly visible above the twin cast iron columns of the centre support. The sheds of Mare's original fabricating facility (Saltash Bridge Works) are in the foreground, the large shed with roof lights being identified as the punching shop. This will now have to be demolished to allow the building of the piers for the Devon approach spans to be completed, some of which are shown in the right foreground. In the distant background the Cornwall approach spans leading to Saltash station are all in position.* SM/SS

Devon, Bristol & Exeter and Cornwall Railways.

In due course, at a Directors' meeting, the Chairman reported[5] that he was

> ...on the span during the whole of that operation, and, notwithstanding the strong breeze which blew, the only vibration that I felt during the whole time from its leaving the shore until it was fixed upon the piers was the 'lift' when it first came afloat. And yet we should recollect that when lengthways with the stream the wind was so strong that the hawsers intended to draw it down against the tide were all slack, and it was let down by the 'preventors', intended to check it in case it went too fast.

Again, the Directors expressed their appreciation of the valuable help the Naval Commander-in-Chief and Admiral Superintendent of Plymouth rendered, through their respective staff, to Captain Claxton.

Fortunately, compared with the movement of the Cornwall span, we have a more comprehensive photographic record of this day's operations. Plates 8.3, 8.4 and 8.5 appear to be views taken soon after this manoeuvre, which clearly illustrate how the truss was settled in place on the two piers, with the Cornwall span in its final location.

Plate 8.6 is a close up view of the end of the truss seated on the stub of the eastern masonry pier.

Raising the Span

Now once again, Brereton was faced with the exacting task of raising this second span to its final position, repeating the operations previously described for the Cornwall truss. The first lift took place on 9 August 1858, while the truss was raised 98 feet to reach the top of the piers by 28 December. The completion of this work, which could justly be described as the key to the whole undertaking was duly acknowledged[6] by members of management and the men employed in the construction who, from the top of the tube, gave three hearty cheers with the unfurling of the Royal Standard. After this 'the event was signalled to a distance by a salute from cannon that had been placed on the bridge'.

The raising and fitting of the 200 ton cast iron standards on the centre pier, and the construction of the cast iron encased brickwork and masonry of the eastern pier portal, quickly followed, thus enabling the truss to be lifted to its final resting place by 16 February 1859. Its inner end was then fixed to the centre pier, while the outer end was eventually located on the expansion rollers installed on the portal of the eastern pier.

However, it should be noted that according to one of Gainsford's reports[7], dated 17 May 1859 (well after the opening of the line, and following Col Yolland's testwork) workmen were still engaged at that time in 'connecting the ends of the two Tubes together over the Centre Pier or putting up Cast Iron covering to it'. This apparently, was the only outstanding work then involved, and could refer to the Butt plates and Hoop, riveted on after both Tubes were in place (see Plates 5.6 and 5.9).

Building of the Devon Approach Spans and Completion of the Bridge

Reverting to the position of the contract in February 1859, it will be seen from Plate 8.3 that the truss had been floated off from its build location on the foreshore between the eastern masonry pier and the large shed with skylights in the roof (the Punching Shop). It will be apparent from the outline details shown in Plate 8.1 that partial dismantling of this building was then necessary in order to build one of the Devon piers while at the same time, with the truss now removed from its foreshore site, work could start on the

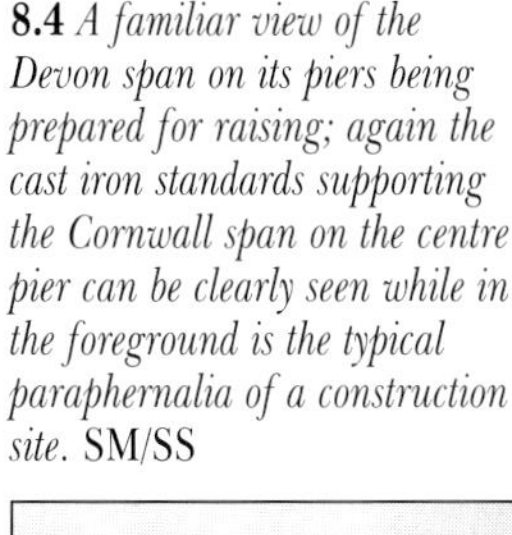

8.4 *A familiar view of the Devon span on its piers being prepared for raising; again the cast iron standards supporting the Cornwall span on the centre pier can be clearly seen while in the foreground is the typical paraphernalia of a construction site.* SM/SS

remaining approach pier. In due course, the main girders were raised and positioned for these last two land spans and the flooring completed.

A report[8] from Brunel, dated 23 February, commented on the 'extraordinary exertions' by the personnel involved, which had enabled the eastern span to have been placed in its final position during December, since when 'the lifting machinery and engines have been removed'. The side piers had been built, flooring laid and ballasted so that within a few days 'the Bridge will be tested by the running of heavy trains across it'.

The *West Briton & Cornwall Advertiser* of 25 February 1859 reported the Bridge nearly complete, with rails laid and the proposal for the first locomotive to cross on 26 February. Plate 8.7 shows work in hand in laying the permanent way to the eastern approaches to the Bridge while Plates 8.8A and 8.8B are two views showing the fabricating shops, largely still extant, with the jetty and overhead crane runway still in position. Plate 8.8C is a later view, with the site facilities removed other than their foundations.

With both the main spans in their final position the public was able, at long last, to appreciate the sweeping grandeur of the completed structure in its unique setting at Saltash, as shown in Plate 8.9. Inevitably, this drew the particular attention of journalists who sought to eulogise, in typical Victorian phraseology, the elegance of its graceful proportions. For instance, the *West Briton & Cornwall Advertiser* commented on the

8.5 *A more distant view of the same site showing the Devon truss seated on its first two sections of the octagonal cast iron columns of the centre pier. The end roadway girders can also be identified on both spans temporarily located above their final position, to facilitate movement of the complete truss during erection.* SM/SS

8.6 *A close up view of the end of the Devon span seated on the eastern masonry pier, showing the diaphragm end of the tube with the two access holes to its interior, the wrought iron support framework and the mass of masonry around the base, ready to build up the pier once lifting is started.* AUTHOR'S COLLECTION

8.7 *Around the time of the building of the Saltash Bridge, the art of stereo photography had just been introduced and evidently an enthusiast had visited the site to record this photo. It shows the trackwork on the Devon approach being completed together with work being carried out on the top of the eastern masonry pier.* RIC

apparent fragility of appearance of the Bridge on account of its immense height even at high water, which '...vanishes immediately the traveller gets on the bridge, where all appears strength and durability which have stood every test. Every confidence may therefore be placed in this masterpiece of engineering skill' and added that

> ...The works have been visited by the leading engineers of the United Kingdom, and from all parts of Europe - to whom it has been a subject of wonder for its lightness in appearance, yet great strength.... which will no doubt during the ensuing summer, be visited by some thousands of persons - it being certainly one of the engineering wonders of the age.

Then, the comment in a small local history[9] to the effect that

> ...old Tamar will be spanned by its double ferruginous bow, presenting with Cyclopean triumph a grand highway of commerce across the broad bosom of the waters. It disputes no territory with the waves; it raises its own dominion over them.

and again from the *West Briton*:

> ...This stupendous structure...crosses the Tamar at Saltash, and unites the counties of Devon and Cornwall in a close and, it is to be hoped, cordial and enduring embrace. This is of all others the viaduct [that] is second to none in the world as it far surpasses in size and in engineering difficulties of the construction even the Britannia Bridge across the Straits of Menai.

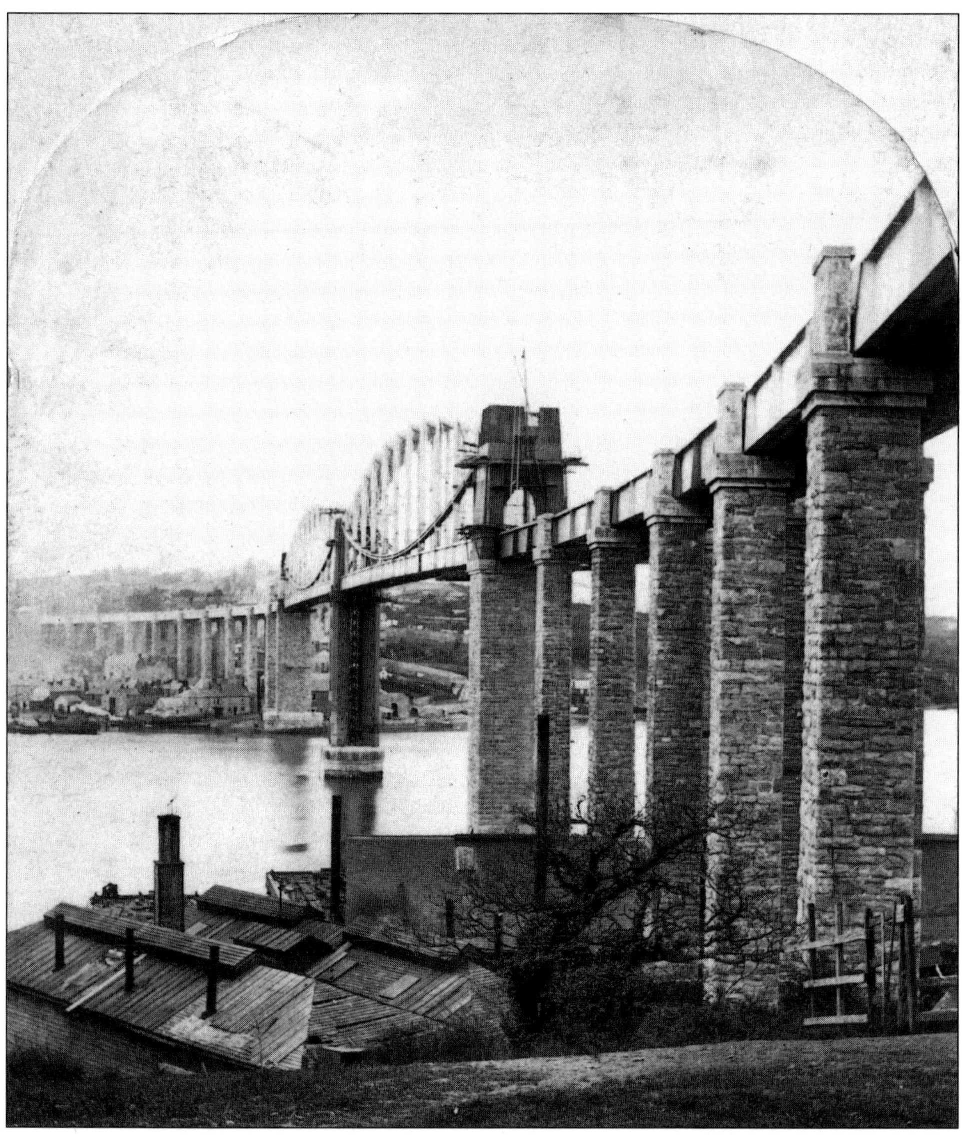

8.8A *A view of the Bridge from the south east during the final stages of completion, with cranework still in position on the eastern portal. This aspect gives a good idea of the extent of the site buildings and facilities of the Saltash Bridge Works which had been constructed on the Devon foreshore, now awaiting final demolition and removal.* COLLECTION STEPHEN ROWSON

While doubtless gratified by such euphoric tributes, Brunel and his staff were more concerned to complete the railway, where work was meanwhile proceeding on finishing the final link in the line from Plymouth to Truro, the erection of the timber superstructure of the viaduct at St Germans. This work had been delayed by unfavourable weather, but eventually it was completed and the first through train to traverse the whole line (including the as yet untested Saltash Bridge) made the journey on 11 April 1859. It consisted of three carriages, drawn by one of the South Devon locomotives, and conveyed Mr Woollcombe, Chairman of that Company, together with other officials from the South Devon and Cornwall Companies. The train returned to Plymouth that same evening, apparently without any untoward incident being reported.

TESTING THE FINAL STRUCTURE

The line was now ready for the Board of Trade inspection, which was carried out by Col W. Yolland CB FRS - a colourful and fiery character (Hall 1990) who had enormous prescience and immense influence on the development of railway safety during his 31 years (1854-1885) with the Railway Inspectorate. He and his staff completed their investigation over the period of 18, 19 and 20

8.8B *A view similar to Plate 8.8A but taken from the north east, showing the overhead runway in more detail, flying scaffolding on two of the approach spans and the Devon truss.*
COLLECTION
STEPHEN ROWSON

April. He issued his formal report, comprising some 26 hand written pages[10], on 25 April 1859, to be followed by a supplementary report of 30 April in connection with certain requirements arising from his original inspection.

In the section dealing with his investigation of the Royal Albert Bridge, he referred to it as 'important as any work of the kind which has as yet been executed in this country'. He gave a brief description of its construction, referring to the drawings and details regarding the calculated operating stresses which had been passed to him by Brereton. He also included the results of the static test which had been applied to the Cornwall span before it was floated off from the dockside (see pages 82-83).

He then turned to the tests which he had himself supervised on 20 April, 'the day being exceedingly favourable'. He had arranged for a spirit level to be 'placed under the roadway and resting on the iron stays at the central pier' which thus enabled him to observe the deflections of the main spans produced by the test train. This was made up of

> ...two heavy engines near the centre, and a number of trucks having their springs

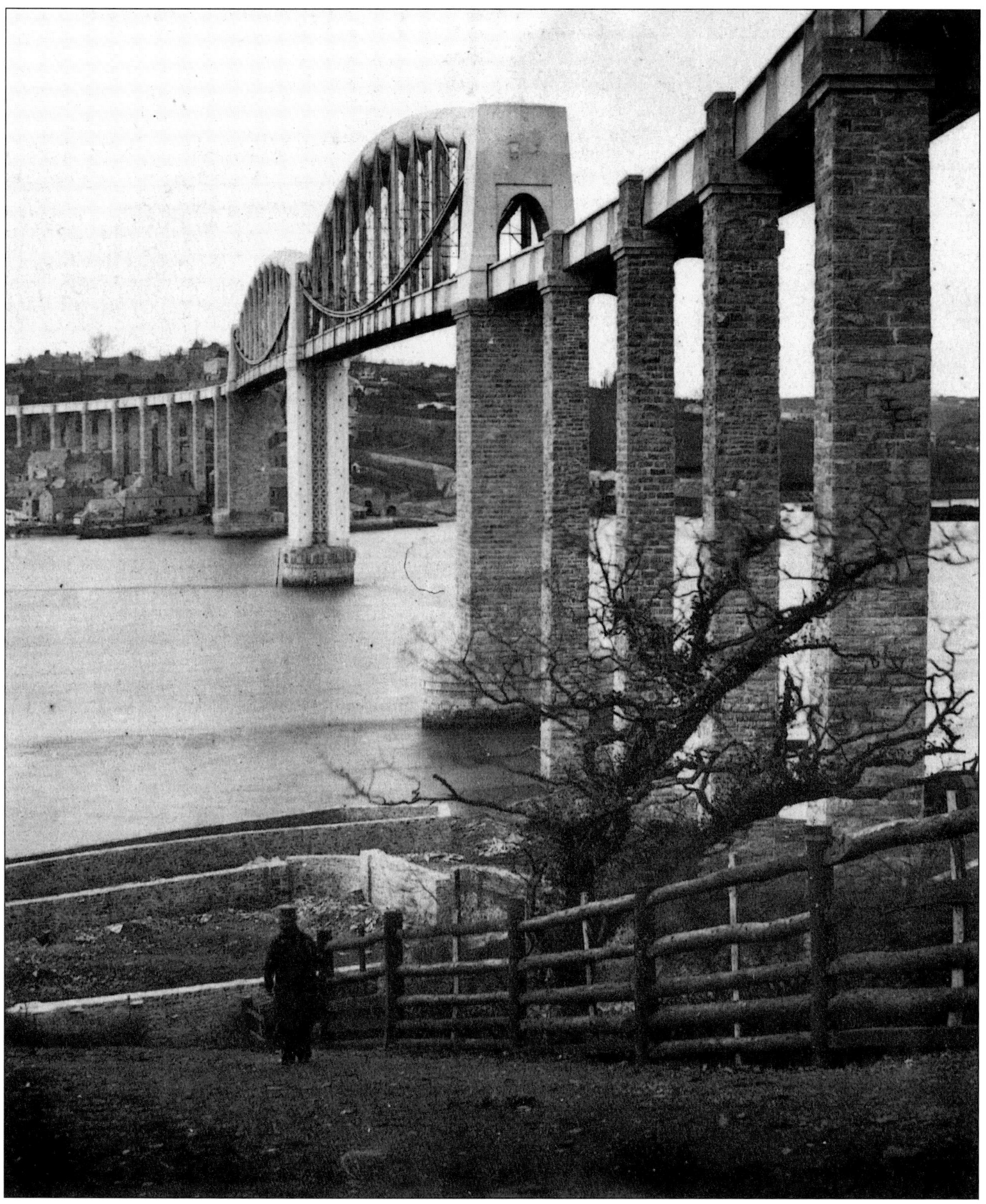

8.8C *A later view of the area from the south east; the Bridge completed and the site facilities removed, leaving their foundations in situ.*
COLLECTION - STEPHEN ROWSON

8.9 *A splendid view of the finished Bridge from the Devon shore showing the immaculate sweep of the broad gauge track on to the approach spans, the graceful formation of the two centre spans followed by the reverse curve across the Cornwall approach spans to Saltash station.* RIC

packed up, loaded with ballast iron etc making up an aggregate weight of 384 tons.

It would seem that two sets of tests were run, the first with two engines and ten trucks and the second with two engines and twenty trucks. Apparently, this was considered to be as large a weight as could possibly have been brought on the viaduct, unless the train was made up of a large number of engines.

The staffs which were to be observed for measuring deflections, were placed at the centres of each of the main spans and midway between the rails, the levels being taken from the top of a spike driven through the floor on to the top of the angle irons of the floor girders; thus the readings observed were the sum of all the deflections, including that of the cross girders carrying the roadway.

Arising from the above loading, Col Yolland reported the following results:

> The east or Devon tube (not previously tested) deflected 1.14 inches
>
> The west or Cornwall tube (tested previously and reported) deflected 1.20 inches

When the weight was taken off there was not the least sign of any permanent set. In amplification of Col Yolland's report, a scale drawing of the deflections under these different loadings was prepared. This also showed the unloaded contour of the roadway, incorporating the camber in each span, in establishing the three foot rise across the structure. These details are reproduced in Plate 8.10, as adapted from the original drawing which, sadly was not of a quality suitable for reproduction.

As part of his test procedure, Col Yolland then tried to register the deflection caused by passing the whole of this train load over the bridge at a speed estimated at 30 m.p.h., but the resulting vibration within the structure prevented the spirit level from remaining sufficiently steady to allow of the staffs being read.

He regarded these results as 'highly

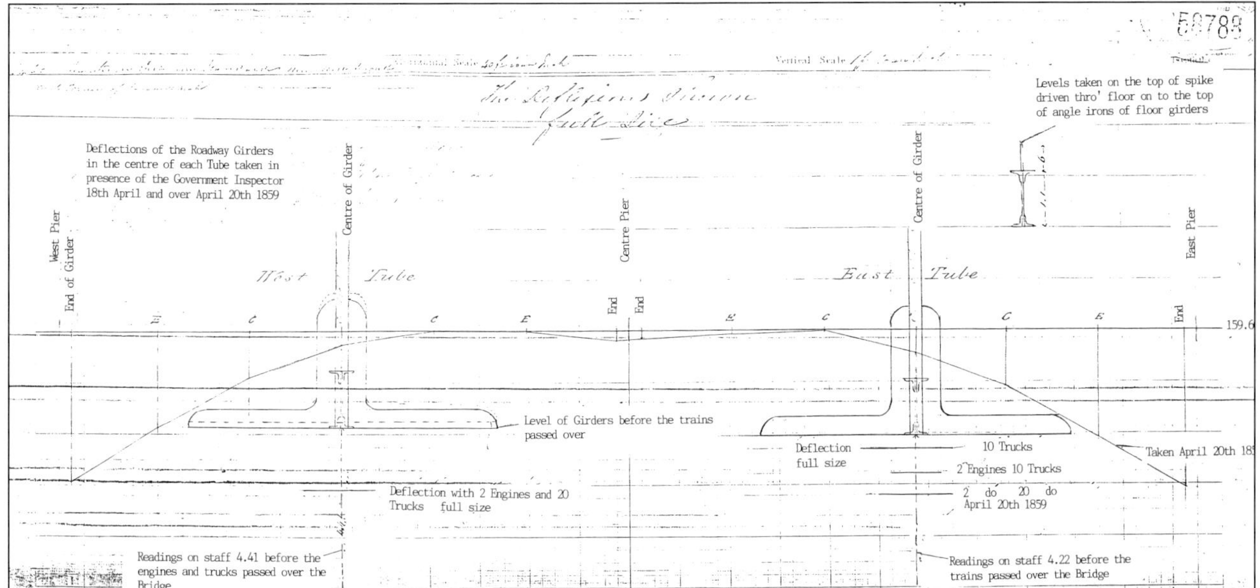

8.10 *A composite drawing prepared at the conclusion of Colonel Yolland's testing of the Bridge, 18-20 April 1859, showing the extent of the deflections of each span under various test loads. The overall quality of the original drawing was not suitable for reproduction so relevant information was extracted to produce this interesting illustration.* RTGW & AUTHOR

satisfactory' and, so far as he knew, he believed them to be greatly superior to anything of a kind that had been attained elsewhere; 'and accomplished at less expenditure of money and materials'.

He further commented that with a load of one ton per foot run and not allowing for any portion of the weight of the ends of the spans immediately resting on the piers, he estimated the amount of the strain on the truss tube at about 4.20 tons/inch^2 of section - and:

> ...allowing 170 tons as the amount of this superincumbent weight, not in any way trying the tube, the strain would be reduced to about 3.80 tons/inch^2.

He also estimated the stress within the girders over the land spans in all cases to be less than 4 tons/inch^2.

No mention was made in this report concerning a speed limit but in the light of Col Yolland's attempted test with the train crossing at 30 m.p.h., together with the sharp approach curves to both sides of the structure, it would seem reasonable to assume that the imposition of the present 15 m.p.h. speed limit would have dated from the opening of the line.

On the basis of these results the Royal Albert Bridge was considered a satisfactory part of the Cornwall Railway, although the final approval for the overall route was delayed until the end of April, pending completion of other work in no way connected with the Bridge.

Personnel Injuries

Throughout this period, contemporary accounts give little or no information regarding any injury or fatality to any member of the considerable number of workmen employed on the project. Having regard to the scope of the works involved, from the excavation for the centre pier below the Tamar to the final height of the main tubes, it would indeed have been an exceptionally safe site if no injuries had been incurred. During this period, 1853 to 1856, the country was engaged in the war in the Crimea and the press fully reported those activities and the casualties incurred; compared with which, a fatality on the Tamar Bridge was obviously less newsworthy.

The situation changed little following peace in the Crimea since 1857 saw the start of the Indian Mutiny, with equally pressing need for newspaper space, again probably at the expense of local news. Accordingly, it has not been possible to make a meaningful assessment of the cost in lives (if any) or injuries in the building of this fine structure, although in the absence of any known graves in Saltash churchyard, local opinion indicates that there were none.

CHAPTER NINE

THE OPENING

1859

During his inspection of the line, Col Yolland conducted his investigation in considerable detail and while his comments regarding the Royal Albert Bridge were without criticism, there were a number of other factors which caused him to conclude his report of 25 April to the effect that, in his opinion, the opening of the line could not be sanctioned. He criticised a number of features including, among others, the absence of man refuges on the long timber viaducts, omission of gradient boards, inadequate top ballast at some locations and unsatisfactory signalling arrangements at some stations. This decision must have caused some consternation within official circles, in view of the arrangements for Prince Albert to attend and perform the opening ceremony of the Bridge, planned for Monday 2 May.

It would appear that on 27 April an official within the Board of Trade must have issued Col Yolland with some emphatic instructions, since he was able to respond in his note[1] of 30 April to say:

> ...In compliance with the instructions contained in your letter of 27th instant I have this day re-inspected the Cornwall Railway between Plymouth and Truro and I have the honor [*sic*] to report for the information of the Lords of the Committee of Privy Council for Trade that the greater proportion of the requirements enumerated in my report of 25th instant have now been carried out, and I am of the opinion that their Lordships sanction for the immediate opening of the line for public traffic as requested in Mr Brereton's letter of the 28th instant may be given in the following conditions.

He then went on to list a change to a covered way at Devonport, the provision of resting places on the viaducts and included an undertaking signed by the Chairman and Secretary of the Company to the effect that

> ...only one engine (or two or more coupled together and forming part of the same train) in steam, shall be run upon the single line, or upon defined portions thereof, at one and the same time.

Brereton and his staff must have worked with great zeal and application over the last few days of April, to have corrected the majority of the points raised by Col Yolland in his first report but evidently, the line was considered to be ready to receive its Royal visitor on 2 May and to open for public use from 3 May.

Plate 9.1 is a view of the Royal Albert Bridge from above Saltash station, the layout of which appears to be in accordance with the details shown on one of Brunel's original drawings of the site, with up and down platforms, a headshunt off the down main line and the bay in the foreground. This was how the station is believed to have been at the time of the Prince Consort's visit. Sometime later the headshunt was removed and the platform widened, as shown in Plate 9.1A, which includes a typical Cornwall Railway train in the station.

In preparation for the opening the Directors had sent out invitations to individuals resident in Truro, as well as those within the Plymouth, Devonport and Stonehouse areas, to be present at the ceremony. It was an occasion looked forward to with considerable anticipation in both Devon and Cornwall. During the morning large numbers of sightseers gathered at all vantage points on the surrounding hillsides, while river steamers brought further visitors from Plymouth and Devonport to witness this great event. The weather, hitherto cold, wet and uncomfortable at last changed to give a morning 'as bright, cheerful and gladdening, as the most ardent promoter of the

9.1 *A view of Saltash station in accordance with one of Brunel's early drawings of the site showing the up and down platforms, the headshunt off the down main line (later removed) and the bay in the foreground; all as at the time of the Prince Consort's visit for the opening ceremony.*
COLLECTION STEPHEN ROWSON

undertaking could desire'. Sadly, this great day was to be marred by the unavoidable absence of Brunel who, through ill health, was compelled to remain on the Continent.

On the grassy slopes of the Devonshire side adjacent to the Bridge, a platform had been erected for the reception of the Royal party, in front of which was stationed a guard of honour composed of a company of the 96th Regiment, with the band and colours. Behind this platform was a battery of artillery under Major Hawkins. Those guests who were to be admitted into the area of the Bridge had been issued with special tickets, identifying the covered seats which they were to occupy adjacent to Saltash station, and giving directions for the order of proceedings.

Meanwhile, arrangements to convey guests to the Bridge included two trains from Plymouth, the first at 10.30 a.m. and the second half an hour later. There was also a special train departing from Truro at 8 a.m., hauled by the locomotive *Argo*. Calling at stations en route to collect its passengers, it reached Liskeard at 10.07 a.m. Unfortunately, on restarting the locomotive broke a connecting rod and the train was stranded, much to the chagrin and annoyance of its passengers. An urgent message was sent to Plymouth for a replacement locomotive which eventually arrived at 12.03 p.m. The driver made a valiant effort to recover the position, reaching St Germans by 12.21, where the train was stopped because His Royal Highness had by then reached the Bridge and was inspecting Coombe viaduct. For the Mayor of Truro and his entourage, together with the other principal guests involved, the day turned into one of great disappointment.

THE ROYAL TRAIN

In order to reach Saltash at noon, the Royal Train had departed from Windsor at 6 a.m., in accordance with the Working Timetable shown in Plate 9.2. The engine was driven by the locomotive superintendent of the Great Western Railway, Daniel Gooch. The train's arrival at the junction of the Cornwall and the South Devon lines was announced by the distant booming of a Royal salute from the citadel and from the flagship in the harbour.

Here, the locomotive had to be run round the train, for the three mile reverse journey down the track of the Cornwall Railway to Saltash. It crossed Brunel's timber viaducts at Stonehouse Pool and Keyham, before dropping down to traverse the 1,200 feet long Weston Mill timber viaduct across the mud flats at Camel Head, and then climbing away to arrive shortly afterwards, amidst the cheers of the spectators, at the eastern end of the Bridge punctually at its prescribed time. However, it would appear that such was the excitement of the occasion different reports record a variation between noon and 12.20 p.m. as the time of arrival. This could perhaps be explained by the difference between 'railway' time and 'local' time, a matter of about 17 minutes.

THE RECEPTION

The train stopped alongside the special platform so that His Royal Highness, with his attendants, could be received by the Earl of Mount Edgcumbe and other dignitaries; the Mayors of Plymouth, Devonport and Saltash in their robes and attended by their mace bearers; Mr Brereton and Mr Gainsford,

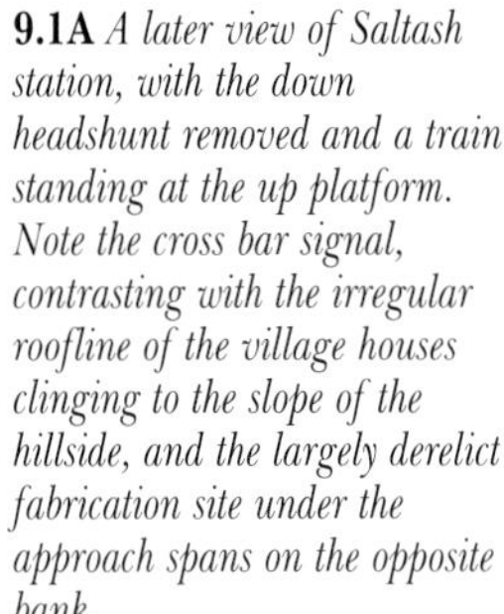

9.1A *A later view of Saltash station, with the down headshunt removed and a train standing at the up platform. Note the cross bar signal, contrasting with the irregular roofline of the village houses clinging to the slope of the hillside, and the largely derelict fabrication site under the approach spans on the opposite bank.*
COLLECTION STEPHEN ROWSON

respectively the acting and resident engineers of the Bridge; and the Chairman, Mr T. Woollcombe, Chairman of the South Devon Railway, with the Devon and Exeter Directors. It was, of course, intended that the Cornwall Directors accompanied by the Mayor of Truro should also be present at this time but, sadly, they were stranded in their train at St Germans.

The various deputations having been presented to His Royal Highness, the Mayor of Saltash tendered an address from the Corporation of that ancient borough, expressing their gratitude at his attendance to inaugurate the opening of the Bridge. In his response the Prince Consort acknowledged his pleasure in being associated with this great event, the linking of Cornwall with the rest of the Kingdom, and paid warm tribute to the enterprising man 'by whom it has been planned and executed', an undertaking which he hoped would lead to increased prosperity in the area.

With His Royal Highness and party once more on board, the train moved slowly forward. On reaching the eastern pier, the Blue Ensign was hoisted, followed on reaching the centre pier, by the firing of a Royal Salute and the hoisting of the Royal Standard and then, on reaching the western pier, St George's ensign was unfurled. Surprisingly, one of the reporters present was to comment[2] that as the train crossed the Bridge

> ...the vibratory and oscillating motion was plainly perceptible to those in the carriages, though, probably the absolute deflection of the arches did not exceed one inch.

The train continued slowly through Saltash station where the card holding guests were seated on a series of elevated platforms, who gave the Royal visitor a rapturous welcome, which he graciously acknowledged by repeatedly bowing. This applause was echoed by the crowds gathered on the surrounding hills, as the train reached Coombe viaduct.

Here he detrained, and examined the structure with keen interest. It was of timber construction[3] and in its way

> ...quite as curious as the colossal iron span of Saltash. Its height from the water is about 120 feet and so slight looks the web of neatly arranged beams, which, rising one upon another, carry the roadway high over all, that it taxes the passenger's confidence in Mr Brunel to the very utmost to venture on it in a heavy train. It has of course, been properly tested and, before proof, was known to be strong enough for what it was required to bear.

His Royal Highness then rejoined his party for the short return journey to Saltash station, where the locomotive was run round the train for its later return to Millbay. Meanwhile, the

BRISTOL & EXETER RAILWAY.

VISIT

OF HIS ROYAL HIGHNESS

THE PRINCE CONSORT,

TO THE

OPENING

OF THE

ROYAL ALBERT BRIDGE,

AT

SALTASH,

ON

MONDAY, 2nd May, 1859.

ROYAL TRAIN TIME BILL.

DOWN.

	DEP. A.M.	ARR. A.M.
WINDSOR	6 0	
Bristol		8 35
"	8 45	
Taunton...		9 35
"	9 38	
Exeter		10 25
"	10 35	
Newton		11 5
"	11 10	
Cornwall Junction		12 0
"	12 5	
SALTASH		12 15

UP.

	DEP. P.M.	ARR. P.M.
SALTASH	—	
Cornwall Junction		—
"	6 50	
Newton		—
"	—	
Exeter		8 15
"	8 25	
Taunton...		9 12
"	9 15	
Bristol		10 5
"	10 15	
WINDSOR		12 50

The following arrangements will be necessary for the proper working of this Train, which must be strictly attended to:—

The 7.50 a.m. Down Passenger Train is to Shunt at Tiverton Junction.

The 8.0 a.m. Goods Train Down will not start from Bristol until after the Royal Train.

The 8.0 p.m. Up Train is to Shunt at Tiverton Junction.

The 9.20 p.m. Short Train from Weston is to Shunt at Yatton.

BRISTOL, 29th April, 1859.

9.2 *A copy of the special Bristol & Exeter Railway timetable issued in connection with the Royal Train journey from Windsor to Saltash and return, 2 May 1859.*

Royal Visitor again left his carriage (Plate 9.3) and retraced his steps to the Bridge, which he crossed in company with the various officials. He showed a lively interest in its various features, Brereton answering his many questions regarding the construction. On reaching the eastern end he duly declared the Bridge to be open, an announcement which was hailed with loud cheers from the vast crowds which were gathered around the Bridge and on the shore.

The After Meeting

The formal ceremony now completed, the Prince Consort descended to the eastern side of the river, to the construction yard of the Saltash Bridge Works on the Devon bank. He was accompanied by the Directors and officials of the Railway Companies together with the Mayors of the boroughs (who had now been joined by the Mayor of Truro). There, in what was probably the works office, he was able to examine plans of the Bridge, some of the viaducts and other works on the line, including a tasteful collection of photographs of the Bridge, taken during its construction, by Mr Cox of Devonport.

Following their introduction to His Royal Highness, the Directors then presented him with the following address[4]:

> To His Royal Highness the Prince Consort
>
> Sir - The Chairman and Directors of the Cornwall Railway Company beg on the present occasion, to express their most grateful thanks for the favour under which they have been permitted to attach the name of your Royal Highness to one of the greatest engineering works of the age; and they desire also to acknowledge the additional honour conferred on the County by the presence of your Royal Highness to-day for the purpose of inaugurating an enterprise which has been brought to a conclusion after years of unexampled difficulty.
>
> The directors recognise in the presence of your Royal Highness, another among the many proofs on record of that truly enlightened spirit which originated and

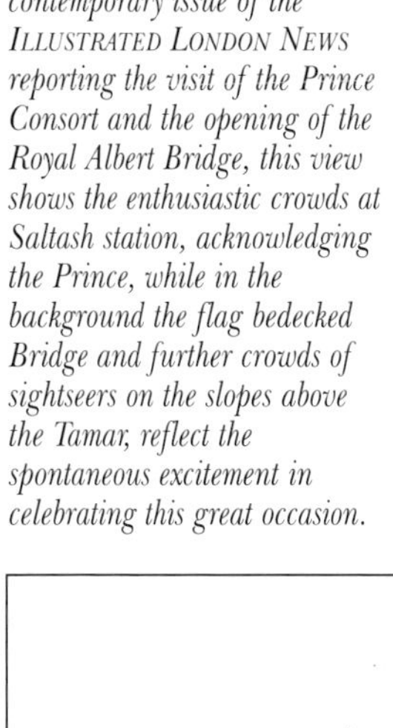

9.3 *Reproduced from a contemporary issue of the Illustrated London News reporting the visit of the Prince Consort and the opening of the Royal Albert Bridge, this view shows the enthusiastic crowds at Saltash station, acknowledging the Prince, while in the background the flag bedecked Bridge and further crowds of sightseers on the slopes above the Tamar, reflect the spontaneous excitement in celebrating this great occasion.*

> seemed an unexampled success for the Great Exhibition of 1851, and which has so beneficially directed, fostered and advanced everything connected with the arts, manufacture and social progress of this great country.
>
> The directors have only to regret the absence through ill health of Mr Brunel, by whom the stupendous structure which bears your royal name was designed and completed, and to whose great talents the county is indebted for the construction of a railway through a district presenting the greatest engineering difficulties.
>
> The directors are assured it would have been Mr Brunel's most anxious wish, and greatest pride, personally to explain to your Royal Highness all those details which you will desire to know, and are so fully able to appreciate; but in Mr Brunel's unavoidable absence, the directors have the satisfaction to know that your Royal Highness will find he has an able representative in Mr Brereton, who has watched and superintended the whole work from its commencement to the present time.
>
> In conclusion, the directors would venture to express a hope that at some future period your Royal Highness would condescend to examine the whole line of railway, and that on such an occasion, you might be accompanied by His Royal Highness the Prince of Wales, whose territory, as Duke of Cornwall, is traversed, and as the directors hope, will be materially benefitted by the opening of the Cornwall Railway.

The Prince Consort acknowledged with great pleasure this address and said he would be informing Her Majesty, the Queen, of the great satisfaction he had experienced in opening this Bridge. The party then retired to a small marquee, erected within the works area, to partake of a 'choice and elegant cold collation, provided by Mr Holmes, of George Street'.

The Afternoon Cruise

The ceremony now completed, the Royal Party embarked on board the Admiralty yacht *Vivid*, Plate 9.4, which had arrived the previous evening from Southampton and moored on the eastern side of the river. Following a royal salute from the battery near the Bridge, the yacht proceeded up the St Germans river so far as the depth would allow; His Royal Highness then transferring to the yacht's boat to be rowed further upstream where he and his party landed, to be met by a guard of the Royal Horse Artillery. They then inspected the fortifications on Tregantle Heights.

Later, they returned through Mount Edgcumbe Park, and travelled on to Cawsand where they re-embarked on the *Vivid* at Barnpool, to cross to the Royal William Victualling Yard. At their Winter Villa, at Stonehouse, the Royal Party was received by the Earl and Countess of Mount Edgcumbe, before returning to the South Devon station at 6 p.m. where the Prince Consort was welcomed by an enthusiastic crowd. This included a guard of honour from the Royal Marines and representatives from the police. He repeatedly acknowledged their cheers and then joined the Directors of the railway companies for dinner. Finally, entraining at 7 p.m., Gooch was again on the footplate for the return journey to Windsor, reached in the early hours of the following morning.

Thus concluded a day which would long be remembered by the inhabitants of Plymouth, Devonport, Saltash and the surrounding neighbourhood. It accorded the Royal Albert Bridge its rightful recognition as an engineering masterpiece, unique in conception and handsome in execution; a worthy tribute to its brilliant engineer.

The Truro Reception

The following day, Tuesday, the Mayor and Town Council of Truro hosted a lunch in the Council Chamber for the Chairman and Directors of the Cornwall Railway Company, the Directors of the other broad gauge companies, officers and other dignitaries, to mark the occasion of the completion of the line between Plymouth and Truro. At 10.20 a.m. the opening train left Plymouth with 14 carriages, conveying some 800 passengers, and hauled by two locomotives. After an uneventful journey they were welcomed at

9.4 *With the formal activities of the day completed, the Prince Consort left Saltash aboard the Admiralty yacht* Vivid, *to cruise the Hamoaze, later returning to Millbay station before departing for Windsor. His leaving the scene of splendour at the ceremonial opening is captured in this fine oil painting by Thomas Valentine Robins, part of the Elton Collection, now housed with the Ironbridge Gorge Museum Trust Ltd.*

Truro station by the Mayor, before the party adjourned to the Council Chamber, which was simply but elegantly decorated for the occasion. Here, they were duly seated by two o'clock for the *déjeuner*, which was 'unexceptionable, and highly creditable to the caterer, Mrs Daniell, of Truro. Substantial justice was done to it'.

This august gathering was marked by a series of toasts and speeches[5], recalling the events of the past years in connection with the building of the railway. The Chairman of the Cornwall Railway, Dr G. Smith (who had recently been appointed to that office), responding to the toast of 'the Chairman and Board of Directors', spoke of the great contribution of his three eminent predecessors, sadly no longer with them, and also of the unique part played by their engineer, Mr I. K. Brunel. In particular, his Royal Albert Bridge had, over the years attracted much criticism, both favourable and unfavourable, and he wanted to take the opportunity of setting the record right. He went on to say

...We have heard a great deal of late - and the longer we live the more we do hear - as to the span which unites the counties of Devon and Cornwall, the Royal Albert Bridge. I have heard very strange opinions as to the origin of this bridge; there are some very wise individuals who, in places of public resort, are very fond of dogmatising on this subject, and who will tell you...that this grand and marvellous structure is due to the ambition of Mr Brunel (laughter). In an evil moment he was tempted to raise up a monument to his engineering ability that should astonish the world. He has done so (cheers). He has completed a work which will yield him world wide fame...Depend upon it people who attribute that bridge to such a cause are utterly mistaken. Some say the bridge proves nothing but a reckless, uncalculating determination of the Board of Directors, and that having once determined on such an erection they stuck to it, regardless of expense. There is no more truth in that than in the other rumour. In fact, I could give you half a dozen equally fabulous accounts of the origin of the bridge; now for two or three facts. In the first place, our Board of Directors had no hand in the matter. The Cornwall Railway laid down a line which they thought the best and cheapest for the county - from Truro to Liskeard and thence to Plymouth...On coming to Saltash it was proposed to cross the Hamoaze by the very simple means of the steam-bridge, like the one in use, only longer and more powerful...They applied to Parliament for an act...for that line of railway and encountered a very formidable opposition...and it was represented to Parliament that it would be very much better to cross the Hamoaze by a bridge. The Cornwall Company never projected the bridge, but Parliament, no doubt influenced in great measure by the objection to crossing the Hamoaze by a steam-ferry...would not sanction the plan. The Directors, had in another session of Parliament to reiterate their application...Were they to risk another [fruitless] application or were they to adopt the suggestion that a bridge should be made?...After the most careful consideration...they suggested two plans to Parliament, but again recommended the ferry. I don't speak in jest, I don't utter a sneer when I say that the wisdom of Parliament overruled their recommendation (cheers); for the ferry was condemned and the bridge sanctioned. Parliament inflicted a serious cost on the Company, but the result has been a beautiful and substantial structure.

He went on to recall the many difficulties which the Board had encountered during the previous thirteen years and acknowledged the great support which they had received from the Associated Companies, without which it would not have been possible to complete the line. However, having now reached Truro, the next task was to finish the route to Falmouth. In conclusion, he paid gracious tribute to the attendance the previous day of the Prince Consort, who had expressed regret that the unfortunate breakdown of the train at Liskeard had prevented him from meeting many of the Cornish ladies and gentlemen. Dr Smith concluded by thanking the gathering for the kind and generous way they had received this toast.

Several of the other dignitaries who were present responded with appropriate speeches, before the party finally broke up at about 7 p.m. for the return journey to Plymouth. Thus ended two days of celebration to mark the opening at long last of the railway between Plymouth and Truro.

At a Board meeting held in Truro on the morning of 6 May, before the arrival of the first train from Plymouth, the Directors had passed a series of resolutions[6] expressing their cordial thanks to the Chairman, Secretary and other officers of the South Devon Railway Company 'for the kind and valuable aid afforded by them on the occasion of the opening of the Royal Albert Bridge'; to Major General Eden, commanding the Western District 'for his disposition of the troops' on this occasion; and to Vice Admiral Sir Barrington Reynolds KCB, Rear Admiral Sir Thomas Pasley and the officers and men under their respective commands 'for the great assistance' which they rendered. The thanks of the Chairman and Board of Directors was also accorded the Mayor and Town Council of Truro 'for the cordial manner in which they were received by them and...[for] their deep interest in the completion of the line'.

Brunel's Visit to Saltash

Later in the month, in weak and failing health, Brunel returned to England and, owing to his condition, arrangements were then made for him to view his completed masterpiece from a couch fitted to a specially prepared platform truck, drawn by one of Gooch's locomotives. On this occasion, in contrast to the festivities of the opening day, no flags flew while all was silent, save the wind moaning through the framework of the mighty spans, the slow exhaust beat of the locomotive and the squeal of the wheel flanges as this unique train slowly crossed the Bridge, to give its lone passenger one last look at the structure which was to remain the enduring tribute to his memory.

During the following weeks he clung tenaciously to life, but finally, surrounded by his family, he died peacefully and without pain

9.5 *Believed to have been published shortly after his death, this engraving represented a tribute to the works of Brunel, including not only the Royal Albert Bridge but also the broad gauge railway track and locomotive of the Cornwall Railway, and a steam driven paddle steamer. The artist, Mr C. A. Scott, shows part of the site fabrication facilities beneath the Devon approach spans still in position, including what appears to be the overhead travelling crane.* SM/SS

in the evening of 15 September 1859. At a meeting shortly after his death, the Directors of the Cornwall Railway decided to commemorate the genius of their engineer by having the letters 'I K BRUNEL ENGINEER 1859' set on the portals at each end of the Bridge, where they stand to this day in recognition of his great work.

The Tribute to Brunel

In his report[7] to the shareholders at their first half yearly meeting, following the death of Brunel, held on the 23 February 1860 in the Council Chamber, Truro, the Chairman, Dr G. Smith took the opportunity of acknowledging the great debt which the Company owed to Isambard Kingdom Brunel

> ...whose works of extraordinary genius had earned for him an European reputation, and whose death will be a loss, not only to this Company, but to the general interests of science throughout the world. It is but an act of justice to the memory of Mr Brunel, to place on record that the whole cost of the erection of that stupendous and beautiful structure, the Royal Albert Bridge, which has elicited the admiration of the whole scientific world, has not exceeded the sum of £225,000. Considering the extraordinary difficulties which were overcome, and the magnitude of the operation, it is believed that there is no engineering work in existence which has been more economically completed.

While in itself a generous tribute, it does not reflect the whole story. The figure of £225,000 not only covered the erection of the Bridge but its entire cost, including the founding of the centre pier on rock at a depth of some 85 feet below high water - a stupendous task. Berridge (1969) quite rightly points out that this overall result provides an unequivocal answer to the criticism made by the mid-Victorian contractor, F. R. Condor, that Brunel was often little concerned with cost.

Likewise, comparison has often been made between this total of £225,000 and the £601,865 cost of Stephenson's double track Britannia Tubular Bridge over the Menai Straits, completed but a few years earlier. It is shorter than Saltash by over 600 feet, but comprises tubular construction throughout its length, whereas the landspans at Saltash, totalling over 1,200 feet, are of 'through girder' formation, a much lighter construction. While this would affect the level of final cost, undoubtedly Brunel's concept of the application of tubular configuration represents a more cost effective arrangement, despite its inherent handicap of the suspension bridge principle.

One further factor needs to be borne in mind, namely, that the Britannia Bridge as evolved by Stephenson, assisted by Fairbairn and Hodgkinson, has formed the basis for all subsequent work on the box girder. Hence, their investigation constituted a key factor in the development of bridge design. However, in arriving at the final formation of the Britannia bridge, Stephenson also employed the architect Francis Thompson. He incorporated extensive masonry, set in proportion to the size and shape of the great tubes and, with the entrances guarded by massive lion statues, rightly gave the whole a monumental aspect.

On the other hand, Brunel, following behind Stephenson, noted the basic results of his rival's investigation and developed these with his own ideas, to produce a lighter and cheaper structure for Saltash. Furthermore, he did not employ an architect since the structure is bare of any architectural embellishment. Nevertheless, the slender towering twin granite piers which carry the curving railway high over the town of Saltash (Plate 7.1) and above the Devon shore, complement the massive wrought iron spans, to create an aesthetic combination of metal and stone. These enormous spans were themselves originally of fairly simple construction, as is apparent from Plate 5.1. Only in recent years, with the addition of bracing and linkage to restrain the suspension chains in their correct curvature in the face of increased train loads, have they taken on a more complicated formation and lost something of Brunel's original simple configuration.

While we must acknowledge the very considerable contribution made by Stephenson and his colleagues in the field of civil engineering, and in particular the application of tubular construction to bridge design, consideration of all the factors involved in Brunel's lifetime - the sheer breadth of his interests from shipbuilding to civil engineering, the originality of his designs, the economics of construction and his overall vision - surely confirm his predominant position as the leading Victorian engineer.

That this was the view largely held at the time of his death was perhaps epitomised by the publication of the engraving reproduced as Plate 9.5, which in a single grand scene reflects the major works of his life - the broad gauge track of the Cornwall Railway, with a typical locomotive and train, a steam driven paddle steamer, both set in a fine picture overshadowed by his greatest work, the Royal Albert Bridge. The artist, Mr C. A. Scott, has captured with accuracy the contemporary scene of this beautiful stretch of the Tamar, as a fitting backdrop to Brunel's achievements.

Robert Pearson Brereton (1818 - 1894)
S K JONES (BRUNEL SOCIETY) COLLECTION

CHAPTER TEN

THE YEARS SINCE 1859

With the completion of the Bridge and the opening of the Cornwall Railway overland communications between the Duchy and the remainder of the United Kingdom were at long last established on a more effective basis. The great divide, which had for so long separated Cornwall from its neighbouring county, Devon, had been bridged, and with it the means to remove the physical and cultural barriers between the two. Almost immediately, the first two benefits to be realised were the introduction of a Night Mail service, giving a daily postal delivery between Penzance and the industrial centres of the country, and the availability of public telegraphic communication from some stations; both bringing immense benefits to Cornwall that had been long overdue.

Our story so far has been concerned with the original development and construction of this Royal Albert Bridge, as conceived by Brunel, and reflected in the overall simple but elegant structure shown in Plate 5.1. His design was intended to cater for the train loads of the mid-nineteenth century, when the heaviest locomotives employed on the Cornwall Railway were the broad gauge 4-4-0 saddle tanks of the South Devon Railway. They had an all up weight of around 40 tons, with a maximum axle loading of just under 14 tons; within their overall length the load density was about 1.38 tons/foot run.

In order to set the story within a contemporary context we should now examine the history of the Bridge over the years following Brunel's death on 15 September 1859. Brereton had then written the Cornwall Directors expressing his wish to continue in office as the Engineer for the Cornwall Railway (letter dated 28 September 1859)[1], and in due course he completed, largely in accordance with Brunel's original plans, the extension to Falmouth.

Although for many years he had been Brunel's principal assistant, particularly as we have seen, with regard to the construction of the Royal Albert Bridge, his personal life is something of an enigma. Following his chief's death he applied for membership of the Institution of Civil Engineers, which was granted on 10 January 1860, at the age of 41. His Application[2] listed an extensive range of major civil engineering contracts on which he had been engaged under Brunel and there can be no doubt regarding his qualification

10.1 *A copy of the advertisement which appeared in the West Briton & Cornwall Advertiser of 9 September 1859, offering the sale of the equipment and stock from the Saltash Bridge Works.*

CORNWALL RAILWAY, SALTASH.

TO CONTRACTORS, BUILDERS, and OTHERS.

MESSRS. FULLER and HORSEY are instructed to SELL by AUCTION, on Thursday, September 8th, and following days, at 11 each day, at the works, Saltash-bridge, Cornwall, on the banks of the Tamar, the

PLANT AND SURPLUS MATERIAL

remaining from and used in the construction of the Royal Albert-bridge, Saltash, including six powerful hydraulic presses used in raising the tubes, two with 22-inch rams and four with 10-inch rams, made on improved principle by Messrs. Easton and Amos, and only used for the tubes at Saltash; two sets of hydraulic pumps, a very powerful overhead travelling crane, one 7-ton wharf crane, two portable 8-ton cranes on trollies, 13 smiths' forges, levelling plates and slabs, a new air machine 9 feet 4 inches diameter, three atmospheric pumps (two by Easton and Amos), 1,000 fathoms chain, 30 pairs sheave blocks, with rope and chain falls, snatch blocks, 1,000 fathoms rope, 20 tons contractors' rails, trollies, 20 anchors and kedges, barge, six boats, mooring buoys, life buoys, sails and rigging, tarpaulings, ladders, wheeling planks, wheelbarrows, carts, 400 loads squared pine timber in logs, 100 loads cut timber, 500 12-feet planks, pile engines and monkeys, 30 tons bar, rod, and plate iron, ten tons pig iron; stores of various descriptions, 20 dozen files, ratchets, smiths' tools, scales and weights, weighing machines, powerful steel yards, iron and wood tanks, erection of plate furnaces, carpenters' benches, grindstones, three tons gun metal castings, the temporary erection of workshops, boarded enclosures, rafters, joists, slating, brick chimney stacks, and numerous other effects.

To be viewed with the machinery, and catalogues had. See preceding advertisement.

Approved bills at three months date will be taken from purchasers to the extent of £50 and upwards.

10.2 *A later view of the Bridge from Saltash station, believed c1870, when painted in a darker colour; note the slotted semaphore signals.* RIC

10.3 *Conversion of the gauge at Saltash station, 17-20 May 1892.* BOB SIMS COLLECTION

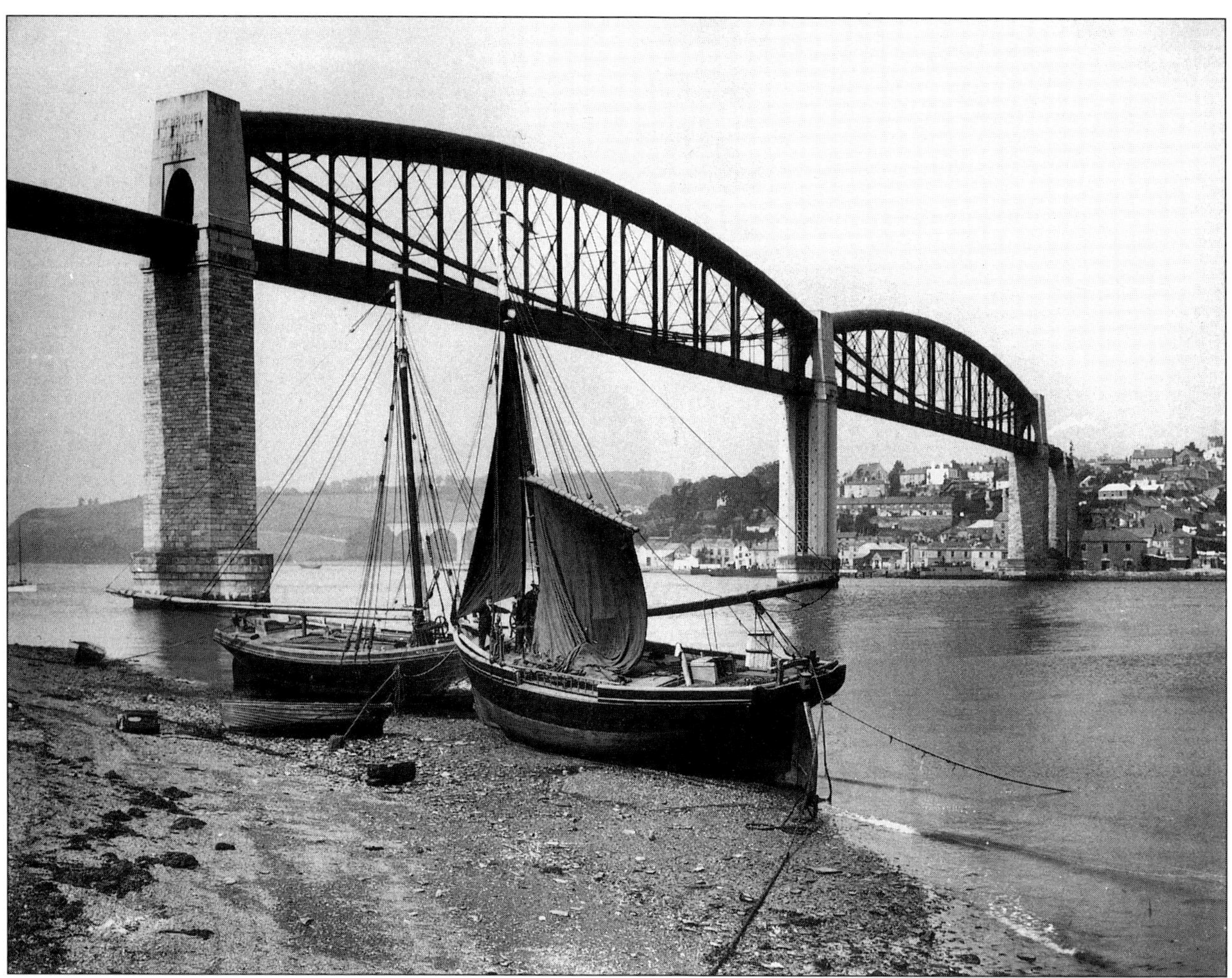

10.4 *A striking view of the Bridge from the north east, taken in 1924, showing the structure very much as built by Brunel and before the introduction of the various modifications intended to counter the distortion of the main chains due to increased loading. With the Tamar road bridge now built alongside Brunel's bridge, this view is no longer possible. The sailing craft in the foreground are on part of the foreshore which incorporated the piled foundation for the building of the main spans.* RtGW

and experience. He was married and he died in 1894[3], but otherwise we know little of his personal life.

With the opening of the railway to Truro, one of the early subsequent developments was to dispose of the fabrication facility on the Devon foreshore (see Plates 8.8A and 8.8B) and to that end the auctioneers, Messrs Fuller & Horsey, were instructed to sell the plant and machinery by auction. Plate 10.1 is a reproduction of their relevant advertisement in the *West Briton & Cornwall Advertiser* of 9 September 1859. This lists in some detail the surviving plant and equipment which had comprised this construction facility.

As already mentioned, in order to complete the piers for the Devon approach spans, once the Devon truss had been floated out, it had been necessary to demolish some of the buildings of the facility. However, reference to the engraving in Plate 9.5 indicates that the artist has included details of the fabrication site, presumably as it existed at that time. Apart from a number of small buildings, it will be seen that it comprised a large building and also the overhead crane and gantry.

Following the September auction, the remaining buildings could be demolished and the land released for sale. At the site today, nestling under the Devon approach spans on the slopes of the hillside, it is difficult to visualise the great activity which had prevailed over a period of some six years, on what was a relatively small area. Firstly, the construction of the great cylinder for the centre pier was to be followed by each massive tubular truss being progressively assembled on its

10.9 *With the work on the span completed, the Erection Wagon, with the old girders slung from the cross beams clear of their replacements, is being slowly drawn off the Bridge, the movement being carefully monitored by the staff, apparently unaffected by the height of these operations.* THE ENGINEER

substantial timber framework, erected on the foreshore.

From its opening, the Bridge continued to carry rail traffic across the Tamar, increasing over the years in both volume and loading, and apart from routine maintenance and painting, the structure remained unchanged throughout the broad gauge years. Plate 10.2 is an overall view of the Bridge from Saltash, c1870, when slotted semaphore signals had been introduced. It reflects the operational environment which prevailed at that time.

Thus, the first significant work to be carried out was the conversion of the trackwork from broad to narrow gauge in May 1892 (Pugsley 1976). Because of the exceptional difficulties in dealing with this conversion, the work[4] was prepared on Sundays several weeks before the 'conversion weekend' of 17-20 May. A separate narrow gauge track was laid inside the broad gauge one, to be connected up at the time of the overall conversion, leaving the original rails to be lifted at leisure. The work of conversion in Saltash station is depicted in Plate 10.3.

Like all ageing structures, over the years the Bridge has demanded ingenuity and patience from the engineers entrusted with its preservation, to ensure that it continues to provide that essential rail link between Devon and Cornwall. In meeting the demands of the late nineteenth century and the subsequent growth in the twentieth century, the Bridge has been subject to some strengthening and design changes, which need to be considered in relation to Brunel's original concept. The following is a résumé of the more important factors which have been involved during this period.

With the abolition of the broad gauge the heavier locomotives of the narrow gauge were able to work into Cornwall. The 4-4-0 'Dukes' and 'Bulldogs' became dominant on the main line services[5], with their increased axle load of around 16 tons. During the Great War some of the services were handled by the heavier 4-6-0 'Star' and 'Saint' classes, with maximum axle loads of nearly 19 tons.

Consequently, as a first step towards accommodating these changes, a total of 401 new cross girders were fixed throughout the structure in 1905 (Plate 5.23). According to Duke Smith[6], the original cross members were placed diagonally with respect to the main girders, and in carrying out this work, to avoid stripping out the flooring completely, the new cross girders were fixed between the old ones and were only as nearly square as these conditions would allow. This situation is very apparent on the two main spans, as will be seen from Plate 11.6, where both sets of cross girders remain in position.

The next significant change came in 1908, when the two land spans adjacent to Saltash station at the Cornish end were reconstructed to enable the double line from the station to be extended on to the Bridge. Thus, the formation of the structure through to the 1920s, very much as Brunel had built it but before the next major phase of modifications was initiated, is shown in the 1924 view of Plate 10.4.

Replacement of Land Span Girders

In 1927 it was decided, in view of the increased weight of modern locomotives and rolling stock, coupled with the onset of corrosion of the thin iron plates adjoining their bearings, to renew the main girders of the fifteen remaining land spans. There then followed a major replacement programme for this work, which included removal of the original cross girders while retaining the 1905 replacements. Over the period April to July 1928 the main girders of the seven Devon approach spans were renewed while from September 1928 to January 1929 those of the remaining eight Cornish approach spans were replaced.

The scope of this operation, carried out with only limited interruption to traffic on Sundays during the above periods, has been well documented[7] and the reader requiring a detailed résumé of the work involved is referred to one or other of these original reports. However, as a tribute to the skill and ingenuity of the engineers and staff employed, and to make our record complete, the operations are summarised in the following paragraphs.

The replacement operation for each span was built around a specially designed erection wagon formed from a lattice girder 95 feet long, 9 feet $\frac{3}{4}$ inch deep and 4 feet $3\frac{1}{4}$ inches wide, weighing about $18\frac{1}{2}$ tons, Plate 10.5, and normally carried on two bogies. This was equipped with special cross traversing beams, capable of conveying the new main girders from the site siding (for the Devon spans located on the Devon side of the Bridge) to the span to be reconstructed, There, following the picking up and temporary removal of the original main girders to the outside extremities of the piers, the new main girders were slewed into position.

To facilitate these operations the cross sleeper track had been temporarily replaced by the original longitudinal timber baulk road which, for the span being replaced, could then be supported from the erection girder by means of special slings, thus freeing the cross girders of its weight. At the same time, a working platform had been provided below the span by underslung scaffolding. Thus, the original cross girders were cut out and the 1905 cross girders unbolted and prepared for fitting to the new main girders.

The plans for each span were prepared in great detail, with much preparatory work being carried out during the week. This enabled the actual occupation of the main line to be kept to the minimum in carrying out the work stages shown in Plate 10.6. This will also be apparent from the summary of the operations involved on the Devon spans, identified as follows:

Propel erection wagon from siding to span under reconstruction;	
Connect cross girders, permanent way &c; lower main girders and lift on stools	1hr 40min
Traverse out old main girders, remove old bed plates and fix new.	30min
Lower and traverse out and set in final position new main girders	30min
Fix cross girders, lower permanent way, adjust and reset erection girder on bogies	1hr 0min
Travel back erection wagon, with old main girders attached, to site for unloading	50min
Total time	**4hr 30min**

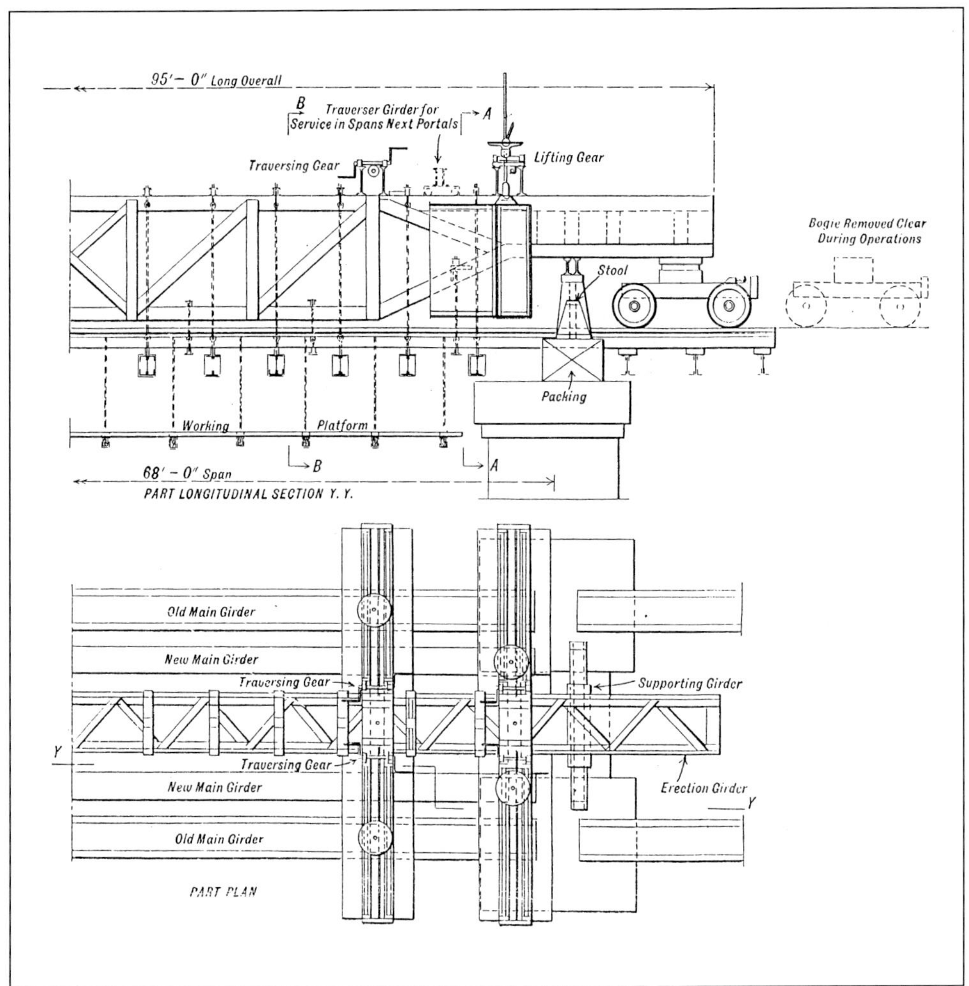

10.5 *For the replacement of the main girders of the approach spans, a special Erection Wagon was used to transport the new girders and recover the original wrought iron members from each span. This illustration shows a part elevation and plan of this special wagon, with its lateral carrying girders and traversing equipment.* THE ENGINEER

10.6 *The progressive operations involved in the removal and substitution of new main girders, using the Erection Wagon positioned for each span. The cross sections AA and BB refer to the corresponding positions identified in Plate 10.5.* THE ENGINEER

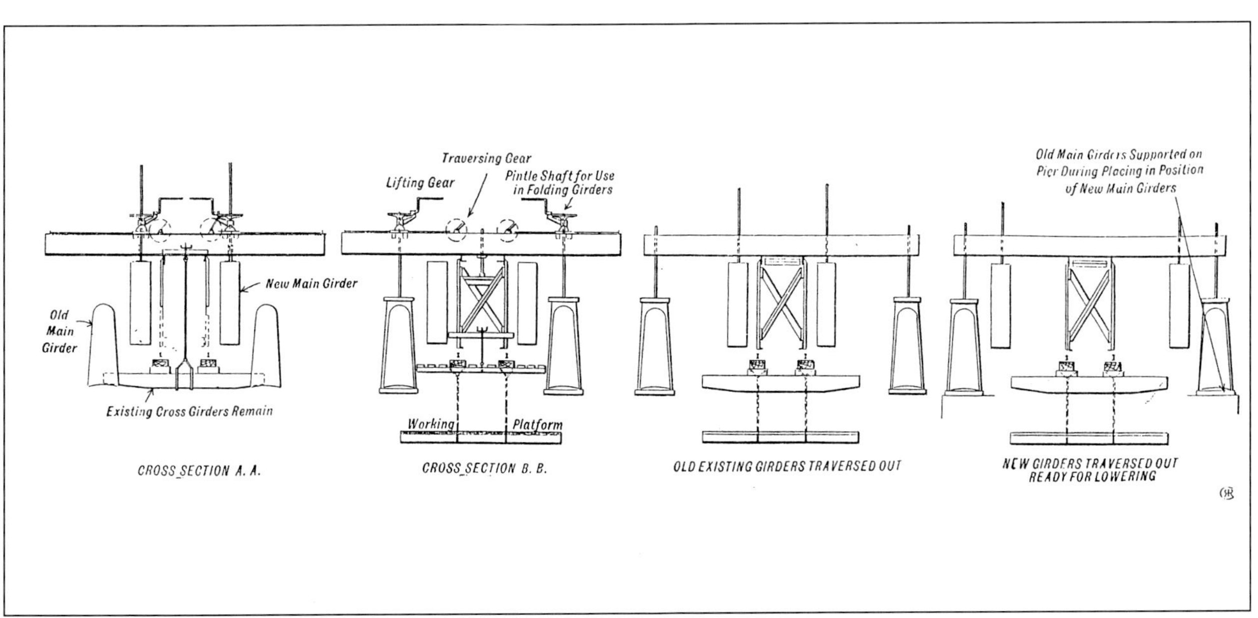

10.7 *A view from the Devon main pier of the Erection Wagon in position on No 4 Devon approach span, showing the old girders moved out to the pier extremities and the new girders dropped into their position, ready for the work of fitting the cross girders, decking and permanent way.*
THE ENGINEER

10.8 *A close up view of the end of the Erection Wagon, the old girders having been slewed out and the new girders being prepared for winching into position on the span.*
THE ENGINEER

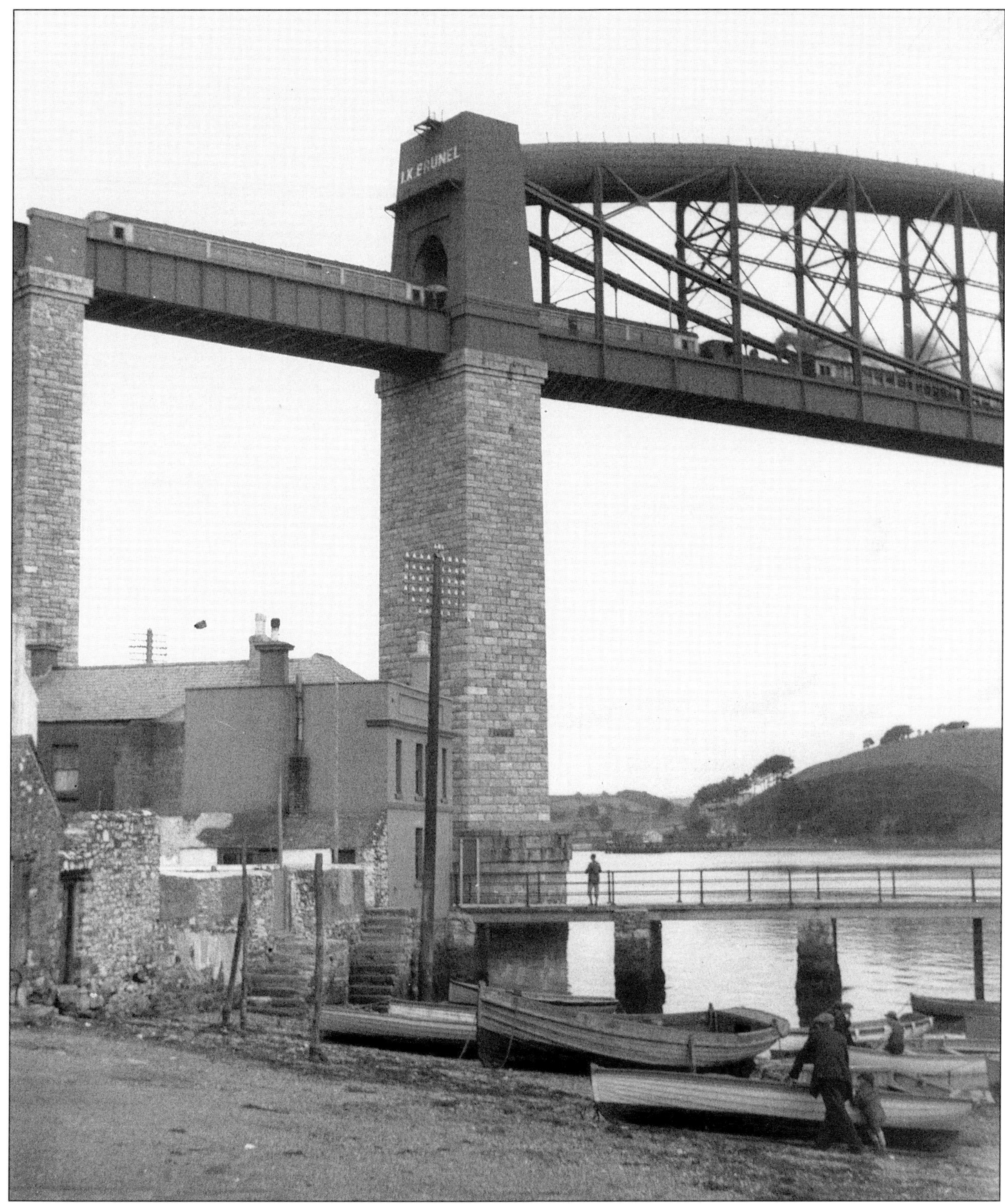

10.10 *As a Saltash bound local auto train crosses the Bridge in July 1936, the horizontal lateral bracing introduced approximately halfway up the verticals can be clearly seen and represents the first of many subsequent additions to Brunel's original simple design. Note also the different cross girder formation of the approach span compared with that of the main span.*
REECE WINSTONE COLLECTION

10.10A *A dramatic view from the Bridge roadway of the various elements of the Devon truss, comprising the massive main support chains on either side; the vertical suspension standards linking the roadway girders to the main tubes; the reinforced transverse bracing between these standards; the diagonal bracing linking the standards with the main tube; the horizontal lateral bracing added halfway up the verticals and extending throughout the span. This 1938 view should be compared with the state of the structure as shown in Plate 5.21, taken in 1927. Note also the shelter referred to in Plate 10.11*
HULTON GETTY PRINT

Because of the platforms in Saltash station it was not possible to propel the erection girder complete with replacement main girders through the station and the preparation work for the Cornwall spans had to be carried out on the short length of double track at the entry to the Bridge; the erection wagon being stored during the week in a special siding at the west end of the station.

The operational procedure for the Cornwall spans was generally similar to that of

the Devon spans. However, in both cases the replacement of the girders immediately adjacent to their respective portals presented an additional problem, since they had first to be drawn out approximately 2 feet 6 inches from their portal before being traversed out to the edge of the pier. This work incurred an additional three hours compared with the time taken for a normal span.

The whole of this reconstruction was carried out by the Company's staff, and on average a total of 46 men worked on each of the 43 Sundays involved in the operation, with no serious accident being reported. Plates 10.7, 10.8 and 10.9 illustrate the various stages in the replacement of one of the Devon spans.

Arising from inspection in 1928, it was noted[8] that at the centre of the Devon span there was considerable movement between the centre pin and the track girder on the down side. In addition, looseness had developed in the main diagonals, attributed to heavy winds over the 70 years since erection.

Accordingly, in the mid thirties horizontal lateral bracing was added half way up the verticals throughout the main spans. This modification, shown in Plate 10.10 will be apparent from a comparison of this illustration with the Bridge as shown in Plate 5.1. At the same time, by doubling up the existing members, much stronger sway bracing was incorporated between the standards above the railway track (Plate 5.14A). All these additions can be seen in closer detail in Plate 10.10A, while with the approach spans in steel, the overall condition of the Bridge in the mid

10.11 *Taken from the foreshore at Saltash in June 1939, this view of the Bridge looking over Saltash Passage towards the Devon Shore clearly shows the modifications introduced by the 1930s; the replacement approach spans and the additional horizontal and lateral bracing. It should be compared with the aspect shown in Plate 5.1. Note also the 'shelters' located at the centre of each main span. It is believed that these had been installed from the late 1920s through the 1930s to facilitate the taking of extensometer readings on the centre hangers; they would also have furnished shelter while welding repairs were carried out to those members pending later modifications.* SM/SS

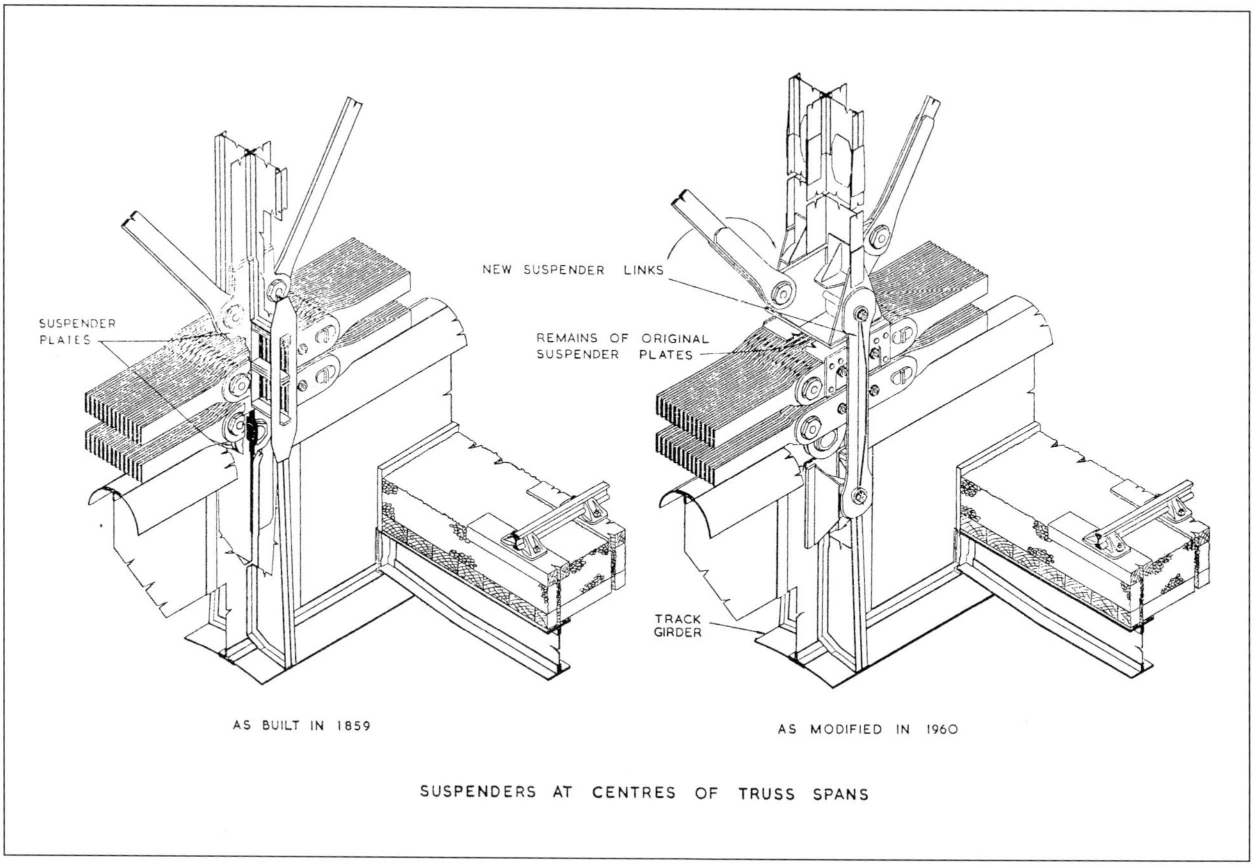

SUSPENDER PLATES

NEW SUSPENDER LINKS

REMAINS OF ORIGINAL SUSPENDER PLATES

TRACK GIRDER

AS BUILT IN 1859

AS MODIFIED IN 1960

SUSPENDERS AT CENTRES OF TRUSS SPANS

10.12 *A diagrammatic illustration of Brunel's original design of the connections for the suspension links at the mid span positions of each main truss and the revised pin jointed suspender links and associated supports introduced in 1960 at these locations.* BERRIDGE

10.13 *A close up view of the Cornwall span showing the outer fixings of the revised suspender links on the mid span connections of the intermediate supports. Note also the problem of sealing the chain entry to the central portal.* AUTHOR

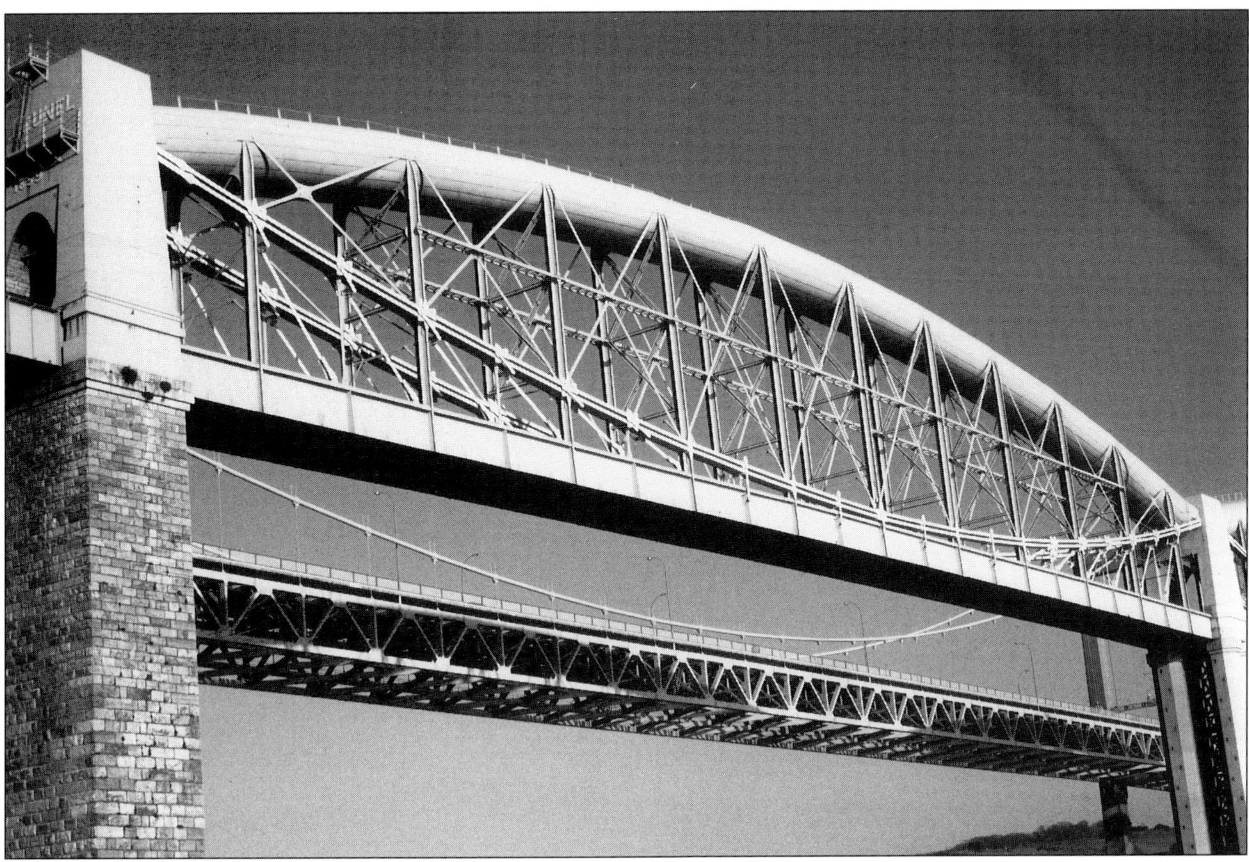

10.14 *Following the extensive investigation into the design during the 1960s, additional radial links were introduced between the roadway girders and each of the intersections between the chains and the main hangers and the intermediate hangers. These can clearly be seen in this illustration, together with the earlier bracing, all of which had been added with a view to keeping the main chains in proper shape in the face of increasing loads.* AUTHOR

1930s is shown in Plate 10.11.

However, both in 1930 and subsequently[9] in 1960 a number of the diagonal members required tightening, with the lower ends on nineteen being replaced and retensioned. A further problem arose due to certain parts of the wrought ironwork proving quite inaccessible for painting and proper maintenance; particularly in the case of the hanger plates below the sets of the middle verticals. Where they passed between the links of the chains, these plates failed through the effects of corrosion-fatigue. Temporary remedial measures were introduced when these failures occurred so as to keep the Bridge in service.

Then, in 1960 work was put in hand to modify these connections altogether (Berridge 1969). In the new arrangements, the plate girders are suspended from the verticals by pin-jointed hangers placed outside the chains where they can be easily accessed for painting. At the same time, the bottom six feet of the centre verticals were cut away and replaced with new members in mild steel incorporating saddle plates. These changes are shown in diagrammatic form in Plate 10.12 with a close up view of the revised links in Plate 10.13. At this same time, the expansion bearings at the ends of the track girders were renewed.

Then, from September 1966 a test programme was initiated to investigate the stresses that would be induced in the two main spans by a train of four axle vehicles each with a gross weight of 100 tons, thus increasing the axle loading to 25 tons. The test programme was limited to these two spans, since the approach spans comprised simply supported bridge decks and were amenable to theoretical assessment.

The scope of this investigation is well covered in the ensuing report[10]; not only did it involve strain gauge tests on the structure itself but also comparative measurements on a 1:50 scale model, to extrapolate from behaviour under existing loads and predict the effect of

10.15 *A close up of part of the Devon truss, showing these modifications in greater detail and also the formation of the main tube contour - straight between each suspension link.* AUTHOR

the new, heavier loads. There followed an exhaustive series of tests over the period November 1966 to April 1967, the results of which were accorded the most careful consideration by the Bridge engineers in relation to Brunel's original design. They were able to make a meaningful analysis of the behaviour of the elements of the Bridge under load, which revealed that the verticals between the chains and track girders were being distorted into an 'S' shape by the moving load.

The solution to this problem was the recommendation to introduce 48 new diagonal members of steel to restrain the shearing action between the track girders and the chains. As will be seen from Plate 10.13 *et seq* these linked each of the chain/standard intersections with the track girders and this allowed the loading on the bridge to be increased to 1.70 ton/ft run[11], without the risk of early fatigue failure. This figure is significantly higher than the 1850 Fletcher design value of 1.20 ton/ft run. Further testing took place in 1988, with the operation of a train comprising two locomotives (one at each end, in radio contact) and fifteen 47 ton loaded wagons. The total length of the train was approximately the same as one span and this resulted in a uniformly distributed load on the span of 1.59 ton/ft run.

These extra members, together with the earlier addition of horizontal lateral bracing, represent a significant overall addition to Brunel's original design. This will be most apparent from the close up view of Plate 10.15, which again illustrates the fact that the contour of each main tube was straight between the chain supports.

All these modifications have been introduced over the years in the face of increasing loads, to stiffen the structure and to try and keep the curve of the chains in proper shape under the influence of a moving load. An appreciation of the scope and extent of these additions, compared with Brunel's original somewhat simplistic design, can be derived from the local view of the Devon span shown in Plate 10.16. However, none of these additions has contributed to any reduction in the loading carried by the chains and the giant tubes themselves; they remain today just as they were built on the Devon shore, all those years ago, incorporating the great flat wrought iron chain links - often referred[12] to as 'treasures' of industrial archaeology - to form the two giant trusses of this elegant and unique structure. They continue to do what they were originally designed and built for - to carry the weight of every train crossing this 'gateway to Cornwall'.

During 1987 it was discovered that the timber supports at the inside bearings of the main tubes had rotted, through water penetrating the casing over the years. These timbers were therefore cut out and replaced by an epoxy mortar over a rubber sheet[13] to give the same resilience as the timber. At the same time, steps were taken to improve the waterproofing of the casing.

Brunel designed his Royal Albert Bridge to cater for the loads of the mid nineteenth century steam age and it says much for his original design that throughout its existence it has, with some modification, been able to accept steadily increasing loads. By the mid twentieth century steam had reached its zenith and the Bridge was able to accommodate all the locomotives then working on British Rail (Western Region). Strict criteria[14] were, however, laid down with regard to the combination of locomotives for double heading, with only one engine permitted to be pulling while a train was actually on the Bridge. Because they were banned from operating in Cornwall, owing to load limitation on some of the viaducts, the original Great Western 60xx 'King' class was not permitted west of Keyham (and hence across the Bridge). Thus, it was not the Royal Albert Bridge which kept the 'Kings' out of Cornwall. While weight does not appear to have been a problem regarding the 47xx in this situation, it is believed other factors may have excluded them.

The extent and scope of the loading of the structure has, of course, changed with the introduction of diesel power, Plate 10.17 (no hammer blow). Consequently, the Bridge engineers have during recent years been more concerned with the effect of the higher axle loading due to heavier freight vehicles. However, with the introduction of welded track across the main spans (thereby eliminating the effect of impact loading) and the singling of the track across St Pinnock and East Largin viaducts, it is currently understood that a 'King' class hauled steam special could operate as far as St Blazey - eminent contemporary testimony to the integrity of Brunel's original proposal.

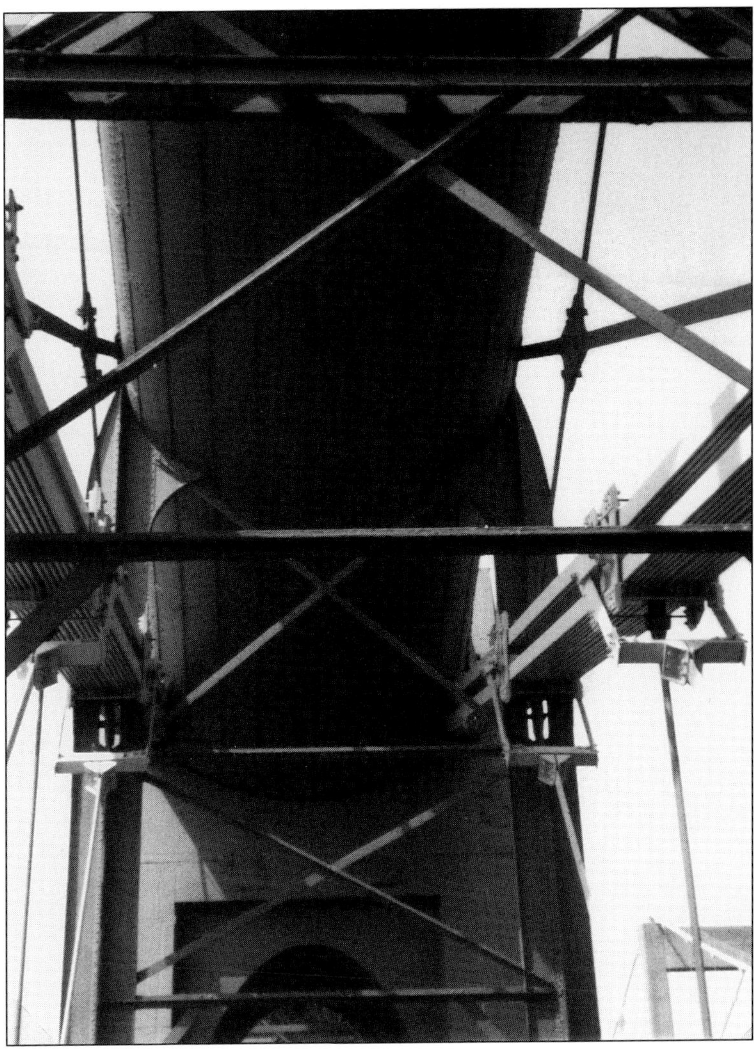

10.16 *Viewing the underside of the Devon tube, showing details of the chains, the original and later additions of cross bracing and the radial links added at each pin joint to connect with the roadway girders.* AUTHOR

The British Standard for bridge design calls for a design life of 120 years. While the original main spans of the Royal Albert bridge have already passed that milestone, on a similar basis, the approach spans, renewed in 1928, still have a considerable design life left. Accordingly, given the continued attention which is currently being lavished upon the whole structure, there seems no reason why it should not continue in service for many years to come.

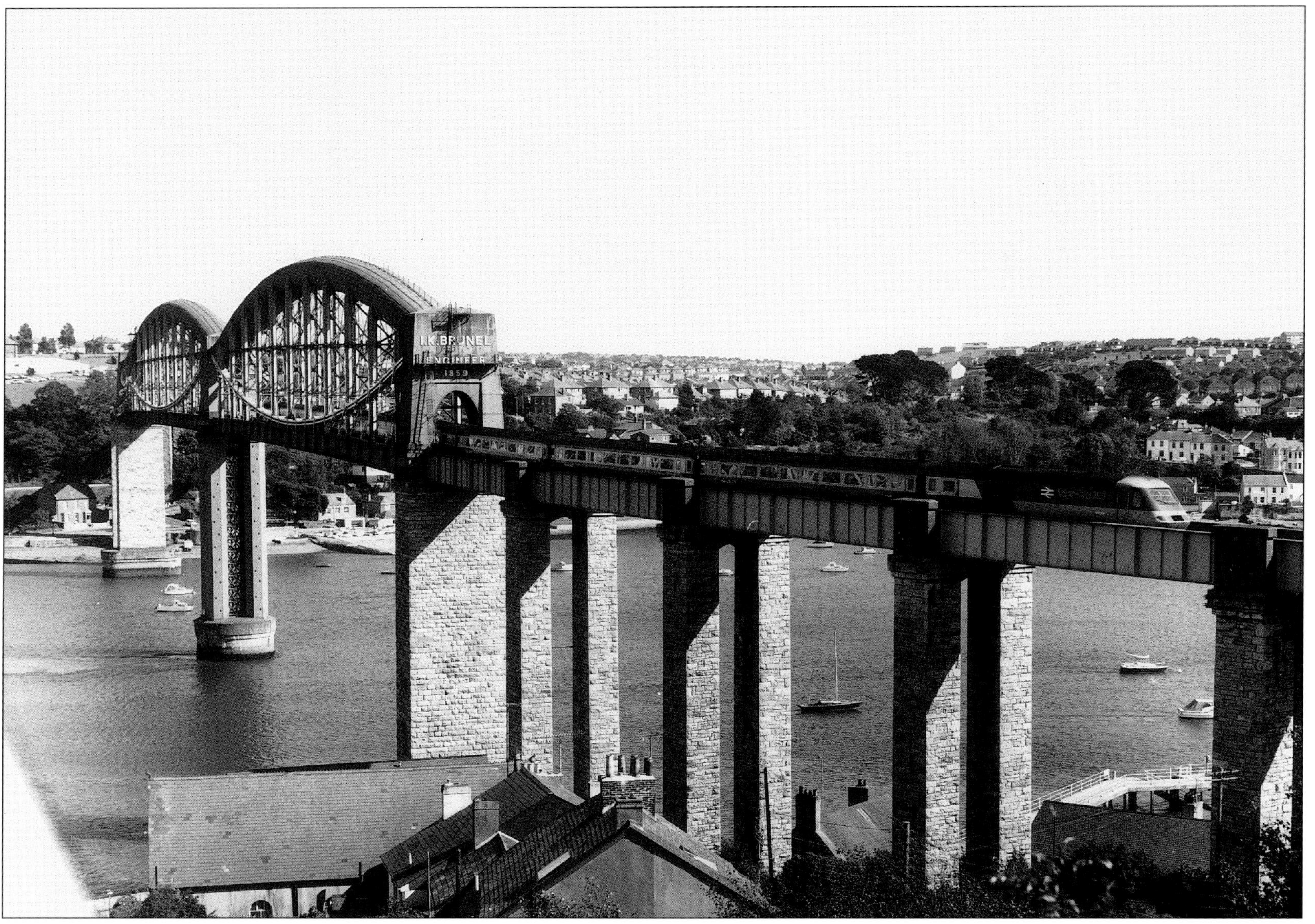

10.17 *The coming of the diesels; a Penzance bound Inter City 125 glides smoothly over the Cornwall approach spans above Saltash, the twin masonry piers standing in true Brunellian majesty in the afternoon sunlight.* RTGW

CHAPTER ELEVEN
REMINISCENCES

Inevitably, with any structure which has been in existence for as long as the Royal Albert Bridge, apart from the design changes which have been covered in the previous chapter, there will have been occasions or events worthy of special note. We now look at a miscellany of information to add an anecdotal dimension to our story.

PROTECTION AND PAINTING

As already discussed, the long term integrity of any structure is largely dependent on the dedication of the personnel involved in its maintenance. Almost from the beginning of its existence, the proper protection of the wrought ironwork from the aggressive salt laden south westerly winds, was of constant concern to the Company. To illustrate the ongoing care and maintenance which the bridge required, even early in its life, the following extracts[1] from the Directors' Minutes of 1865-1870, are of interest.

In June 1866, ref. 175 'the Directors approved of an outlay of from £300 to £400 during the following three or four months in painting part of the Saltash Bridge'.

Then in May 1867, Minutes ref. 102 recorded that 'The Engineer reported the RAB will require painting throughout at a cost of £1,700 and the committee ordered a brown colour paint to be used'. These instructions were followed in July 1867, ref.167, for 'the piers of the Saltash Bridge to be painted Granite color [*sic*]'; and then in April 1868, the Committee ordered 'the letters of Mr Brunel's name on the Saltash Bridge to be painted at a cost of £2'; ref. 367.

And so, throughout the ensuing years the records of the Company carry reference to the ongoing requirement of painting. A particular difficulty concerned Brunel's tendency to pay more attention to the appearance of his bridges than to making adequate arrangements for painting the ironwork. For instance, he tidied up the ends of his girders by masking them with masonry, or cast iron; this left room for the rain to drive in but no space for the paint brush.

Accordingly, we can but admire the application over the years of all those staff who, often working at great heights in all winds and weathers, applied the essential paint to protect the wrought iron from the ravages of those salt laden winds which daily sweep up the Hamoaze; or who climbed into almost inaccessible locations to make sure all was well with Brunel's masterpiece.

With regard to the exterior painting, the practices prevalent up to the 1930s and even later, are well illustrated in Plates 11.1, 11.2 and 11.3 which show the painters, devoid of any hard hats or weather protection, slung from bosun's chairs or simple rope supports; apparently indifferent to the height and exposure of their position, as they applied paint by brush from their small pots. Frequent refilling must have been the order of the day. It is believed that at some time this work was carried out by a firm of contractors from Cardiff, who attended at Saltash approximately every five years, to paint the structure from end to end.

The methods they then adopted would today be condemned as utterly unsafe; the regulations of the Health and Safety Executive insist on proper safeguards, the men working from scaffolding or from permanent ladderwork, like that now installed within the cast iron columns of the centre pier, where hitherto men had merely climbed down the structure using its internal reinforcement for foot holds. Such is the change in standards over the years, that when working on the main spans over the water, even from scaffolding, a high speed rescue craft manned by two specialists in rescue and safety at sea, is on constant patrol in case a workman should fall from the Bridge.

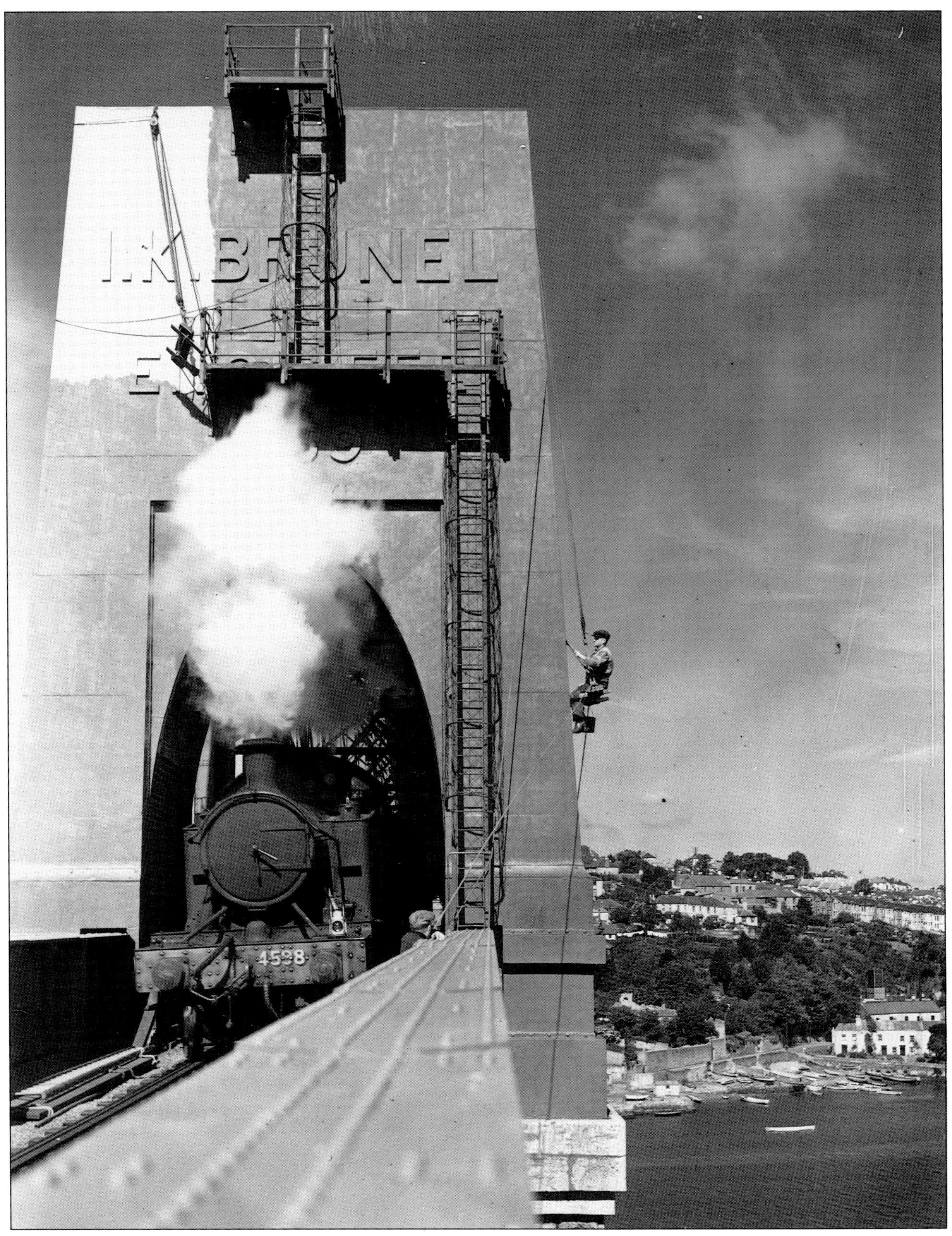
I.K.BRUNEL

Nevertheless, the erection of such scaffolding, at heights in excess of 100 feet above the Tamar, and the maintenance personnel working at the locations involved, in the often bitter and inclement weather of Saltash Passage, call for men of particular courage and dedication, not to be tempted to take short cuts in the face of the harsh environment, at the expense of the long term safety of the structure.

Currently, under the management of Railtrack Great Western, the Bridge is subject to a regular painting and inspection cycle[2], so that each major element is examined as part of a six year routine. Under this arrangement, the Devon approach spans are painted in year one; the Cornwall approach spans in year two; the tube, hangers and diagonals on the Devon span in year three; with the Cornwall main span following in year four; the Devon track girders in year five and finally the Cornwall track girders in year six. Painting does not necessarily go on throughout each year but some idea of the scope of the work involved may be gathered from the extensive scaffolding seen in Plate 11.5, during the painting of the Devon span in 1994.

THE TUBES

Of course, those great curved tubes reaching out between the massive piers, have always been subject to inquisitive interest, particularly bearing in mind their dark, cavernous interior (see Plate 5.8B). It is reported that during the war they became the home of wild pigeons and at night, staff from Saltash, particularly those with poaching skills, were not averse to climbing into the tubes to capture the birds and thus augment the frugal rations of the day.

Although subjected to intense air attack during the Second World War, the Bridge never received a direct hit - only several near misses. Consequently, it was peppered on many occasions with shrapnel and a correspondent recalls going through the tubes in 1946 and seeing the shrapnel holes in the walls of the tubes, then being repaired.

We are fortunate in having the recollections of another correspondent who also had the experience of a conducted tour over and through the tubes in the 1950s. He recalls the opportunity arose one day in discussion with the Bridge Foreman at Saltash when he mentioned his interest. Arrangements were made for such a tour the next day, at the conclusion of his shift at Saltash. The itinerary was to walk over the tubes from the Cornwall side and then return through them. At that time the Bridge was being painted and apparently there was a large patch of white showing on the Cornwall span where the paint had peeled off.

According to his guide, whenever paint flaked off the Bridge it exposed the original white lead coating. He was of the opinion that this latter protection was superior to that which they were now applying. As they climbed the structure and reached the top of the Cornwall tube, our correspondent noticed that his guide was wearing hob nailed boots, which were in sharp contrast to his own thick rubber soled footwear. Questioned if it was not dangerous to wear hob nailed boots, his companion pointed out that he took great care to be sure where he was stepping, whereas with rubber soles it was possible to become over confident - a fatal attitude when working on top of the Bridge or within the centre pier supports.

Once on top of the tubes there was little to be seen except the magnificent views, although despite their elliptical shape the tubes did give an illusion of width. They climbed to the peak of the Cornwall span and then descended to the top of the centre pier, then to climb over the Devon span and so down to the entrance to the tubes on the Devon portal. Once inside, there was an impression of their sheer size and the atmosphere invoked by the fact that they had been constructed over 100 years previously. As will be seen from Plate 5.8B the tops of the tubes were painted white and the bottoms tarred. The ventilation holes in the bottom produced a camera obscura affect, the waves and the outline of passing craft could be seen projected on to the white tube top.

There was an air of cleanliness within the interior, which was particularly significant since apparently the last time the insides of the tubes had been painted was in 1924, by staff

11.1 (opposite page) *A fascinating view of the eastern portal of the Bridge, on 18 July 1938, as 2-6-2 tank No 4598 emerges at the head of an up local goods train. Our interest centres on the painter, slung in a bosun's chair, as he applies paint to the vast surface of the portal - assisted by his mate on the bridge deck who, by an additional line, was able to position him as necessary.* HULTON GETTY PRINT

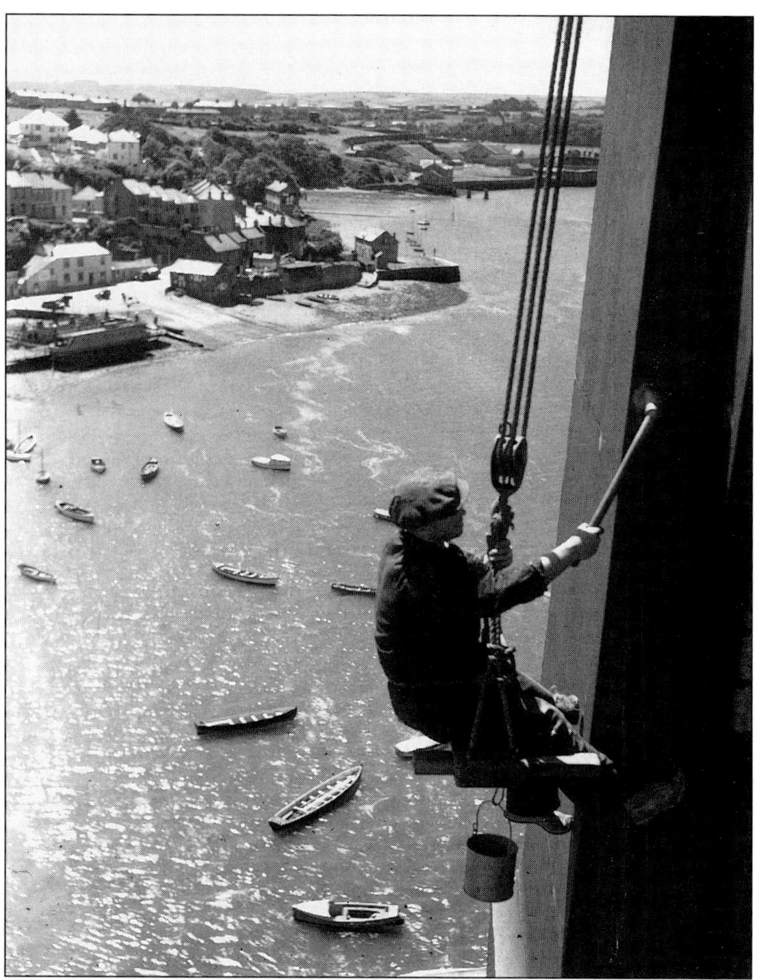

11.2 *High above the Tamar, this painter is wearing no safety harness while the cradle itself is hung on a large hook beneath the pulley block secured only by means of a knot. The paint pot obviously required frequent refilling.*
HULTON GETTY PRINT

from St Blazey. There was evidence of birds nesting in the corners of some of the supports while in the middle of the Devon tube, pieces of plywood were hung to act as a visitors' book. Among recent signatories were the names of some engineers from the Japanese State Railways who had visited the Bridge. Our correspondent naturally added his name.

While they were traversing the inside of the tubes, a freight train crossed the Bridge (steam hauled, of course) and it was possible to sense the rocking of the structure in time with each beat of the locomotive; while once the train had left the Bridge, the structure could be heard creaking as it recovered its normal unloaded position.

As a conclusion to his tour, our visitor was invited to walk up one of the chains and also to descend inside one of the cast iron centre piers - offers which he discreetly declined. Altogether a fascinating experience, the memory of which has remained with him all these years.

ALMOST A PUBLIC CROSSING

Before the advent of the Tamar Road Bridge in 1961, Brunel's structure provided the only means of crossing the Tamar, once the ferries had stopped operating of an evening, and it was often used as such by Saltash residents to get home after a 'night out' in Plymouth. In fact, it appears that the Bridge was widely used during those years as a pedestrian and cycle crossing, such users placing their lives at risk, since trains crossed the Bridge throughout the day and night, both signal boxes being open 24 hours.

A fireman recalls that he was given special dispensation to reside in Saltash, on compassionate grounds, but this often involved him in cycling across the Bridge, on the south side, in the early hours to get to his duty at Laira sheds; hopefully, he would get across without meeting a train, which could result in a drenching if the fireman was washing down the footplate.

However, this situation was assisted to some extent during the Second World War, when it was decided that timber decking should be laid between the rails to enable road vehicles to cross the Bridge in the event of an emergency. A short lane from Vicarage Road was made to gain access to the Devon side while an exit was already in existence between the Bridge and the station at Saltash. The laying of these timbers presented problems with the locking bars on the facing points at each end of the Bridge where the lines converged from double to single track.

By regulation, facing points on passenger lines had to be fitted with a facing point lock (FPL), which ensured that the point was locked in its proper location before the signal protecting it could be cleared to the 'off' position. In addition, a locking bar longer than the wheelbase of the longest vehicle in use was also fitted which was raised by the lever operating the FPL. Thus, a vehicle occupying the point and standing on the locking bar prevented the signalman from operating the FPL lever.

With the trackwork decked in, the normal arrangement for a FPL and locking bar was inoperative. To overcome this problem, it was decided to replace the locking bars with small track circuits, a proposal introduced in 1941. By this arrangement, when a train was standing on the short track circuit, the FPL lever was electrically locked in the reverse position, thus preventing the signalman from operating the lever. However, because of the problems likely to arise should there be a track circuit failure, the decking was removed at the end of the war, and locking bars restored from 1 September 1946.

The presence of the timber decking also posed a problem with the Automatic Train Control ramp for the Royal Albert Bridge Up Distant signal. Accordingly, an additional Distant signal arm was fitted to the Saltash Up Inner Home signal and the ATC ramp moved to that position. Again, once the decking had been removed the additional arm was taken away and the ATC ramp restored to its original position, as from the above date.

Owing to wartime security, little or no information has come to light regarding the occasions when road vehicles actually crossed the Bridge. Indeed, it would appear that the density of rail traffic would have made it difficult to fit in such a crossing, other than in a dire emergency; but the timber decking must have made personnel crossings, despite the threat of trespass, that much easier.

While it would appear that ordinary human beings made regular use of the Bridge, there was an incident in the early 1950s when a pedigree cow made the crossing. It seems that on the day in question, around lunchtime, the beast in question was being unloaded at Saltash from a horsebox on the end of the 5.30 a.m. ex Paddington train. The following auto train from Plymouth was held at signals on the Bridge, while this operation was in progress, watched with interest by the driver in the leading trailer car and the fireman on the footplate. Suddenly, the cow broke loose from its attendants and charged down the platform and out on to the Bridge, towards the waiting train. The fireman reacted promptly to this situation by opening the cylinder drain cocks, in the hope of scaring the animal. However, undeterred by the noise and steam, the beast squeezed past the train and with hind legs kicking high and scattering the ballast, set off for St Budeaux, the attendants in hot pursuit. Apparently, it was several hours later before it was finally cornered and recaptured at Bull Point.

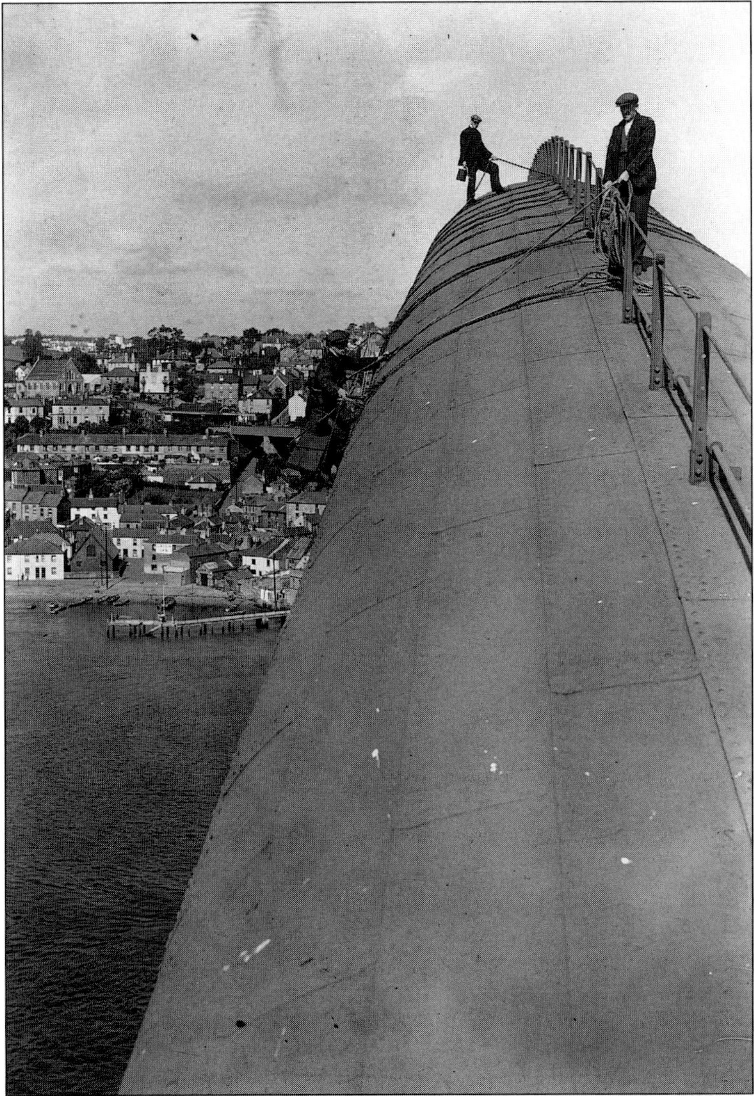

11.3 *Again, these painters working without adequate safety harness appear oblivious to their dangerous position, high above the Tamar, walking on the curved surface of the main tube as they steadily work their way across the structure.* HULTON GETTY PRINT

COLLECTING THE SINGLE LINE TOKEN

Trains entering the single line section across the Bridge had to be in possession of the appropriate token. This sometimes led to an embarrassing situation if a down train, travelling up the gradient from St Budeaux

11.5 *This 1994 view of the two main spans of Brunel's masterpiece spanning the Tamar on a calm, sunny morning probably shows the Bridge to best affect, although the Tamar roadbridge in the background sadly adds confusion to the scene. The morning of 1 September 1857 most likely reflected a very similar calm as Brunel prepared to float out the Cornwall span from the Devon shore to its final location. The extensive scaffolding erected on the Devon span in this view as it was being repainted shows how safety standards today have changed in comparison with the conditions illustrated in the previous plates.* AUTHOR

11.6 (opposite page) *A magnificent view of the Bridge, floodlit for its Centenary celebration, showing the double cross girders within the main spans, compared with only single members on the left hand approach span. Note the additional horizontal and lateral bracing and the absence of the access ladders and platforms on the portal.* A. BOWDEN

entered the single line section of the Bridge, and the fireman failed to pick up the token from the stand alongside the track. The driver had immediately to stop the train, while the fireman faced the humiliation of walking back to collect the token. His journey, in both directions, was usually subject to ribald comments from passengers, annoyed at the delay, leaning out of the carriage windows, questioning the hold up.

There is also a corollary to such events, in that as the down train came off the Bridge, the fireman surrendered the token on the down platform at Saltash by hooking it on the stand as the train passed through the station. However, there were occasions apparently when the momentum of the token was such that instead of staying on the stand, it leaped off the end and dropped down into Albert Road, which passed under the station at that point. This unhappy turn of events involved the Saltash signalman in having to search the road to find the token, as without it he could not authorise any further train movement.

A NAVAL OCCASION

With the War over in 1945 and large numbers of Royal Naval vessels returning to Devonport to pay off and lay up, a unique event occurred in the early 1950s. The story is told by the signalman on duty that morning in the Royal Albert Bridge signal box. He noticed a ship proceeding up stream which had an exceptionally tall mast, and he was of the immediate opinion that it would not clear the Bridge. He was right; he saw the mast strike the Devon side main span, break off and fall to the deck. It was not possible to see the actual ship from the box and it was only later that he ascertained it was the monitor, HMS *Roberts*, which was armed with two 15 inch guns.

On seeing the collision, the signalman immediately rushed to the Electric Train Token instrument to send the 'Obstruction Danger' signal to his colleague in the Saltash box. He also had noticed the mast strike the main span and likewise he immediately took action to register the danger. The signalmen conferred by 'phone and notified Plymouth Control of the incident; reporting the Bridge closed until the structure had been examined.

Arrangements were initiated for the duty Civil Engineer Officer to attend at the Bridge without delay (apparently arriving by taxi) to carry out his examination, the line being closed to traffic in the meanwhile. The extent and scope of the damage is not known, but it would be reasonable to assume that Brunel's substantial wrought iron members must have fared significantly better than the light top mast of a monitor. In due course, the Bridge was opened once more to traffic.

THE CENTENARY

In 1959 preparations were put in hand to celebrate the centenary of the Bridge. Firstly, the structure was repainted and the access ladders and platforms temporarily removed from the end portals so that Brunel's name could be more clearly seen. Arrangements were made to floodlight the Bridge as shown in Plate 11.6. The lights were switched on for 2 May 1959, the anniversary of the opening, and finally switched off on 15 September, to mark the date on which Brunel had died 100 years before. This illustration is of particular significance in that it clearly shows the original and the 1905 cross girders as fitted to the main spans, compared with only the 1905 members on the approach span; the original, lighter cross members having been removed when the latter were replaced in the 1920s.

The town of Saltash established a committee to organise events to recognise the great occasion; in particular, the local school children were encouraged to record their impressions of the event and history of the Bridge. Indeed, the Junior School took the

I.K.BRUNEL
ENGINEER
1859

11.7 *On the occasion of the 125th anniversary of the opening of the Bridge, the public were allowed to walk across this famous structure. Here the crowd is passing under the Cornwall portal; note the brickwork and masonry lining.* AUTHOR

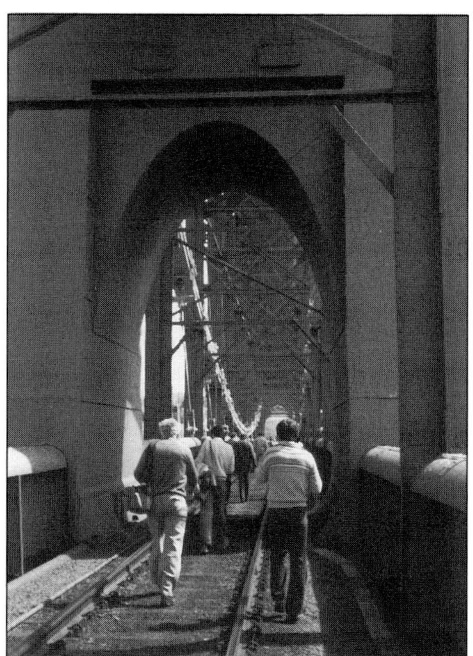

11.8 (right) *A similar view as the crowd proceed under the all cast iron centre pier portal. Note the ends of the roadway girders fitting closely to the cast iron shroud of the portal, to look neat and tidy, but leaving space for rain to enter between the two but inadequate room to insert the paint brush.* AUTHOR

opportunity to introduce a new cap badge, which featured the Royal Albert Bridge - probably one of the most unusual insignia of any school. Photographs of the celebrations were combined in an album placed within the Town Hall archive so that there would be a record for posterity.

THE 125TH ANNIVERSARY

As a fitting conclusion to this story of Brunel's masterpiece, it is appropriate to record the commemoration of the 125th anniversary of the Bridge in May 1984. To mark that date, British Rail ran a special train from Penzance to Saltash where, once the passengers had detrained, a plaque was unveiled on the down platform to record the 125 years of the Bridge's existence. The train then proceeded empty to St Budeaux while the passengers enjoyed the unique experience of being allowed to cross the Bridge on foot; Plates 11.7 and 11.8 record the occasion, with the crowds passing respectively under the Cornwall portal and the centre pier portal, as they made their way across the structure. These views clearly show the difference in portal construction.

THE FUTURE

The Bridge is properly listed Grade 1 and as such demands ongoing care and attention to preserve this fitting memorial to a great engineer. Such is the veneration in which he is still held that the gracious tributes paid to the work when it was first completed are complemented by a contemporary comment[3] - 'Even today, the simplicity of the two oval arched tubes seems modern, making Brunel's creation seem a century (newer) and not (older) than the neighbouring suspension bridge'.

Railtrack Great Western continues to invest considerable funds in its maintenance and in this work they are supported by the valuable contributions from the Railway Heritage Trust. With their aid[4] substantial remedial work has been carried out on both of the main tubes and their respective hangers, the decking, both end portals and the centre portal. Additional work, which should be of lasting benefit in preserving this unique structure as a memorial to its designer, is the projected removal of the access ladders and gallery from each of the end portals, so that the tribute I K BRUNEL ENGINEER 1859 will be clearly visible. The Railway Heritage Trust has indicated its ready support in this further work which will include provision of alternative means of access to the tubes.

Accordingly, with the continued application of such dedicated interest and care we can but hope that Brunel's 'Gateway to Cornwall' will still be in service carrying trains across the Tamar on the occasion of its 150th anniversary in the year 2009.

This 1924 view of Saltash Passage from the Devon shore shows the Bridge, substantially as Brunel built it, with the wrought iron approach spans in their characteristic design and the main spans free of the strengthening members introduced in the 1930s and later. An evocative scene with the 'steam bridge' in operation, having ferried over a few local passengers and their hand cart etc. while a contemporary touring car, with passengers awaits to drive on board. The spare steam ferry is beached, out of use. ALAN KITTRIDGE COLLECTION

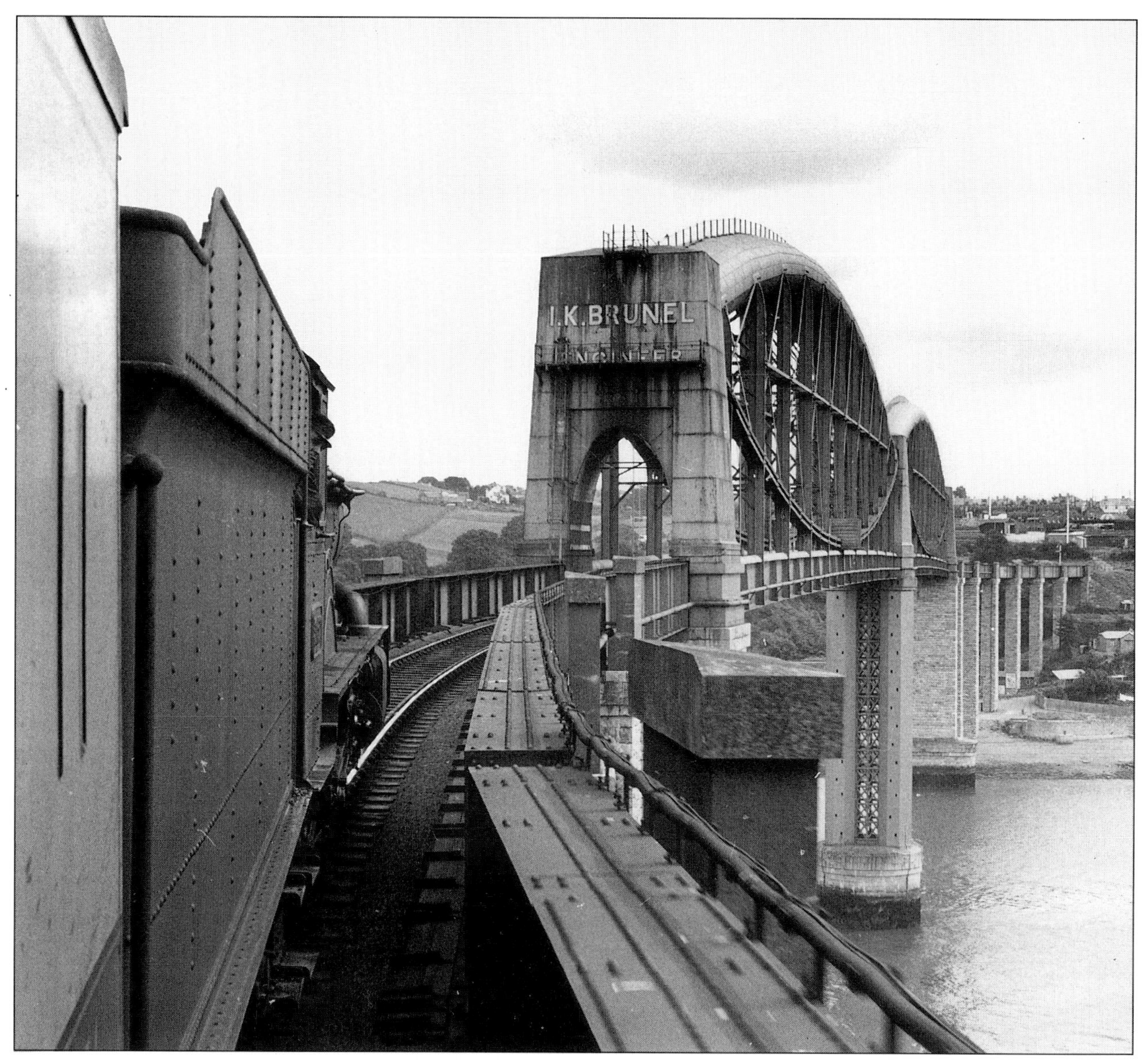

A dramatic view of the Bridge, believed taken in the late 1940s, from the window of a carriage on an up express as, hauled by a GWR 'Castle' class locomotive, it slowly rumbles on to the Cornwall approach spans, high above the village of Saltash nestling below Brunel's masterpiece. The 3ft rise to the centre pier can be clearly seen, together with the shelters erected around each of the centre hangers (see Plate 10.11). Even with the replacement of semaphore signals by their colour light successors, the introduction of diesel motive power and the appearance of the Tamar suspension bridge but a short distance away, this scene has changed little over the years and still holds a special fascination for most rail travellers. SM/SS

REFERENCES

Abbreviations:

ICE Institution of Civil Engineers
P&DJ *Plymouth & Devonport Journal*
PRO Public Record Office, Kew
RCG *Royal Cornwall Gazette*
WB *West Briton & Cornwall Advertiser*

Chapter One - The Great Divide

1. Proc ICE 1836 Vol 1 pp99-108
2. *Devon Historian*, No 33 October 1986

Chapter Two - The Coming of the Railway - 1835 to 1859

1. RCG, 6 September 1859
2. WB, 16 April 1841
3. WB, 27 September 1844
4. WB, 22 November 1844
5. WB, 20 September 1844
6. WB, 27 September 1844
7. WB, 20 September 1844
8. WB, 4 October 1844
9. WB, 25 October 1844
10. Parliamentary Papers HC (89) XXXIX 19-7 mf:49.281
11. WB, 6 June 1845
12. P&DJ 3 September 1857
13. WB, 6 June 1845
14. PRO RAIL 1066/719
15. WB, 25 July 1845
16. PRO RAIL 134/1
17. RCG, 6 September 1859
18. P&DJ, 3 September 1857
19. Brunel, 1870
20. P&DJ, 3 September 1857
21. WB, 24 July 1846
22. RCG, 6 May 1859

Chapter Three - The Initial Design Investigation - 1847 to 1849

1. P&DJ, 3 September 1857
2. *Trans. Newcomen Soc.* Vol XXXVI 1963/4
3. PRO RAIL 134/2
4. Proc ICE Vol 21 1861/2 p268
5. PR0 RAIL 134/2
6. PRO RAIL 134/19
7. PRO RAIL 134/19
8. PRO RAIL 134/19
9. PRO RAIL 134/19
10. PRO RAIL 134/2
11. WB, 1 September 1848
12. PRO RAIL 134/2

Chapter Four - The Prototype - 1849 to 1853

1. Proc ICE 1847-8 Vol VII p138
2. Clark, 1850
3. Waters, 1856
4. Clark, 1850
5. Berridge, 1969

Chapter Five - The Final Design - 1853

1. PRO RAIL 134/2
2. Proc ICE Vol 14 1855 p492
3. Proc ICE Vol 69 1882 p200
4. Proc ICE Vol 31 1870-71 p162
5. *New Civil Engineer* 16 November 1989
6. PRO RAIL 134/15

Chapter Six - The Contract Let: Construction: The Centre Pier - 1853 to 1856

1. PRO RAIL 134/2
2. PRO RAIL 134/3
3. WB, 4 March 1853
4. PRO RAIL 134/19
5. WB, 2 September 1853
6. Corlett, 1990
7. WB, 9 September 1859
8. WB, 2 September 1853
9. Proc ICE Vol 21 1861/2 p268
10. PRO RAIL 134/19
11. PRO RAIL 134/17
12. PRO RAIL 134/2
13. PRO RAIL 134/19
14. PRO RAIL 134/17
15. Proc ICE Vol 21 1861/2
16. PRO RAIL 134/19

17. WB, 1 September 1854
18. WB, 10 August 1855
19. PRO RAIL 134/19
20. PRO RAIL 134/15
21. PRO RAIL 134/17
22. PRO RAIL 134/17
23. PRO ZJ1/289
24. PRO RAIL 134/3
25. PRO RAIL 134/3
26. WB, 5 October 1855
27. WB, 7 March 1856
28. PRO RAIL 134/19
29. WB, 5 September 1856

Chapter Seven - Construction: The Cornwall Span - 1854 to 1858

1. PRO RAIL 134/17
2. PRO RAIL 134/17
3. PRO RAIL 134/17
4. *Railway Magazine*, November 1973
5. Proc ICE Vol 8 1849 p273
6. Proc ICE Vol 30 1869-70 p270
7. WB, 6 March 1856
8. WB, 6 March 1857
9. Humber, 1864
10. PRO RAIL MT29/20
11. *Railway Magazine*, November 1973
12. Author's conversation with Mr Brian Ward
13. See Plate 7.3A
14. PRO RAIL 134/19
15. PRO RAIL 134/19
16. WB, 4 September 1857
17. WB, 6 May 1859
18. Brunel, 1870
19. P&DJ, 3 September 1857
20. PRO RAIL 134/19
21. Railtrack papers
22. PRO RAIL 134/19
23. Proc ICE Vol 69 1882 p198 et seq
24. Binding, 1994
25. Proc ICE Vol 69 1882 p200
26. RCG, 5 March 1858
27. PRO RAIL 134/19
28. WB, 6 August 1858

Chapter Eight - Construction: Completion and Final Testing - 1857 to 1859

1. PRO RAIL 134/19
2. Wood & Tozer, c1859
3. PRO RAIL 134/19
4. Wood & Tozer, c1859
5. WB, 6 August 1858
6. WB, 6 May 1859
7. PRO RAIL 134/19
8. WB, 25 February 1859
9. Wood & Tozer, c1859
10. PRO RAIL MT29/20
11. WB, 6 May 1859

Chapter Nine - The Opening - 1859

1. PRO RAIL MT29/20
2. *Illustrated London News*, 14 May 1859
3. *Illustrated Times*, 7 May 1859
4. RCG, 6 May 1859
5. RCG, 6 May 1859
6. PRO RAIL 134/3
7. WB, 2 March 1860

Chapter Ten - The Years since 1859

1. PRO RAIL 1014/30
2. ICE Application dated 12 November 1859
3. Proc ICE Vol 118 1893/4 p466
4. Clinker, 1978
5. Letter to author from Mr John Copsey
6. Proc ICE Vol 230 1929/30
7. Proc ICE Vol 230 1929/30 and *The Engineer*, 21 June 1929
8. Proc ICE Part 1 1974
9. Proc ICE Part 1 1974
10. Proc ICE Part 1 1974
11. *New Civil Engineer*, 16 November 1989
12. *Railway Magazine*, November 1973
13. *New Civil Engineer*, 16 November 1989
14. Woodfin, 1972

Chapter Eleven - Reminiscences

1. PRO RAIL 134/9
2. *New Civil Engineer*, 16 November 1989
3. *The Independent* 7 June 1996
4. Railway Heritage Trust - Annual Report 1995/6

UNITS

The engineering units used throughout this book are those current in Brunel's lifetime. They may be converted to SI units as follows:
Length: 1 foot = 12 inches = 0.3048 metres
Force: 1 ton = 2,240 pounds (lb) = 9964 newtons
Stress: 1 ton/in^2 = 2,240 lb/in^2 = 15.44 newtons/mm^2
Speed: 1 mile per hour = 1.609 km per hour

Other units involved are:
Weight: 1 ton = 20 cwt
1 cwt = 112 pounds (lb)

Money: £1 = 20 shillings = 100p
1 shilling (s) = 12 pence (d)

GLOSSARY

Cast Iron
An alloy of iron containing a carbon content of 2.0 to 6.0%, together with other impurities. It is not appreciably malleable at any temperature. Being a brittle material, it is strong in compression but weak in tension; in the ratio of approximately 6 to 1.

Coffer Dam
A temporary wall serving to exclude water from any site normally under water, so as to facilitate the laying of foundations or other similar work; usually formed by driving a double row of piles, until a double timber wall exists all round. Sluices are usually incorporated so as to control the flow of water into and out of the area thus created.

Crab
A machine for hoisting or handling heavy weights.

Greenstone Dyke
Associated with the well known outcrops on Dartmoor and Bodmin Moor, originating from the Cornubian granite batholith, were extensive sheet like bodies known as dyke swarms, which spread throughout the older Devonian sediments. These dykes cut through the existing bedding and are generally known as 'Greenstone', composed of alkali rich, medium grained, slightly metamorphosed igneous rock.

Holliday Lamp c1820
Burnt oil from tar, the oil being vaporised by the heat of the flame and burned through small orifices in a rose burner.

Kentledge
Scrap iron, rails, heavy stone, etc, used as loading on a structure - e.g. on the top section in sinking a cylinder caisson.

Lewis Bolt
Foundation bolt with a tapered and jagged head which is securely fixed into a hole in the anchoring masonry by having molten lead run around it.

Lucigen Lamp
A creosote burning lamp, the oil being forced from the reservoir by high pressure through a spiral heated by the flame of the lamp, the heated oil being ejected partly as vapour and partly as fluid and burning with a large and highly luminous flame. However, impurities in the oil often choked the passages which frequently extinguished the light. Oil often escaped unconsumed which, in a confined space, settled on adjacent surfaces to make them slippery and unsafe.

Walings
Horizontal struts forming part of a timber framework.

Wrought Iron
Made in the puddling furnace by decarburising pig or cast iron and then hammered and rolled to form bars, rods, sections, plates and sheets. Chemically, it is iron in its commercially pure form with a carbon content of up to 0.25% and with the smallest practicable content of other elements. It is highly ductile, with an average tensile strength of 21/25 tons/in^2 and an elongation of 20/35%. It has excellent resistance to corrosion.

BIBLIOGRAPHY

Primary and documentary sources and articles in magazines and journals are given as references in the text.

Anderton *et al, Dynamic Stratigraphy of the British Isles*, George Allen & Unwin 1979

Beckett, D. *Brunel's Britain* David & Charles 1980

Berridge, D. *The Girder Bridge*, Robert Maxwell 1969

Biddle, G. *The Railway Surveyors*, Ian Allan 1990

Bowden & Mills *Brunel's Royal Albert Bridge*, Watts 1983

Brunel, I. *Life of Isambard Kingdom Brunel*, Longmans Green 1870

Charlton, T. M. *A History of Theory of Structures in the Nineteenth Century*, Cambridge University Press 1982

Chrimes, M. *Civil Engineering 1839-1889,* Thomas Telford 1991

Clark, E. *The Britannia and Conway Bridges*, Day & Son 1850

Conder, F. E. *The Men who Built Railways* (ed. J. Simmons), Thomas Telford 1983

Corlett, E. *The Iron Ship*, Conway Maritime Press 1990

Dempsey, G.D. *Practical Railway Engineer*, John Weale 1855

Hall, S. *Railway Detectives*, Ian Allan 1990

Humber, W. *Treatise on Bridge Construction*, Lockwood & Co. 1864

MacDermot, E. T. *History of the Great Western Railway vol 2*, Ian Allan 1982

Polsue, J. *Lake's Parochial History of the County of Cornwall Vol IV*, EP Publishing Ltd

Pugsley, A. *Works of Isambard Kingdom Brunel (edited)*, Cambridge University Press 1976

Rankine, W. J. M. *Manual of Civil Engineering*, Charles Griffin & Co. 1885

Resal, H. *Trait de Mecanique Generale*, Gauthier-Villars, Paris 1881

Robins, F. W. *The Story of the Lamp*, Oxford University Press 1939

Rolt, L. T. C. *Isambard Kingdom Brunel*, Longmans 1957

Sekon, G. A. *A History of the Great Western Railway*, Digby Long & Co. 1895

Various *The Locomotives of the Great Western Railway*, RCTS 1968 *et seq*

Vaughan, A. *Isambard Kingdom Brunel - Engineering Knight Errant*, John Murray 1991

Vignoles K. H. *Charles Blacker Vignoles: romantic engineer*, Cambridge University Press 1982

Woodfin, R. J. *The Cornwall Railway*, Bradford Barton 1972

Waters, I. *Brunel's Tubular Suspension Bridge over the River Wye*, Moss Rose Press Chepstow 1856

Wood & Tozer *History of the Royal Albert Bridge*, Wood & Tozer c1859

STATISTICCS

Statistics and chronology of the Royal Albert Bridge

Major Dimensions

Length of each Main Span (Two)	455ft
Overall length of each Main Truss	461ft
Distance between chain eye attachments	450ft
Height of tube centre above roadway	72ft
Height of roadway above HWOST	100ft
Devon Approach Spans (East/West)	3 @ 69ft 6in
	1 @ 72ft 6in
	1 @ 78ft 0in
	1 @ 83ft 6in
	1 @ 93ft 0in
Cornwall Approach Spans (East/West)	1 @ 93ft 0in
	1 @ 83ft 6in
	1 @ 78ft 0in
	1 @ 72ft 6in
	5 @ 69ft 6in
	1 @ 67ft 6in
Total Overall length of Bridge	2,187ft 6in

CHRONOLOGY

Cornwall Railway Act of Parliament	3 August 1846
Contract with C. J. Mare	January 1853
Launch of Great Cylinder	May 1854
Great Cylinder finally positioned	February 1855
C. J. Mare Bankruptcy	21 September 1855
Testing of Cornwall Span	Summer 1857
Floating of Cornwall Span	1 September 1857
Start of Cornwall Span lifting	25 November 1857
Cornwall Span in position	19 May 1858
Floating of Devon Span	10 July 1858
Start of Devon Span lifting	9 August 1858
Devon Span in position	16 February 1859
Testing of Bridge	20 April 1859
Opening Date	2 May 1859

MATERIALS USED IN CONSTRUCTION

Wrought Iron	2,650 tons
Cast Iron	1,200 tons
Masonry & Brickwork	17,000 yards^3
Timber	14,000 ft^3

INDEX

CORNWALI

CONTRACT

SALTASI

Genera

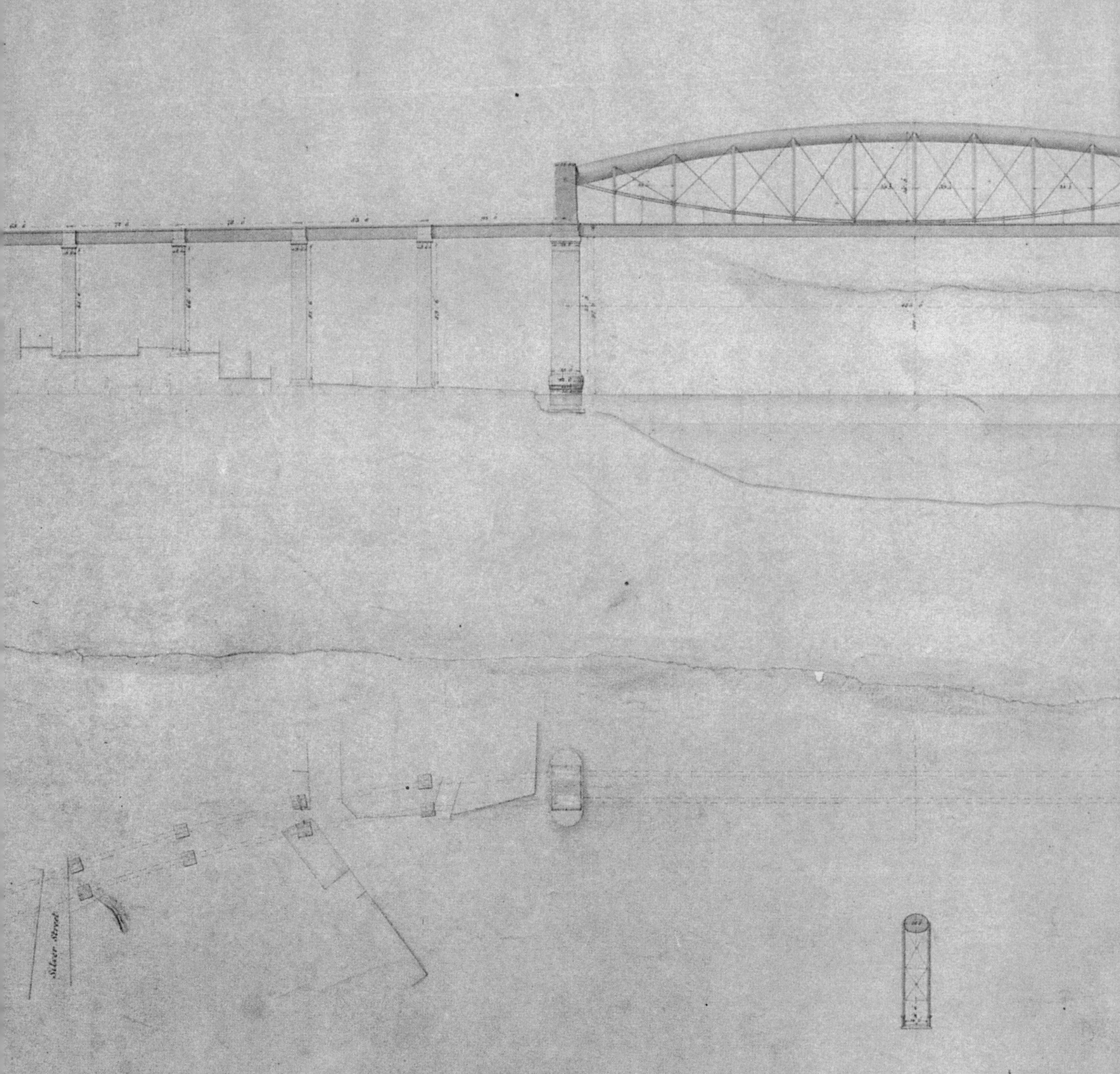